Sun-Earth-Man:
a Mesh of Cosmic O

GH01086837

HOW PLANETS REGULATE SOLAR ERUPTIONS, GEOMAGNETIC STORMS, CONDITIONS OF LIFE, AND ECONOMIC CYCLES

by
THEODOR LANDSCHEIDT
Belle Côte, Nova Scotia, Canada B0E 1C0

I AM A CHILD OF EARTH AND STARRY HEAVEN

URANIA
TRUST

First published 1989

Published by the Urania Trust,
396 Caledonian Road, London, N1 1DN England.

Typeset by Mike Kelly Photosetting
Biddestone, Wiltshire.
Printed and Bound by
Butler & Tanner Limited
Frome, Somerset.

ISBN 1–871989–00–0

CONTENTS

VITA THEODOR LANDSCHEIDT

Theodor Landscheidt was born in Bremen in 1927. He studied philosophy, law, and natural sciences at the University of Goettingen where he earned his doctorate. He was, until his recent retirement, a West German High Court judge. He is the Director of the Schroeter Institute for Research in Cycles of Solar Activity, and is on the board of directors of the International Committee for Research in Environmental Factors at the Free University of Brussels. He has been elected a member of various German academies and of the American Geophysical Union.

Since 1974 Landscheidt has made long-range forecasts of energetic solar eruptions and geomagnetic storms. When checked by astronomers and by the Space Environment Services Centre, Boulder, Colorado, his predictions have been shown to have a quality better than 90%. He successfully forcast the end of the Sahelian drought and has correctly identified the turning points in various economic cycles.

Special publictions dealing with research in cycles:

Landscheidt, T. (1976): Beziehungen zwischen der Sonnenaktivitaet und dem Massenzentrum des Sonnensystems, Nachrichten der Olbers-Gesellschaft 100, 2–19

Landscheidt, T. (1980): Saekularer Tiefpunkt der Sonnenaktivitaet, Ursache einer Kaelteperiode um das Jahr 2000?, Jahrb. d. Wittheit zu Bremen 24, 189–220

Landscheidt, T. (1981): Swinging Sun, 79-Year Cycle, and Climatic Change, J. interdisc. Cycle Res. 12, 3–19

Landscheidt, T. (1983): Solar Oscillations, Sunspot Cycles, and Climatic Change, in McCormac, B. M., ed.: Weather and Climate Responses to Solar Variations, Colorado Associated University Press, Boulder, pp. 293–308

Landscheidt, T. (1984): Cycles of Solar Flares and Weather, in Moerner, N. A. and Karlèn, W., eds.: Climatic Changes on a Yearly to Millenial Basis, D. Reidel Publishing Company, Dordrecht, pp. 473–481

Landscheidt, T. (1984): Funktionen kosmischer Organismen: Schwingungen der Sonne und irdische Resonanzen, in Resch, A., ed.: Geheime Mächte, Andreas Resch Verlag, Innsbruck, pp. 37–130

Landscheidt, T. (1986): Long Range Forecast of Energetic X-Ray Bursts Based on Cycles of Flares, in Simon, P. A., Heckman, G., and Shea, M. A., eds.: Solar-Terrestrial Predictions: Proceedings of a Workshop at Meudon, France, June 18–22, 1984, National Oceanic and Atmospheric Adminstration, Boulder, pp. 81–89

Landscheidt, T. (1986): Long Range Forcast of Sunspot Cycles, in Simon, Heckman, and Shea, pp. 48–57

Landscheidt, T. (1986): Cyclic Distribution of Energetic X-Ray Flares, Solar Physics 107, 195-199

Landscheidt, T. (1987): Wir sind Kinder des Lichts – Kosmisches Bewusstsein als Quelle der Lebensbejahung, Verlag Herder Freiburg, Basel, Wien

Landscheidt, T. (1987): Long Range forecasts of Solar Cycles and Climatic Change, in Rampino, M. R., Sanders, J. E., Newman, W. S., and Koenigsson, L. K., eds.: Climate History, Periodicity, and Predictability, van Nostrand Reinhold Company, New York, pp. 421–445

Landscheidt, T. (1988): Solar Rotation, Impulses of the Torque in the Sun's Motion, and Climatic Variation, in press for Climatic Change.

I. INTRODUCTION

The mass-man of our age, so aptly described by José Ortega y Gasset in "The Revolt of the Masses", is dominated by the principles of mechanistic materialism. This anachronistic view of life was au fait with the world view of the exponents of science in the 19th century which looked at the universe as a mechanical device, an assembly of separable parts subject to local effects caused by local interaction. Meanwhile, the avant-garde of scientists has overthrown these local theories that split the world into separated parts which can only be influenced by their immediate environment. The new interpretation of the Einstein-Rosen-Podolsky paradox and the violation of the Bell inequality provide irrefutable evidence of the inseparability and non-locality of the fundamental processes in the universe.[1] This epochal achievement in the history of human knowledge has not yet been valued appropriately. There are even scientists that have never heard of Bell's theorem and those sophisticated experiments that prove its violation. All experts, however, agree on its paramount importance in the history of science.[2]

The unanimous message of mystics of all ages that all entities in the universe are interconnected and constitute an indivisible whole [3] is proven now by unequivocal physical experiments that have been replicated again and again.[4] From this undeniable unity, connectedness, and inseparability follows that any action or configuration in any distant part of the universe can influence processes in the solar system inhabited by man. This is also valid for the interrelations of Sun and planets within the solar system and especially the Earth's connections with other cosmic bodies in the solar system environment.

To look at the solar system and its constituent parts as a whole that embraces a complex web of holistic interrelations, is a premise of traditional astrology, which seemed antiquated, but turns out to be trend-setting. Thus, it appears promising to subject the astrological thesis of an influence of celestial bodies on the Earth and life on its surface to a new test. The quality of the astrological body of theses matches the holistic results of modern research, as it represents the archetype of an integrating science. Astrology of this brand was a historical reality in the era of Kepler, Galileo and Newton. It is well known that Kepler was both an astrologer and one of the creative founders of modern science. Book IV of his principle work "Harmonics Mundi" with the heading "Book on Metaphysics, Psychology, and Astrology" is evidence of this, as well as his papers "De fundamentis astrologiae certioribus" and "De stella nova". Those who pretend that Kepler was not really engaged in astrology should read these writings.

Galileo, the other master scientist, was also an astrologer. Figure 1 from Owen Gingerich[5] shows on top a drawing of the Moon made by Galileo after his construction of an astronomical telescope in 1609. On the same page is the start of a horoscope he cast for Cosimo II di Medici. This concurrence is typical of the holistic approach of Kepler and Galileo. They did not talk about interdisciplinary research, they lived it. Kepler was not only an astronomer and astrologer, but also a meteorologist, mathematician, harmonist, philosopher,

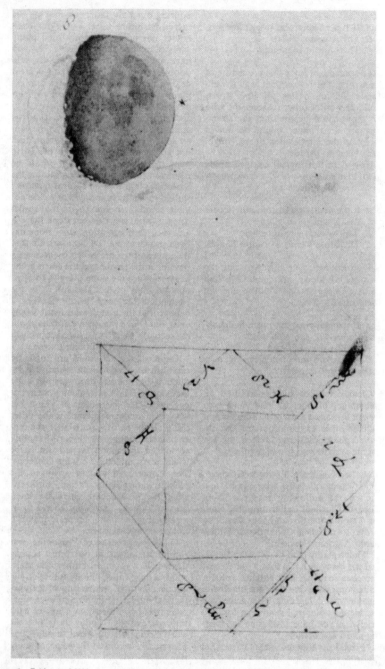

Figure 1: Evidence of Galileo's interdisciplinary work uniting astronomy and astrology: on the same page a drawing of the Moon oberserved by means of Galileo's new astronomical telescope and the start of a horoscope he cast for Cosimo II di Medici.

theologian, and mystic. Newton, last but not least in this trinity of creative scientists, wrote much more papers on alchemy, theology, and metaphysics than on physics and mathematics.[6] In hundreds of nights, spent in his unhealthy alchemic laboratory, he searched for the noumenal light, bearer of life and mind, quite different from the phenomenal light he dealt with in his optics.[7] Kepler, Galileo, and Newton integrated the knowledge of their age. This was a necessary condition of their creativity.

In our days, astrologers and scientists do not live up to their great predecessors who initiated a new age in science. There are few exponents who coalesce astrological views and modern scientific knowledge to create new paradigms. Most scientists do not realize that their findings confirm fundamental astrological ideas, and most astrologers do not see that creative scientists transgress the frontiers of traditional astrological knowledge. In our time, astrology's faculty to integrate diverging fields of knowledge is merely a dormant potentiality. Faint-hearted astrologers timidly defend the old saying "as above, so below" in reducing it to a mere analogy, whereas scientists like the dynamic systems theorist Erich Jantsch[8] and the Nobel-prize recipient Ilya Prigogine[9] boldly claim that there is interdependent coevolution of microcosmic and macrocosmic structures regulated by homologous principles which go back to common cosmic roots that converge in the cosmic-egg phase of our universe. Even Operations research, a rather practical field of knowledge, follows the basic rule that the behaviour of any part of a system has some effect on the system as a whole. The application of such rules, however, is restricted to the narrow limits of human activity in society, technology, and economy. Scientists lack the boldness of astrological imagination that could stimulate a projection of basic insights upon the dimensions of the solar system, the realm of Sun, Earth, and planets that induced creative ideas in Kepler, Galileo, and Newton. The result of the experiments suggested by Bell's theorem begs for a new synthesis that integrates fundamental astrological ideas and modern scientific knowledge.

Thus, let us try such a new kind of genuine interdisciplinary approach. It will yield intriguing results which show that Sun and planets function like an intricate organism regulated by complex feed-back loops. The Sun that makes the planets revolve around its huge body, is again influenced by the giant planets Jupiter, Saturn, Uranus, and Neptune that make it revolve around the common centre of mass of the solar system. This very irregular motion regulates the Sun's varying activity which again influences the planets and so on. This feed-back loop will be revealed by deciphering a kind of Rosetta stone of planetary forcing. We shall come to know how the tidal planets Mercury, Venus, Earth, and Jupiter and the giant planets cooperate in regulating or modulating essential features of the Sun's activity: the former by special effects of tide-generating forces and the latter via the Sun's oscillations about the centre of mass. And Jupiter, this massive planet just below the level of a binary star, is the link between both groups; it is the only planet involved in both functions, thus playing a central part.

Accordingly, special Jupiter configurations, that will be described in detail, prove to be related to variations in the Sun's rotation, the incidence of energetic solar eruptions, geomagnetic storms, variations in the ozone column in the

Earth's atmosphere, rainfall, temperature, rise and fall in animal populations, economic cycles, interest rates, stock prices, variations in the gross national product, phases of general instability, and even historical periods of radical change and revolution. In addition, consecutive Jupiter configurations constitute long-term cycles the harmonics of which point to short-term cycles that appear in various time series of solar-terrestrial events. The most significant harmonics form ratios that reflect consonances and even the major perfect chord in musical harmony. This new precise realization of the Keplerian "music of the spheres" makes it possible to "compose" predictions of the Sun's activity and its terrestrial response. Such forecasts have been checked by scientific institutions and reached a high level of reliability. Details of these data will be presented as well as the foundations on which they are based , so that the reader can judge for himself the dependability of the new results.

II. EXAMPLE AVAILS TEN TIMES MORE THAN PRECEPT

Samuel Smiles was convinced that example is one of the most potent of instructors, though it teaches without a tongue. Here is such an example which demonstrates the fertility of a new kind of multidisciplinary approach that integrates mathematical, physical, astronomical, biological, economical, psychological, sociological, harmonical, and astrological knowledge in a simple, but enlightening way and thus reflects the unity and connectedness of our world as proven by the violation of Bell's inequality therom:

1. FEED-BACK LOOPS, AN ARCHETYPE OF MORHOGENESIS

It has been mentioned already that Sun and planets form complex feed-back loops. Figure 2, the lithograph Drawing Hands by Maurits Cornelis Escher, is a representation of such feed-back systems. A left hand draws a right hand, while at the same time a right hand draws a left hand. Levels which are ordinarily seen as hierarchical – that which draws and that which is drawn – turn back on each other, creating a tangled hierarchy. According to Douglas Hofstadter[10] such strange loops are at the core of creativity. The solar system, too, embodies feed-back loops of this kind. The Sun, the central body and main force in the system, looked at as being in a higher hierarchical position, is in its turn influenced by the seemingly inferior planets that make it oscillate around the common centre of mass and regulate its varying activity, which again influences the planets etc. As the planet Earth and its complex surface features are also involved in this cyclic entanglement of feed-back loops, the yield of these intricate processes is beyond imagination. Even human creativity seems to be involved. Enlightenment in artists, scientists, or mystics that manifests itself in acts of creation concurs with solar light emanations released by energetic solar eruptions.

This may seem inconceivable to some readers, but seemingly simple dynamic systems that comprise loops or cycles do not necessarily possess simple dynamic properties. Even extremely simple mathematical models of non-linear dynamic feed-back systems provide surprising evidence of unfathomable structural complexity. Take an initial number, the seed, square it and add a constant. Feed the result, the output, back into this functional process as new input. Do this over and over again to see if some pattern emerges. The respective output values, when plotted in the plane of complex numbers, reveal the existence of so-called "attractors" that reign over separate domains into which they attract special output. Such attractors at zero and infinity, for instance, could represent the polar tension created by the antagonistic qualities concentration and dissipation. Surprisingly, this discloses a hidden connection between feed-back loops or similar cyclic features and centres of polar tension diametrically opposite in nature. At the boundary between the realms of competing attractors, where their influence approaches zero as a limit, wonders of creativity emerge, patterns delicately poised between order and chaos. Computers can be converted into a kind of microscope for viewing such boundaries. Figure 3 shows an example of a microscopic boundary pattern made visible by H. O. Peitgen and P. H.

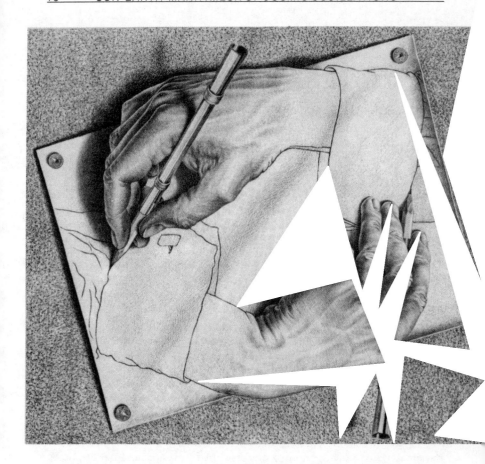

Figure 2: The lithograph ''Drawing Hands'' by Maurits Cornelis Escher – a representation of ''strange loops'' which according to D. Hofstadter create a tangled hierarchy. The Sun and the planets embody such a feed-back system.

Richter.[11] Mathematically expressed, it is a Julia set; Peitgen and Richter call it seahorse tail. It winds down and down, going on forever. There is infinite regression of detail. The large tail encompasses complete smaller seahorses that show different features, thus representing a wealth of explicit forms.

One of the peculiar things about the boundary is its self-similarity. If we look at any one of the fractal corners or bays, we notice that the same shape is found at another place in another size. An arbitrary piece of the boundary contains all the essential structure of the whole boundary. The boundary is invariant under this transformation.[12] This mathematical theorem was expressed by Gaston Julia and Pierre Fatou as early as 1919. It supports an astrological thesis, the dictum of the Emerald Tablet: ''*Quod est inferius, est sicut quod est superius. Et quod est superius, est sicut quod est inferius, ad perpetranda miracula rei unius*'': As below, so above, as above, so below; this accomplishes the wonders of oneness.

Figure 3:   Boundary pattern, called Julia set, elaborated by H. O. Peitgen and P. H. Richter. Julia sets carry incredibly complex dynamics emerging from boundaries between domains of antagonistic attractors that compete for influence. In border regions with polar tension transition from one form of existence to another takes place: from order to disorder, magnetic to non-magnetic state, or however the opposite entities are to be interpreted that meet at the boundary.

At the core of those creative patterns that grow out of the boundary region there exists a central form that represents the implicit order as we find it in cell nuclei. Zooming in for a close computer look discloses it. It is shown in Figure 4 elaborated by Peitgen and Richter.[13] Mathematicians call it Mandelbrot set after its discoverer. It regulates the form of Julia sets and thus may be considered as a pre-image of central regulation. The proportions of the Mandelbrot set provide a wealth of clues to musical harmony including the major perfect chord. It will be shown in a later chapter that even the ratios of harmonics of cosmic cycles are precisely reflected in this core structure. There is mathematical proof that all Mandelbrot sets that emerge in the universe of the complex plane are interconnected, though there is an infinity of them. Everything is held together by extremely thin lines. Thus the infinite set of Mandelbrot sets may viewed as a pre-image of the unity of all core structures in the universe, a special reflection of the wholeness of the universe proved by the violation of the Bell inequality.

Figure 4: Mandelbrot set, elaborated by H. O. Peitgen and P. H. Richter, which controls the structure of a wealth of diverse Julia sets. According to Peitgen and Richter it reminds of the genetic organisation in higher organisms. Its proportions express consonant intervals in musical harmony and the major perfect chord.

2. THE HALLMARK OF ALL BORDERLINE PHENOMENA: INSTABILITY AND ABUNDANCE OF FORMS

Those boundaries that separate the realms of antagonistic attractors that compete for influence are a model of reality. They represent the qualities of the phase boundary between magnetism and non-magnetism, laminar flow and turbulent flow, cyclicity and non-cyclicity, order and chaos etc. Because of its fractal character the border is infinitely long. By definition, it has infinitesimal width. Thus, its sensitivity is such that the stroke of a butterfly's wing can change the fate of macrocosmic systems, as the meteorologist E. N. Lorenz put it. This is why we do not know whether the solar system will continue to be stable or not. An infinitesimal difference in the initial conditions not accessible to calculation could lead to the dissolution of order in the planetary system. The physicist and mathematician Henri Poincaré provided evidence of this as early as the end of the 19th century.[14] A wealth of boundaries with such qualities is to be found in the solar system. This refutes the often repeated argument against astrology that the energy level of any planetary influence is much too low.

It is inherent in the conditions of emergence of boundaries that their creative potential is irresolvably linked to instability. However, it is just this instability in dissipative systems far from the state of thermodynamical equilibrium which, according to Ilya Prigogine, Hermann Haken,[15] and Erich Jantsch, can lead to a spontaneous formation of new structures out of germs of gestalt or even out of chaos. If there is a boundary transition from one polar quality to the opposite one, instability will arise, but new patterns will emerge too. Our knowledge of the prototypal quality of boundaries can help us to judge the function of special boundary states and transitions properly. This for example, applies to zero phases in cycles, critical days in biorhythms, the boundary between consciousness and subconsciousness, the transition from waking to sleeping with its Kekulé-effects, creative acts of artists, eureka moments, mystic experience, birth, death, the balance in mathematical formulae, and interdisciplinary research. Mesocosmic man lives just on the boundary between the realms of the attractors microcosmos and marcrocosmos. This explains man's instability, the dominant quality of all borderlines between chaos and order, but also the unfathomable depths of man's creativity and destructiveness. A crisis in the development of individuals or collectives is again a boundary state. The Swiss writer Max Frisch put it thus: a crisis could be productive if only the tang of catastrophe would be taken from it.

The Earth's surface and the wealth of fractal structures growing out of this small boundary region is a further example. Such spherical surfaces are most interesting. Kepler thought them to be a perfect symbol of God's creative functions. Surfaces of material spheres are phase interfaces where symmetry breaking occurs; the invariance of vertical translation relative to the surface is no longer valid.[16] New structures can emerge. The Sun's surface, too, shows such boundary qualities. It separates the realms of two competing attractors: one that represents contraction and transforms dying suns into neutron stars or even black holes, and another one that represents expansion and dissipating radiation. The borderline between these realms, the Sun's surface, shows the attributes of all boundaries: instability and a wealth of structures. The complex patterns of solar activity – sunspots, faculae, prominences, eruptions, and flares – arise from the Sun's thin, unstable surface layer. As will be shown, this surface activity is linked up with the Earth's surface activity. This is together a connection between two boundary regions in the defined sense.

It has been shown at international conferences of astronomers, geophysicists, and climatologists, but also at astrological research conferences in London, that impulses of the torque (IOT) in the Sun's irregular oscillations about the invisible centre of mass of the solar system, induced by the giant planets, regulate the incidence of energetic solar eruptions and their terrestial response.[17] Details will be given in a later chapter. Strong impulses of the torque occur when the Sun's centre, the centre of mass, and Jupiter, the weighty centre of the world of planets, are in line. These heliocentric conjunctions of Jupiter and the centre of mass again are a boundary phenomenon. They mark a zero phase in the Sun's motion about the centre of mass, in which the torque acting on the Sun reaches zero, changes sign, and shows a more or less sharp increase in the new direction. The Sun changes from approaching the centre of mass to receding from it or vice versa. Just this boundary phenomenon releases instability together with a wealth of new patterns in the Sun's surface that is followed by corresponding effects in the Earth's surface region. These terrestrial responses, that will be dealt with in detail in another chapter, range from geomagnetic storms to abundance in wild life and economic change.

3. VARIATION IN WILD LIFE ABUNDANCE, A PARADIGM OF TERRESTRIAL EFFECTS OF SOLAR SYSTEM BOUNDARY EVENTS

Now we are ready to make an interesting point in our example. Figure 5, after Edward R. Dewey,[18] shows the cyclic variation in Canadian lynx abundance for the years 1735 to 1969. The data are based on records of the offerings of lynx skins by trappers, particularly to the Hudson's Bay Company. As the efforts of trappers to earn a livelihood are fairly constant, biologists feel that the records of skin offerings constitute a rather reliable index of the abundance of lynx. The ordinate axis in Figure 5 indicates the yearly number N of offered lynx skins. Flat triangles mark the epochs of conjunctions of Jupiter with the centre of mass. These epochs show an obvious connection with extrema in the lynx abundance. The pattern, however, is rather complex. There are longer periods with epochs that coincide with peaks, as before 1789, other protracted periods with epochs that concur with troughs, as after 1867, and phase jumps from minima to maxima as before 1823 and 1867. Such phase changes appear in almost all time series of solar and terrestrial data and are thought to pose intricate questions. The first three arrows in the plot point to periods of instability resulting in phase jumps that started about 1789, 1823, and 1867. Even these periods of change show a distinct pattern: the epochs of Jupiter conjunctions on the left of the respective arrows always coincide with a maximum in lynx abundance, whereas the epoch on the right concurs with a minimum. This regular pattern of instabilities yields different results depending on whether the foregoing epochs of Jupiter conjunctions go along with maxima or minima in the time series. Only the instability event starting in 1933 resulted in a different pattern: there was no phase change, but an anomalous period with very small numbers of lynx and poor variations in the abundance.

Fortunately, our knowledge of the fundamental quality of boundaries, derived from mathematical feed-back cycles and physical phase transitions, when combined with astronomical facts and astrological imagination, enables us to explain and predict such instability events. The centre of mass of the solar system is an attractor as defined above. Hermann Haken, the founder of synergetics, a new discipline dealing with nonequilibrium phase transitions and self-organization in physics and biology, has focused attention on profound analogies between completely different systems when they pass through an instability and then build up new macroscopic spatio-temporal patterns. Haken explicitly states that the equations of celestial mechanics follow the rules of synergetics, and he stresses in addition that centres of mass of systems of astronomical bodies play an important part in nonequilibrium

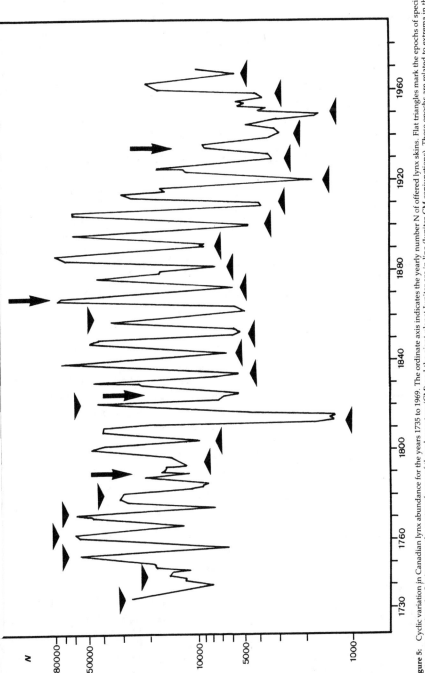

Figure 5: Cyclic variation in Canadian lynx abundance for the years 1735 to 1969. The ordinate axis indicates the yearly number N of offered lynx skins. Flat triangles mark the epochs of special configurations when the Sun's centre, the centre of mass of the solar system (CM) and the giant planet Jupiter are in line (Jupiter-CM conjunctions). These epochs are related to extrema in the lynx abundance. The phase pattern of this relationship or major anomalies in the distribution depend on major solar instability events the starting epochs of which (1789, 1823, 1867, and 1933) are designated by arrows. Major instability events occur when the centre of mass, an attractor, remains for years in or near the Sun's surface, a boundary region.

phase transitions as they act as order parameters that function like attractors.[19] As has been shown already, the Sun's surface is a boundary in terms of the morphology of nonlinear dynamic systems. Thus, it makes sense that the major instability events starting about 1789, 1823, and 1867, and later about 1933 and 1968, occurred just when the centre of mass remained in or near the Sun's surface for several years.

When the Sun approaches the centre of mass (CM), or recedes from it, there is a phase when CM passes through the Sun's surface. Usually, this is a fast passage, as the line of motion is steeply inclined to the surface. There are rare instances, however, when the inclination is very weak, CM runs nearly parallel with the Sun's surface, or oscillates about it so that CM remains near the surface for several years. Fixing the epochs of start and end of such periods involves some arbitrariness. The following definition is in accordance with observation and meets all requirements of practice: major solar instability events occur when the centre of mass remains continually within the range 0.9 — 1.1 solar radii for 2.5 to 8.5 years, and additionally within the range 0.8 — 1.2 solar radii for 5.5 to 10 years. The giant planet Jupiter is again involved. In most cases major instability events are released when Jupiter is stationary near CM.

The first, sharper criterion yields the following periods:

1789.7 — 1793.1	(3.4 yr)
1823.6 — 1828.4	(4.8 yr)
1867.6 — 1870.2	(2.6 yr)
1933.8 — 1937.3	(3.5 yr)
1968.4 — 1972.6	(4.2 yr)
2002.8 — 2011.0	(8.3 yr)

The first decimal is only given to relate the results rather exactly to the criterion. The epochs of the onset and the end of the phenomenon cannot be assessed with such precision. The second, weaker criterion yields periods which begin earlier:

1784.7 — 1794.0	(9.3 yr)
1823.0 — 1832.8	(9.8 yr)
1864.5 — 1870.9	(6.4 yr)
1932.5 — 1938.3	(5.8 yr)
1967.3 — 1973.3	(6.0 yr)
2002.2 — 2011.8	(9.6 yr)

Henceforth, the starting periods 1789, 1823 etc. of the first criterion will be quoted.

In case of major instability events that affect the Sun's surface and the incidence of features of solar activity displaying in this thin, sensitive layer, the instability seems to spread out in the planetary system and seize all events in time series that are connected with the Sun's activity. The instability pattern in the abundance of lynx is only one example of this effect. The rhythm induced by Jupiter conjunctions with the centre of mass, however, does not

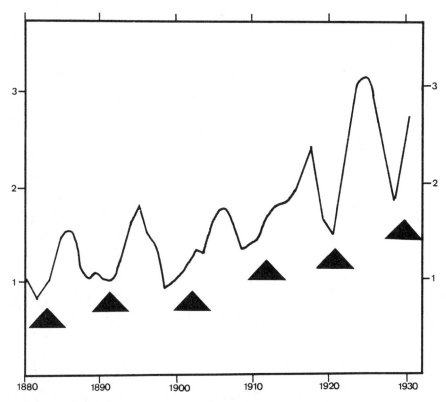

Figure 6: Cycle of Atlantic salmon abundance after E. R. Dewey. The ordinate axis indicates the catch of salmon per rod per day in the Canadian Restigouche Salmon Club 1880 to 1930. Flat triangles mark epochs of Jupiter-CM conjunctions. Their consistent connection with minima in the abundance is in phase with that of the Canadian lynx. This relationship was not disturbed by phase anomalies, as there were no major solar system instability events during the period of observation.

show any disturbances if there are no major instability events. Figure 6, after Edward R. Dewey,[20] presents a cycle in Atlantic salmon abundance. The ordinate axis indicates the catch of salmon per rod per day in the Canadian Restigouche Salmon Club covering the years 1880 to 1929. Flat triangles indicate the epochs of Jupiter conjunctions. The consistent connection with minima in the abundance is in phase with that of the Canadian lynx and the Chinch bug in Illinois. Calculations show that there was no major instability event between 1880 and 1929.

Major instability events seem to affect nearly everything in the solar system. They do not only mark turning points in long-term solar activity, but also influence planets as a whole. Figure 7, after Malcolm G. McLeod,[21] shows the response of the secular variation in the Earth's magnetic field. The upper curve presents the time rate of change of the northern component of the field. The triangles mark the starting epochs of periods of major instability in the Sun's surface about 1933 and 1968. The geophysical literature is replete with papers on the geomagnetic jerk around 1968.

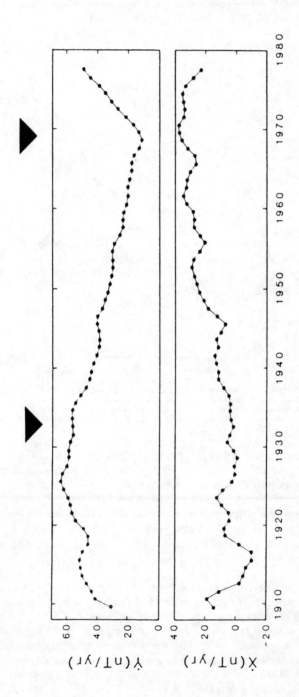

Figure 7: The curve in the top graph after M. G. McLeod presents the time rate of change of the northern component of the Earth's magnetic field. Triangles mark the starting epochs 1933 and 1968 of major instability events in the solar system. They seem to have left their mark in the secular variation of the geomagnetic field.

4. CONJUNCTIONS OF JUPITER WITH THE CENTRE OF MASS,
A COSMIC INDICATOR OF TURNING POINTS IN ECONOMIC
CYCLES

Human activity is involved too. Economy is an expression of such activity.
Figure 8, after Samuel Benner and Edward R. Dewey,[22] shows the ups and
downs in the U.S. pig-iron prices from 1834 to 1900. Flat triangles mark Jupiter
conjunctions with the centre of mass. The fat arrow points to the boundary
event that began in 1867 and resulted in a phase jump from minima to maxima.
Epochs of Jupiter conjunctions that before had been connected with troughs
in the prices shifted to a connection with peaks. Incidentally, since 1954 all
peaks in U.S. long government bond yields have coincided with epochs of
Jupiter conjunctions and all valleys with phases in the middle between such
epochs. The next peak is to be expected about 1990–91.

Figure 9 presents the yearly percental variation in the gross national product
of West Germany. Flat black triangles designate epochs of Jupiter conjunctions
with the centre of mass, while white triangles indicate second harmonics of
cycles formed by consecutive conjunctions. The fat arrow points to the epoch
of the major instability event initiated in 1968 when the center of mass began
to stay in or near the Sun's surface for years. The corresponding change in the
pattern of the percental variation is obvious. Before this boundary event all
epochs of Jupiter conjunctions and second harmonics were related to sharp
single-peaked maxima, whereas after the event Jupiter conjunctions were
connected with minima in the variation of the gross national product, and
second harmonics with broad maxima forming a double peaked plateau. The
white triangles that mark the epochs of second harmonics always point to the
same position in the plateau, just before the second peak. The next major
instability event will not begin before the year 2002. Thus it is to be expected
that the pattern will be permanent in the current millenium.

A forecast can be read from the plot. In 1988 the growth will probably be
less than 2%, in 1989 it could be negative, and in 1990, the epoch of a Jupiter
conjunction, it will reach a minimum. The first, higher peak is to be expected
in 1992, and the position on the plateau near the second, lower peak, indicated
by a white triangle, will be reached in 1994. The plots of the gross national
products of other countries might display somewhat different details. They
should be, however, in conformity with the basic pattern: connection of the
extrema with the epochs of Jupiter conjunctions and phase jump around 1968.
The relation to the epochs of Jupiter conjunctions might be masked by lags
that may be different for different countries. The respective lags, however,
should show a consistent pattern with a change after 1968. A list of the epochs
of Jupiter conjunctions with the centre of mass, the only prerequisite for such
studies, is given in Table 1.

5. MULTIDISCIPLINARY FORECAST OF STOCK PRICES

Variations in stock prices, another very complex expression of man's activity,
are also influenced by solar instability events. This seems incredible at first
sight. But if the violation of Bell's inequality and the resulting oneness of all
features of reality are taken seriously, there is no inconsistency in the

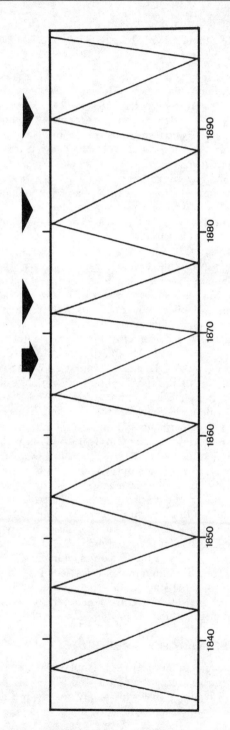

Figure 8: Cycle in U.S. pig-iron prices 1834 to 1900 after E. R. Dewey. Flat triangles indicate the epochs of Jupiter-CM conjunctions. The fat arrow points to the starting epoch 1867 of a major instability event that resulted in a phase jump in the time series. Before 1867 the epochs of Jupiter conjunctions were consistently connected with minima and afterwards with maxima.

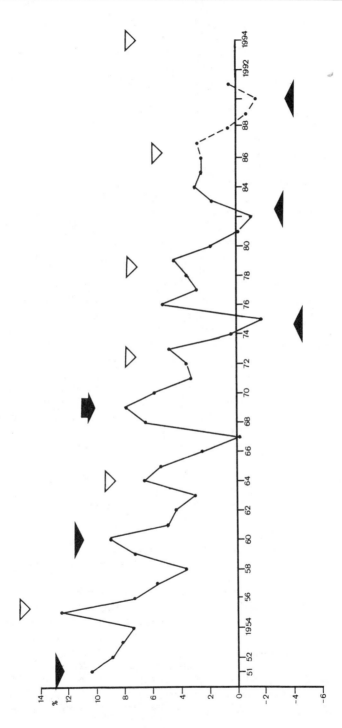

Figure 9: Yearly percental variation in the gross national product of the Federal Republic of Germany 1951 to 1986. Flat black triangles designate epochs of Jupiter-CM conjunctions. White triangles indicate second harmonics of cycles formed by consecutive conjunctions. The fat arrow points to the starting epoch of the major instability event 1968 that changed the pattern of the relationship of Jupiter-CM constellations with extrema in the gross national product. The next minimum in this economic time series is to be expected in 1990.

hypothesis that enhanced instability in the unstable boundary region of the Sun, the center of energy display and regulation, releases instability, too, in a peripheral feature in the Earth's unstable surface like man. It is imaginable that people involved in the sale and purchase in the stock market who are psychologically unsteady and plagued by unstable autonomous nervous systems or hormones, might act differently from well-balanced, optimistic people. Experts acknowledge that a large part of variations in share prices cannot be explained by economic laws and facts.

Figure 10 after Edward R. Dewey[23] presents percental deviations of U.S. stock prices from the 9-year moving average trend for the years 1830 to 1942. Triangles point to epochs of Jupiter conjunctions. The fat arrows mark the epochs of major instability events beginning in 1867 and 1933. The same pattern emerges as in other time series: before 1867 the Jupiter conjunctions coincided with negative extrema in the deviations, whereas after the major instability event they concurred with positive extrema. After 1933, the starting epoch of the next boundary event, the pattern changed again, as was to be expected. The Jupiter conjunction in 1942 indicated a negative extremum instead of a positive one as before.

The turning points of stock prices after World War II continued to match the Sun's phases of instability. Figure 11 is an illustration of this. It presents the German share index published by the Frankfurter Allgemeine Zeitung (F.A.Z.). The rather complex connection with solar instability events requires some explanation. The patterns that emerge from instability and concomitant processes of dynamic self-organisation may be quite different, as they can be influenced by infinitesimal differences in the initial conditions. Thus, it seems natural that different time series that follow identical cyclic periods regulated by Jupiter conjunctions with the centre of mass, may show different phases when they have passed through an instability event. Even within the same time series it may occur that the ups and downs in the data show unexpected responses after periods of major instability. This depends on how many different phases can be realized in the cycle of a special time series. In most cases there are only two. The cycle of stock-prices, formed by consecutive Jupiter conjunctions, is more complex. It shows three different phase states: coincidence of epochs of Jupiter conjunctions with maxima, minima, or mean values in between, just in the middle of the curve ascending from minimum to maximum.

Such mean phases are designated in Figure 11 by small horizontal arrow heads. Before the start of the major instability event in 1968, marked by a large short pointer, the epochs of Jupiter conjunctions in 1951, 1959, and 1967, indicated by arrows, consistently coincided with respective mean phases in the ascending branch of the curve. This pattern changed after 1968. From then on the epochs of Jupiter conjunctions coincided with bottoms in stock prices. The respective epochs in 1970, 1974, and 1982 are again indicated by arrows. This pattern will be preserved until 2002, the epoch of the start of the next major instability event. Thus, the epoch of the next minor instability event, the conjunction of Jupiter with the centre of mass in 1990.3 (April 20, 1990), points to the coming turning point where stock prices reach their bottom and begin to rise again. Such turning points indicate a global trend that affects all

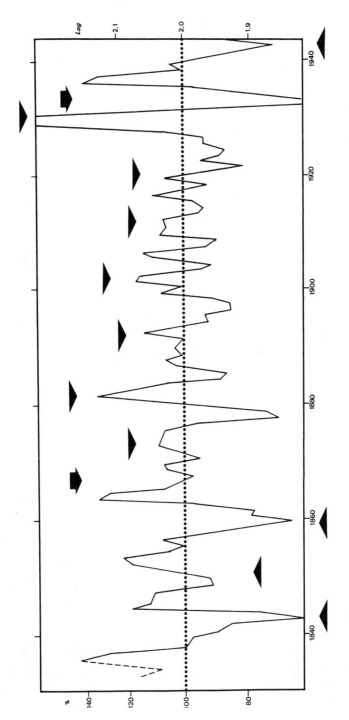

Figure 10: Percental deviations of U.S. stock prices from the 9-year moving average trend for 1830 to 1942 after E. R. Dewey. Triangles point to epochs of Jupiter-CM conjunctions that are related to extrema in the deviations. Fat arrows mark the beginning of predictable major instability events in 1867 and 1933 that changed the pattern of the relationship.

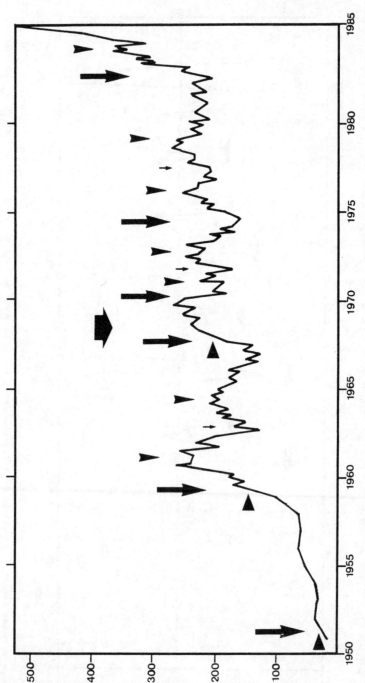

Figure 11: German index of share prices published by the Frankfurter Allgemeine Zeitung (F.A.Z) since 1951. Epochs of Jupiter-CM conjunctions are marked by large arrows. The starting epoch of the major instability event 1968 is indicated by a large fat pointer. The relationship of Jupiter-CM conjunctions with main phases in the course of stock prices shows a different pattern before and after 1968. Before this major instability event the epochs of conjunctions coincided with index ordinates just on the trendline, as marked by small horizontal pointers, whereas after 1968 the conjunctions met bottoms and will continue to do so until the beginning of the next major instability event about 2002. Arrow heads and small pointers indicate secondary tops and bottoms within cycles formed by consecutive Jupiter-CM conjunctions. These patterns made it possible to predict the recent top turning point in stock indices.

important stock exchanges such that the average of their indices is a good match. The indices of individual stock markets may fall several months behind the exact date of the turning point or show a premature release. Thorough knowledge of the state of the special market of interest remains a necessary condition for making appropriate use of the fundamentalist tool offered here. Chart techniques alone are not sufficient to foresee major change. Black Monday, the stock market crash on October 19, 1987, is evidence of this. A combination of expertise, chart techniques, and a general survey of the fundamental turning points will yield more satisfying results than less holistic attempts in the past.

Further analysis of the data in Figure 11 reveals that the fifth harmonic of the cycles formed by consecutive conjunctions of Jupiter and the centre of mass plays an important part with respect to the detailed pattern of cycles in stock prices. There are two subcycles in the respective cycle that comprise two maxima, marked in Figure 11 by vertical arrow heads, and an intermittent minimum, indicated by a small arrow. The epoch of the first peak is at 1/5 of the respective length of the cycle of Jupiter conjunctions, the intermittent trough at 2/5, and the second peak before the final bottom phase at 3/5. The epochs can be calculated by means of a simple formula: first peak: epoch of preceding Jupiter conjunction + 1/5 length of cycle; intermediate valley: epoch of conjunction + 2/5 length of cycle; second peak: epoch of conjunction + 3/5 length of cycle. For the years 1959 to 1982 the mean deviation from this pattern was 0.22 years; the standard deviation reached $\sigma = 0.18$ yr.

The current cycle was initiated by the conjunction of Jupiter with the centre of mass on October 31, 1982 (1982.83), and will be terminated by the conjunction on April 20, 1990 (1990.3). The length of the cycle is 7.5 years. One fifth of this length is 1.5 years. Accordingly, the first peak in the international average of stock indices was to be expected in 1984.3, the intermittent valley in 1985.8, and the second peak in 1987.3. In the case of vigorous hausses like that in the roaring twenties and again after 1982, the two peaks grow together in forming one ascending branch that reaches its top at the epoch of the second peak. The intermittent valley becomes apparent only by a temporary reduction in the pace of rising. On this basis, a forecast was published in January 1986 that pinned down the turning point in the recent boom to 1987.3.[26a] It was explicitly stated that after this date the average of international indices would fall down to a bottom around 1990.3. Recommendation was given to sell before 1987.3 (end of April 1987). The mean of the indices of ten of the most important stock exchanges reached the turning point in 1987.25. Those that walked beyond this cliff in the bull market were shaken by the crash initiated on Black Monday.

The third phase state that emerges in cycles of stock prices is by no means restricted to indices of shares. Figure 12, after Edward R. Dewey,[24] presents another example, the rate of immigration into the U.S.A. from 1824 to 1950. The ordinate axis indicates smoothed percental deviations from trend. Large pointers mark the starting epochs of major instability phases in 1867 and 1933. Before 1867 the epochs of Jupiter conjunctions, designated by arrow heads, coincided with extrema in the immigration rate. After 1867 this relation was subjected to a change: the epochs went along with zero phases, intersections

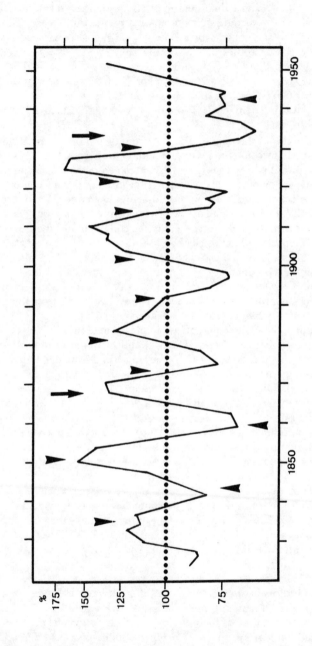

Figure 12: Variations in the rate of immigration into U.S.A from 1824 to 1950 after E. R. Dewey. The ordinate axis indicates smoothed percental deviations from the trend. The major instability events beginning about 1867 and 1933 are marked by arrows. Arrow heads designate the epochs of Jupiter-CM conjunctions. Before 1867 these conjunctions matched extrema in the immigration rate. After 1867 this pattern changed; epochs of Jupiter-CM conjunctions met zero phases on the 100 % trend line. The next major instability event about 1933 initiated a further change.

of the curve with the x-axis that represents time. This pattern changed again after the major instability event starting about 1933.

6. BORDERLINE PHENOMENA IN HISTORY, ART, AND SCIENCE

The special constellation of Sun and planets that makes the centre of mass and the Sun's surface coalesce, is also reflected in the fields of sociology, art, and science. The years that followed 1789, 1823, 1867, 1933, and 1968 were periods of radical change and revolution, a break-down of old structures and the emergence of new forms and ideas. The following examples give an impression of the turning-point function of these epochs, a proper expression of the basic quality of boundary effects as explained in the beginning:

About 1789 to 1793: Great French revolution; spread of modern democracy; first modern constitution in U.S.A.; invention of lighting gas; Mozart, The Magic Flute.

About 1823 to 1828: Monroe doctrine; end of the Spanish empire in South America, Simon Bolivar; Greek war of independence against the Turkish rule; Decembrist conspiracy in Russia; non-Euclidian geometry; foundation of thermodynamic theory; Ohm's law in electricity; Brownian movement; first synthesis of an organic compound (urea) from inorganic substance; invention of steam locomotive, electromagnet, sewing machine, ship's propeller, and aniline dye; Beethoven, Ninth Symphony, Missa Solemnis; Schubert, Seventh Symphony.

About 1867 to 1870: Alaska bought by U.S.A.; nihilism in Russia; Karl Marx, The Capital; foundation of first Social Democratic Party; Maxwell's equation describing the interrelation of electric and magnetic fields; concept of periodic table of chemical elements; Kekulé's concept of six-carbon benzene ring; invention of dynamo, spark-ignition engine, type-writer, rotary press printing, reinforced concrete; dynamite; impressionism in art.

About 1933 to 1937: Great economic depression, collapse of the world market; Stalin's dictatorship, forced collectivisation of agriculture; start of Japan's Far Eastern expansion; breakthrough of Hitler's national socialism; Goedels revolution in logic; discovery of neutron, positron, meson, and heavy hydrogen; creation of electron-positron pairs from energy and vice versa; discovery of nucleic acid in cell nuclei; invention of television, jet engine, and electron microscope.

About 1968 to 1972:   Upheavals and rebellions of students all over the world; spread of hippies; Cultural revolution in China; six day Arab-Israeli war; new economic structures in Czechoslovakia, suppressed by Russian invasion; turning point in Vietnam; space travel; astronauts on the Moon; Glomar Challenger expedition, plate tectonics; first Aids infections; ecological movement; Gnostics of Princeton; Pop art.

The next major instability event will start about 2002 and last till 2011. This is an exceptionally long period. It is impossible to predict the details of its historic effects. But the basic quality of all boundary functions will be evident: the years past 2002 will prove to be another turning point, a period of instability, upheaval, agitation, and revolution, that ruins traditional structures, but favours the emergence of new patterns in society, economy, art, and science. Furthermore, the rhythm in terrestrial time series that shows a connection with the Sun's activity will change again. Perhaps people at the beginning of the third millenium will be better prepared to realize the dangers and chances of cosmic periods of change like these. Possibly, the holistic results presented here will contribute to such awareness.

7. SOLAR TORQUE CYCLES, PRECAMBRIAN CLIMATE, AND CLASSICAL ASTROLOGICAL CONJUNCTIONS

This is the end of our comprehensive example which demonstrates the fertility of a genuine holistic approach that integrates basic astrological ideas with modern scientific knowledge. A single notion taken from the fields of mathematics and physics, a simple model of feed-back loops or cycles, seemingly infinitely apart from astrological views, when looked at in an unbiased multidisciplinary way, has been shown to yield new results that profoundly change our perspective. Critics may object that impulses of the torque (IOT), even if initiated by conjunctions of Jupiter and the centre of mass, show no relation to traditional astrological constellations. But actually conjunctions and oppositions of the giant planets play a vital part in the Sun's irregular motion about the centre of mass (CM). The Sun reaches extreme positions relative to CM when traditional constellations are formed by Jupiter, Saturn, Uranus, and Neptune. When Jupiter on one side of the Sun is in opposition to Saturn, Uranus and Neptune on the other side, the Sun's centre and the centre of mass CM come together, whereas the two centres reach their greatest distance when all of the four giant planets are in conjunction. The synodic cycle of Jupiter and Saturn with a period of 19.86 years and cycles of double (39.72 yr), fourfold (79.44 yr), eightfold (158.9 yr), and 16-fold (317.8 yr) length are of paramount importance in solar torque cycles. They even appear in the solar cycle in Precambrian time, 680 million years ago, derived from records covering more than 16.000 years. According to G. E. Williams[25] the so-called "Elatina cycle" of solar activity, that shows a strong relation, too, with climatic cyclicity, has an average duration of 314 years. This is near to the 16th subharmonic (317 yr) of Jupiter's and Saturn's conjunction cycle. The harmonics of 79 and 157 years in the "Elatina cycle" match the fourth (79 yr) and 8th (158 yr) subharmonic of the synodic cycle of Jupiter and Saturn. A further classical constellation, the triple conjunction of Jupiter, Saturn, and Uranus, the period of which is 317.7 years, is immediately related to the "Elatina cycle" and together to torque cycles. As will be shown, one of the most important torque cycles has a mean period of 13.3 years. It can be derived from the conjunction cycles of Jupiter and Neptune (12.8 yr) and Jupiter and Uranus (13.8 yr). The mean of both synodic cycles (13.3 yr) matches just the torque cycle of this length. Interestingly, the remaining harmonics of the "Elatina cycle" of 52, 63, and 105 years can be derived from the 13.3-year torque cycle. They are near its 4th (53 yr), 5th (66 yr), and 8th (106 yr) subharmonic. There are many other relations that connect traditional astrological constellations with torque cycles, solar activity, and terrestrial effects. This shows that traditional astrology had hands on something, the precise contours of which, however, can only be worked out by unprejudiced investigations that make interdisciplinary use of modern means of research. Astrologers should follow the respective pieces of advice given by H. Eysenck.[25a]

III. PREDICTIONS OF SOLAR ERUPTIONS BASED ON PLANETARY CONSTELLATIONS

The extensive example presented in the initial part of this monograph was intended to give a first survey of the advantages of a holistic approach and the new kind of multidisciplinary techniques that integrate basic astrological views and modern scientific knowledge. In the following part, a body of evidence will be presented that supports the fundamental astrological concept of the influence of planetary constellations on terrestrial phenomena. It is shown how planets modulate the Sun's variable activity and thus indirectly influence diverse effects of solar-terrestrial interaction. These connections were tested by long-range predictions of solar activity and related terrestrial events checked by astronomical and geophysical institutes. John Addey's dictum "that astrological effects can be best understood in terms of cosmic periods and their harmonics", is substantiated by cyclic patterns formed by consecutive conjunctions of Jupiter with the centre of mass of the solar system. Such cycles and their harmonics emerge in time series of the Sun's rotation, energetic solar eruptions, geomagnetic storms, and weather. The abundance of wild life and economic cycles have already been dealt with in the introductory part.

The dependability of the forecasts in question, that were based on planetary configurations in the solar system, forms a sharp contrast to what scientists think of predictions based on planetary constellations. At the Fifth Astrological Research Conference, "Exploring Astrology", held in London on November 22 – 23, 1986, the critic Geoffrey Dean was engaged in spreading "bad news for astrologers", as he put it. In his paper "Does Astrology Need To Be True?" he covered the same topic. He especially dealt with surveys of astrological predictions that proved spurious: "What most surely appears . . . is the perfect inanity of the astrological undertaking . . . what was announced did not happen, what happened was not announced." Geoffrey Dean, too, reviewed his own analysis of J. H. Nelson's daily forecasts of shortwave radio quality based on heliocentric planetary positions. With respect to his evidence that Nelson's relatively simple technique did not work he concluded: "Yet for 30 years Nelson was convinced he saw a correlation that in fact did not exist. So we should not be surprised that astrologers, working with generally vaguer events and far more complicated techniques, can see correlations even if none actually exist." Eventually, Geoffrey Dean stated: "The astrologers' response to these five surveys, which are the only ones I know of, has not been to generate surveys of their own. Instead there has been either silence or brusque dismissal. . . " [26]

This statement is not true, and Geoffrey Dean knew well that it was not in accordance with facts. He was present at the Second Astrological Research Conference, London, November 28/29, 1981, when the positive yield of long range forecasts of energetic solar eruptions and their terrestrial effects was presented that was based on constellations of planets. These results were reviewed in a conference report in *Correlation*[26a] and thoroughly explained in papers published in proceedings of international science conferences and

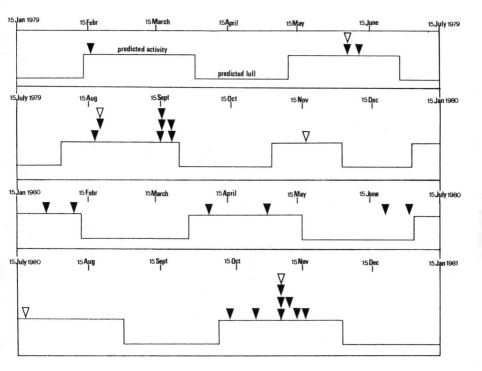

Figure 13: Result of yearly forecasts of energetic solar X-ray bursts equal to or greater than class X2 (black triangles) and proton events (white triangles) for 1979 to 1981. Out of 29 events observed, 27 fit the periods of predicted activity.

scientific and astrological journals.[27] Geoffrey Dean cannot argue that predictions of solar activity, even if based on planetary constellations, have nothing to do with astrology. He explicitly holds that the hypothesis of a planetary modulation of the Sun's activity and an indirect influence on life on Earth would be entirely compatible with astrological tradition.[28] This is why he thought it worthwhile to write a critical analysis of the forecasts of shortwave radio quality by John H. Nelson.[29]

Figure 13 shows the result presented at the Second Astrological Research Conference. The forecasts in question, covering the years 1979 to 1981, were published one year in advance respectively and checked by the astronomers W. Gleissberg, J. Pfleiderer and H. Wöhl, as well as by the Space Environment Services Center, Boulder, U.S.A.[30] Each of the four frames presents the data for half a year. Elevated rectangles mark periods of predicted eruptional activity in a quantitatively defined range, whereas troughs indicate predicted lulls. Epochs of observed energetic eruptions of the defined classes are marked by triangles. Black triangles point to flares accompanied by X-ray bursts equal

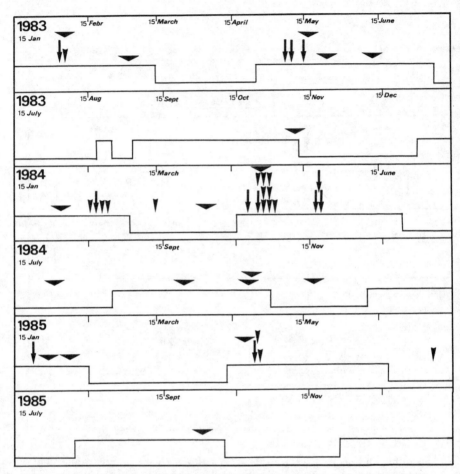

Figure 14: Outcome of a long-range forecast of energetic solar-terrestrial events covering the 3-year period 1983 to 1986. Out of 46 events observed, 41 match the periods of predicted activity: all of 12 X-ray bursts equal to or greater than class X2 (marked by arrows), 14 of 16 proton- and polar cap absorption events (indicated by arrow heads), and 15 of 18 geomagnetic storms (marked by flat triangles).

to or greater than ($\leq$) class $X2$, and white triangles designate proton events $\leq$ 50 particles at 10 MeV. Out of 29 energetic events observed in the forecast period January 1979 to January 1981, 27 met the predicted periods of enhanced activity. It can be seen without any statistical evaluation that this is a good fit. A Pearson-test yields χ^2 (1 degree of freedom) = 20.9; $P < 0.00001$.

Some of the terms used in this part might seem rather technical. This should not deter the reader from going on, the thread of the argument will prove easy to follow. Technical details, which are necessary to convince experts, may be neglected by readers who only want to grasp the essential connections. (There is an extensive glossary in the appendix that explains most of the technical terms.)

In January 1983 a new long-range forecast was issued that covered a period of three years. Besides energetic X-ray flares and proton events, strong geomagnetic storms were included in the prediction. The data were again checked by astronomers and the Space Environment Services Center. Figure 14 shows the result of the forecast. Out of 46 energetic events observed January 1983 to January 1986, 41 fit the periods of predicted activity. These include all of 12 observed X-ray bursts $\leq X2$, marked by arrows, 12 of 14 proton events $\leq$ 50 particles at 10 MeV, and both polar cap absorption events $\leq$ 2 dB, indicated by arrow heads, as well as 15 of 18 magnetic disturbances $A\kappa \leq 50$, marked by flat triangles. A Pearson-test yields $\chi^2 = 16.3$ (1 degree of freedom); $P < 0.00006$). The astronomer Hubertus Wöhl, member of the Fraunhofer Institute for Solar Physics, Freiburg, who checked the forecast, published the result of his evaluation, commenting that the 3-year forecast was "very successful".[31]

A replication of the evaluation of the prediction experiment by means of observed events of less eminent categories again yields a good fit. Out of 62 observed events, 55 hit the periods of predicted activity. A Pearson-test reaches $\chi^2 = 21.3$; $P < 0.00001$. Events whose distribution is subjected to a χ^2-test should be quite independent. This condition is not fulfilled within the time series under consideration, as energetic solar events form clusters. The chance, however, that such clusters coincide with periods of predicted lulls is as good as that of accumulations in periods of predicted activity, if the pattern, the forecast is based upon, is not valid. Thus, the Pearson-test may nevertheless give useful evaluations of the goodness of fit of predicted and observed events. If not, it can be seen quite without tests of statistical significance that the prediction was successful.

The forecast for the year 1982 ran a special risk as it dealt with very rare events, namely energetic flares accompanied by X-ray bursts greater than class X9. Since 1970 only two such events had been observed when, according to the January 1982 forecast, events greater than X9 were to be expected January 15, 1982, to January 14, 1983. Highest probability was assigned to the period from the end of September to the middle of December 1982, and second highest probability to the period from April 29 to June 24, especially April 29 to May 5, and May 22 to June 9, 1982. The observations fit this prediction. X-ray bursts X12, X12.9, and X10 occurred on June 6, December 15, and December 17, 1982. The foregoing X10 event, observed on July 5, 1974, was also predicted in a forecast issued February 20, 1974, and checked by the Space Environment Services Center, Boulder.

IV. CYCLES OF SOLAR ERUPTIONS

1. SOLAR-TERRESTRIAL EFFECTS OF FLARES

The set of checked predictions, presented above, is based on a body of connections that go back to constellations of planets. The controversial thesis that events on Earth are influenced by planets would get substantiation if there were evidence that even the huge Sun and its varying activity are subject to planetary regulation. As to solar activity, attention is usually focused on sunspots; they are spectacular and well documented. But the magnetic energy stored in or above sunspot groups solely constitutes a potential for solar-terrestrial interaction, which is actually released if there are solar eruptions. Thus, energetic solar eruptions are a sharper criterion of immediate solar-terrestrial relations than sunspots.

Flares are the most powerful and explosive of all forms of solar eruptions, and the most important in terrestrial effect. Large flares release energy equivalent to the explosion of more than 200 million hydrogen bombs in a few minutes' time, sufficient to meet mankind's energy demands for a 100 million years. Momentary temperatures exceed 20 million ° K, which is hotter than in the searing interior of the Sun. Ultraviolet and X-ray radiation increases dramatically and causes multiple geophysical effects in the upper atmosphere. Flare effects include corpuscular emission, cosmic ray events, Forbush decreases, aurorae, sudden ionospheric disturbances, radio noise storms, disturbance of navigation on the terrestrial surface and of satellite operation in space, geomagnetic disturbances, short-wave fade out, polar blackout, disruption of telephone connections, power-line failures, computer malfunctions by "mad electrons", and ionization of the atmosphere. Coronal holes, that also contribute to such ionization, are again released by energetic flares.[32]

Geomagnetic storms, another effect of energetic solar eruptions, have caused extensive power blackouts in cities, states, and provinces of the United States and Canada. There are records of baby booms, especially for New York, that occurred nine months after these events. Besides strong power surges on long lines, telephone and microwave relay circuits can seriously be impaired. In Canada there is current legal as well as scientific interest in the possible effects of the large magnetic storm on February 8, 1986, caused by solar eruptions that were initiated by an X-ray burst of class X3. Just at this time a head-on collision between a freight train and a passenger train occurred, and scientists question whether potentials induced by magnetic disturbances could have affected operation of a microwave device that was supposed to control the red light that should have stopped the freight train.[33] Magnetic storms also curtail geophysical exploration studies, destroy vital communication links and can produce significant radiation hazards to both astronauts and airline passengers. Further terrestrial flare effects are increased incidence of lightnings and atmospherics, changes in weather, variations in chemical reactions, increase of electric potentials in the atmosphere as well as in trees and in man, coagulation of colloids, increase in myocardial infarction, leucopenia, psychic instability and traffic accidents.[34]

2. SOLAR ERUPTIONS AND HUMAN CREATIVITY

Flares also seem to stimulate human creativity. There are intriguing examples of scientific discoveries, creative intuition of artists, and mystic vision that concurred with highly energetic flares. The recently published book "Children of the Cosmic Light" [35] deals with this facet of the Sun's boundary creativity. Here are some examples. The trappist monk Thomas Merton, author of "The Seven Storey Mountain", had a mystic experience on December 3, 1968, as described in his diary.[36] Figure 15, after Armstrong et al,[36a] shows the incidence of solar eruptions in 1968 that emitted energetic particles. The arrow points to the date that relates strong surface activity of the Sun to a human boundary event. Unfortunately, direct measurements of the intensity of energetic effects of solar eruptions, as presented in Figure 15, are merely available for a few decades after World War II. As to observations of flares themselves, the situation is not much better. Observations of flares in white light are very rare. The vast majority of flares can only be observed in a selected region of the spectrum. Not until the invention of the spectrohelioscope by Hale in 1926 was there any hope of studying flares systematically. Since this instrument was not fully developed until 1931, the 17th solar cycle of the late thirties was the first during which flares could be studied systematically. Even then flare lists were not complete.

In addition, the recorded optical intensity of flares has meanwhile proved to be a poor indicator of the actual energy involved and of its terrestrial effect.[37] Energetic X-ray bursts emitted by flares are a sharper criterion, but they can only be observed by satellite instrumentation available since the late sixties. There is, however, a proxy means that points to energetic solar eruptions: major geomagnetic storms that have been recorded for more than 120 years. If such major storms occur, there must have been a preceding energetic solar eruption, a strong ejection of solar plasma. There may sometimes be energetic solar eruptions that do not release strong magnetic storms due to the solar system geometry; eruptions near the Sun's limb, especially east of the central meridian, produce only small storms or none at all, no matter how large. But the actual incidence of a major magnetic storm is a dependable indicator of corresponding energetic eruptions that eject fast solar plasma. There is a host of indices to measure geomagnetic disturbances. The indices aa published by P. N. Mayaud[38] form a time series, the quantitative homogeneity of which is acknowledged to be good. It begins with the year 1868.

Exact dates of mystic experience are rare; real mystics do not talk much. All dates, however, that have become known show coincidence with aa-indices far above the level of the annual mean (am). Gopi Krishna, who practised Tantric Yoga, had his first mystic experience at Christmas 1937.[39] During deep meditation he was overwhelmed by a wave of fluid light and ineffable blissfulness. This did not only occur at sunrise, but also at the time of strong solar boundary activity that released a strong magnetic storm on Earth (aa = 75; am = 19.1). In the same year, but under quite different circumstances, Arthur Koestler had a mystic experience, aptly described in his autobiography, when he was under sentence of death during the Spanish Civil War. His experience was released when he was meditating in his prison cell on the

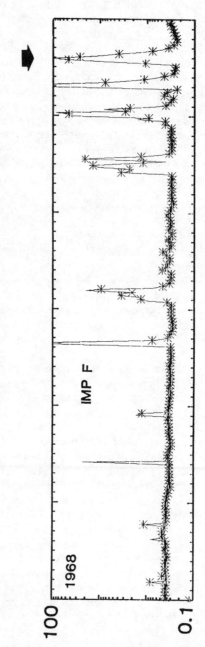

Figure 15: Incidence of solar eruptions in 1968 that emitted energetic particles, after Armstrong (1983). The arrow points to the date of December 3, when the trappist monk Thomas Merton had the mystic experience as described in his diary. This is an example of links between energetic surface activity of the Sun and human boundary events.

nature of prime numbers and Euclid's proof of the infinity of the sequence of prime numbers. Koestler's report is of great importance as he was well respected as a critic, writer, journalist, and scientist. His experience occurred on February 17, 1937, when there were solar eruptions pointed to by a strong magnetic storm ($aa = 55$; $am = 19.1$). Richard Maurice Bucke, [40] who coined the term Cosmic consciousness, has recorded two other data of mystic experience: J. W. W., January 20, 1885, and Paul Tyner, May 11, 1895. The respective geomagnetic indices are: $aa = 74$; $am = 15.5$ and $aa = 64$; $am = 18.2$. Three persons that did not want their names published gave the following dates of their mystic experience: June 4, 1950 ($aa = 59$; $am = 24.4$); July 19, 1959 ($aa = 241$; $am = 30.2$); June 26, 1963 ($aa = 67$; $am = 21.3$).

This is a rather eclectic sample; it is very difficult, however, to find such rare events at all that in addition are exactly dated and occurred after 1868, the beginning of the aa-record. Fortunately, Nicholas Kollerstrom has gathered another sample of acts of creation, though for another purpose. At the 5th International Astrological Research Conference, held in London, on November 22–23, 1986, he presented a sample of 17 eminent discoveries of scientists, aptly called Eureka moments. [41] Eleven of these data lie after the beginning of Mayaud's aa-index. Two were cancelled. Fermi's direction of the first controlled nuclear chain reaction in 1942 was no real act of creativity; it was only a phase in a technical development the mental basis of which was founded earlier. And Shockley's invention of the transistor, dated as 1947, is given as 1948 by several other sources. The remaining nine cases confirm the connection between boundary events on the Sun and human acts of creativity. Particles that are ejected by solar eruptions can reach the Earth within a few hours to four days. Thus, if it is assumed that Eureka moments concur with energetic solar eruptions that in most cases release strong geomagnetic storms, it seems reasonable to expect such storms on the Eureka day or one of the three following days. The observations confirm this working hypothesis:

Mendeleyev: 1 March 1869; concept of periodic table of chemical elements; $aa = 64$; $am = 20.9$

Edison: 7 November 1877; invention of phonograph; $aa = 57$; $am = 9.3$

Roentgen: 8 November 1895; discovery of X-rays; $aa = 100$; $am = 18.2$

Becquerel: 1 March 1896; discovery of radioactivity; $aa = 89$; $am = 18$

Loewi: 28 March 1921; discovery of chemical transmission of nerve impulses; $aa = 42$; $am = 16.6$

Fleming: 3 September 1928; discovery of Penicillin; $aa = 54$; $am = 17.7$

Tombaugh: 18 February 1930; discovery of the planet Pluto; $aa = 50$; $am = 28.6$)

Szilard: 12 September 1933; concept of atomic fission theory; $aa = 71$; $am = 16.4$

Watson: 28 February 1953; discovery of the molecular structure of gene substance; $aa = 92$; $am = 22.2$.

This result can be subjected to a statistical test, though the sample is rather small. Mayaud gives two half-daily values of the aa index for each Greenwich day. For the range of four days after the nine Eureka events the number of aa values thus amounts to 72. Statistically, the mean of these aa values, $\bar{x}_1$ = 29.13, and the standard deviation of their distribution, σ_1 = 21.56, are characteristic parameters of this first group. They set off against the parameters of the second group formed by the nine annual means of geomagnetic activity related to the years of the Eureka events: $\bar{x}_2$ = 18.66; σ_2 = 4.89. The statistical t-test evaluates whether the difference between the means of both groups is significant. The test yields t = 3.47 for 63 degrees of freedom (df). As the first group is known and expected to have a higher mean than the second group, the rules valid for single-sided distributions apply: $P < 0.0007$. The probability P that this result has been produced by random sampling is smaller than 1 in 1400. This points to a highly significant difference between the aa indices in both groups in accordance with the working hypothesis proposed above. When monthly means are chosen instead of yearly means, the difference between both groups continues to show highly significant results.

This example shows that significant results can emerge in very small samples. If so, this indicates strong relations that are of practical importance. Connections that only become visible when thousands of cases are investigated may be of theoretical interest; in practice, however, they are often of negligible weight. Naturally, the relation between solar boundary events and human creativity has to be corroborated by replications making use of new data. In this respect, it is a significant that Suitbert Ertel has established a relation between human acts of creation in various fields of art and science, and sunspot cycles of different length.[42] His highly significant results, corroborated by many replications, are based on a quite different, independent approach and careful statistical analysis of large bodies of data. Unfortunately, Ertel's voluminous work has not yet been published.

As has been stated in the beginning, instability indicative of boundary states is a pre-condition of creativity. Heavy geomagnetic storms that are linked to solar instability events are themselves an expression of strong instability in the Earth's magnetic field. It is not out of the question that this magnetic instability may induce instability in the electric activity of the brain cells, evidenced in electroencephalograms, or of the autonomous nervous system.[42a] Certainly, such instability cannot produce a creative potential other conditions of which are not fulfilled. But if there is a creative potential, it may be stimulated or triggered by instability.

According to Arthur Koestler [43] there is a remarkable form of blindness which often prevents even an original thinker from perceiving the meaning and significance of his own discovery. It resembles an "anti-body reaction" directed against new ideas irrespective of whether it is a new pattern created by others or oneself. Kepler nearly threw away the elliptic orbits of planets; for nearly three years he held the solution in his hands without seeing it. After the breakthrough of the new concept Kepler confessed: "The truth of Nature, which I had rejected and chased away, returned by stealth through the backdoor, disguising itself to be accepted. Ah, what a foolish bird I have been."

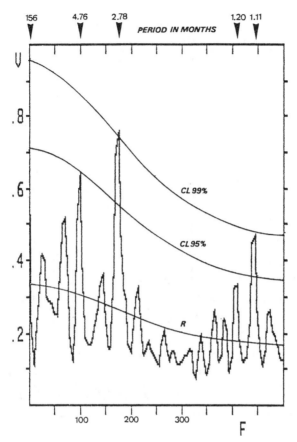

Figure 16: Blackman-Tukey power spectrum of flare-generated X-ray bursts equal to or greater than class X1 observed 1970 to 1982 by means of satellite instrumentation. The frequency f of investigated cycles is measured in millicycles per sampling interval of half a month. The ordinate axis represents the relative variance V of the respective frequencies. Periods of outstanding peaks, pointing to cycles of flares, are indicated on top of the figure. The significance of the deviation of prominent peaks from the Markov red noise (R) can be evaluated by means of the confidence level curves CL. The result provides evidence of cyclic features in the distribution of energetic solar flares.

Koestler aptly remarks that the defence mechanisms which protect habits against the intrusion of novelty account both for our mental inertia and mental stability. It seems plausible that strong instability in the Earth's magnetic field, that affects the basic electric conditions of brain functions, may release mental instability which makes it easier to overcome mental inertia.

Inversely, unshaken inertia would prevail when the geomagnetic field keeps quiet. There are examples that seem to point to such effects. Irène Curie and Frédéric Joliot were talented physicists; they were awarded the Nobel prize for the synthesis of new radioactive elements. On January 18, 1932, they made an observation the significance of which they did not grasp. Thus, they missed the discovery of the neutron, a fundamental subatomic particle. When the young physicist Ettore Majorana, a disciple of James Chadwick, read the report of the Joliot-Curies, he remarked sarcastically: "These fools, they have

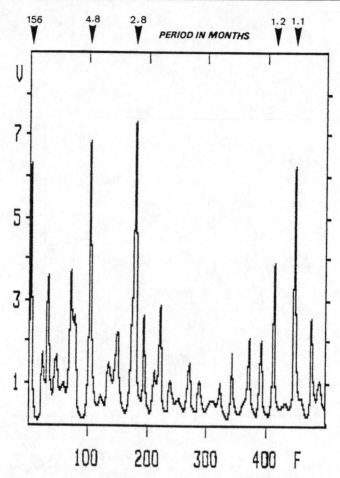

Figure 17: Maximum entropy spectrum of the same sample of X-ray bursts equal to or greater than class X1 as presented in Figure 16. The analysis based on the Burg-algorithm includes 312 data points and has a filter length of 82 coefficients. The frequency f is measured in millicycles per sampling interval of half a month. The ordinate axis indicates the relative variance of the respective frequencies. The outstanding peaks conform with those in the spectrum of Figure 16. This points to a cyclic pattern in the investigated sample of X-ray flares.

discovered the neutral proton and do not see that."[44] The Earth's magnetic field was unusually quiet at that time. The mean value of the Mayaud index for January 18 to 22, 1932, was $aa = 5$ and the standard deviation $\sigma = 0.8$, wheras the annual mean reached $am = 19$. However, when the physicist Klaus von Klitzing on February 5, 1980, observed facts that pointed to a quantized Hall effect, he at once fully realized the theoretical meaning of his finding;[45] it was a genuine Eureka moment that won him the Nobel prize. This time there was strong geomagnetic activity around the date of observation. The Mayaud index reached $aa = 67$ on February 6, 1980 ($am = 18.1$). As energetic flares were continually monitored by means of satellite instrumentation, there is confirmation that the strong geomagnetic activity around the date of discovery coincided with an X-ray burst of class X2 and a proton event.

3. SUCCESSFUL SEARCH FOR CYCLES OF FLARES

With respect to the multiple effects of energetic solar events, there is urgent need to develop a dependable flare forecast. Cycles of flares, if they existed, could be a help in this endeavour. But the general opinion of astronomers is that flares show a stochastic distribution. Research in solar eruptions seems to follow the same type of history as that of sunspots. It took more than 200 years to find out that they form a cycle of 11 years. Credit for this discovery has to be given to the pharmacist Schwabe; professional astronomers thought that sunspots were stochastically distributed. Fortunately, the delay with flares will be shorter. It has been shown that there are distinct cycles of energetic flares.[46] Energetic X-ray bursts below 12 Å are the hallmark of highly energetic X-ray flares and proton flares. They are a good general indicator of the geophysical significance of flares. X-ray bursts can only be observed by satellite instrumentation (SOLRAD/SMS/GOES). Such data in the 1 to 8 Å range are available from 1970. They beg for an analysis of their distribution over time.

Accordingly, all X-ray events $\geq$ X1 reported 1970 to 1982 in the Ursigrams of IUWDS and the prompt reports of Solar-Geophysical Data have been subjected to spectral analysis. Figure 16 presents the Blackman-Tukey power spectrum [47] of these flare-generated X-ray bursts. The weighted numbers of the observed bursts were summed within equidistant sampling intervals of half a month. The weights were derived from the X-ray class of the respective bursts. Thus, for example, the value 9 was assigned to a sampling interval comprising one burst X5 and two bursts X2. The resulting time series includes 312 data points. The frequency f is measured in millicycles per sampling interval of half a month. The ordinate axis designates the relative variance V of the respective frequencies. The spectrum shows prominent peaks at 156, 4.8, 1.2, and 1.1 months. The amplitudes around 1.1 months are near the highest resolvable frequency, though not beyond the limit defined by the Nyquist frequency. Yet an analysis based on a sampling interval of ¼ month yields the same result.

There are indications that the most pronounced peaks are real. R in Figure 16 designates the adopted Markov red noise, an appropriate model of random variability in spectra based on the Fourier cosine transform of estimates of the autocorrelation function.[48] The significance of the deviation of prominent peaks from the Markov red noise level can be evaluated by means of a special x^2-test.[49] The resulting confidence levels CL are marked in Figure 16. The peaks at 2.8 and 1.1 months are significant at the 99% level while the peak at 4.8 months reaches the 95% level. Two further peaks approach this zone of significance. The peak around 156 months is at 83%, and the peak at 1.2 months at 90%.

These results are replicated by another approach. J. P. Burg [50] has developed a new form of spectral variance analysis, the maximum entropy spectral method (MEM), which shows much higher resolution than earlier methods, especially at lower frequencies. The new method reaches an exactness and sharpness that matches the optical spectra. Meanwhile, the MEM is practised in several scientific fields including astronomy and geophysics. Figure 17 shows the result of the maximum entropy spectral analysis applied to the same time series of X-ray bursts comprising the same sampling intervals of half a month. The calculation based on the Burg-algorithm covers 312 data points and 301 frequencies. The filter length of 82 coefficients is in accord with the suggestion of most authors not to go beyond 30% of the number of data points.[51] The extreme sensitivity of the MEM can lead to spectral shifts or spectrum instability, especially when the filter length is extended beyond 30 to 40% of the length of the time series. Experiments with different filter lengths up to 40% show that the spectrum presented in Figure 17 is stable. There is no shift in the outstanding frequencies. The MEM spectrum shows the same prominent peaks at the same frequencies as in the Blackman-Tukey power spectrum. A narrower sampling interval of ¼ month does not change the result.

It is a disadvantage of the MEM that an acknowledged reliability test of spectral peaks does not yet exist. According to the simple and useful "rule of thumb" expressed by Stuart *et al.*,[52] a spectral peak is regarded to be significant if it contains at least three computed points which deviate from the noise and has a maximum two or three times greater than the surrounding noise level. According to this standard the peaks in Figure 17 marked by period pointers deviate significantly from the noise. As these are the same peaks as in the Blackman-Tukey spectrum of Figure 16 that proved to be significant at confidence levels going up to 99%, there is sufficient evidence supporting their reality. A further replication is contributed by dividing the data set in half. The maximum entropy spectra for each half again set off the peaks around 4.8, 2.8, 1.2, and 1.1 months; only the 156 months period is lost, as was to be expected.

V. PLANETARY CONTROL OF THE SUN'S MOTION ABOUT THE CENTRE OF MASS OF THE SOLAR SYSTEM

The prominent cyclic features are consistently present in all spectra examined. Thus, there are sufficient reasons to propose the working hypothesis that the incidence of X-ray flares in the 1 to 8 Å range shows a cyclic pattern. Where do these flare cycles come from? As to predictions, this is a crucial question because the analysis is based on the rather small time-span of 13 years. If there are strong variations in the actual period of cycles, forecasts of flares and connected terrestrial events will go astray if it is not clear which changes will occur. It will be shown that the prominent amplitudes in the spectra indeed represent quasi-cycles with wide variations in their periods. The knowledge of the mean period of such quasicycles is no real help in predictions. The 11-year sunspot cycle with a range of variation from 7 to 17 years is an example of this. As long as it is not known how the cycle is regulated, there will be no solid basis for predictions. Without a reasoned physical background to guide selection, there is a severe risk of finding accidental patterns in diverse and varied data sets. The statistical analysis of past data does not constitute a reliable means to foresee future change in the data pattern. Thus, it is of both practical and theoretical importance that the spectrum can be exactly related to the variation in astrophysical quantities and to calculable planetary configurations by an approach following the fundamental rule of Operations research that the behaviour of any part of a system has some effect on the behaviour of the system as a whole. The results were tested by extended forecast experiments described above.

The first process involved are impulses of the torque (IOT) in the Sun's motion about the centre of mass of the solar system (CM) that were mentioned already. They are induced by special heliocentric constellations of the giant planets Jupiter, Saturn, Uranus, and Neptune. Figure 18 shows the ecliptic positions of CM relative to the Sun's centre for 1945 to 1995. The heliocentric representation and the line marking the limb of the Sun make it easy to see whether CM is to be found above or below the Sun's surface; most of the time it is on the outside of the Sun's body. The distance of both centres varies from 0.01 to 2.19 solar radii. It takes 9 to 14 years to complete one revolution. In relation to the galactic centre only CM follows an elliptic path around the centre of mass of the Milky Way system, whereas the Sun describes a very irregular helix around the elliptic line of motion of CM. The planets' paths are still more complicated. There is mutual interdependence. While the planets make the Sun oscillate around CM, the Sun induces a still more intricate dance of the planets about the centre of mass of the solar system. Newton was the first to see this: "Since that centre of gravity is continually at rest, the Sun, according to the various positions of the planets, must continually move every way, but will never recede far from that centre."[53] In 1928 Ludwig Zehnder [54] suspected a connection of the Sun's motion with the 11-year sunspot cycle. Paul D. Jose [55] made a thorough computer analysis of this special relation in 1965. Unfortunately, his predictions for the 11- year sunspot cycle No. 21, based on his analysis, failed to be accurate.

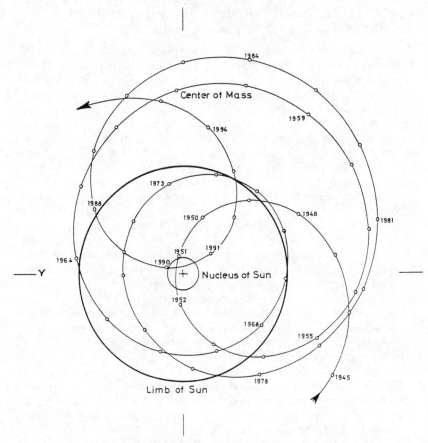

Figure 18:   Position of the centre of mass of the solar system CM in the ecliptic plane relative to the Sun's centre CS for the years 1945 to 1995. Heliocentric representation and marking the limb of Sun make it easy to see whether CM is above or below the Sun's surface. The distance of both centres varies from 0.01 to 2.19 solar radii.

VI. PLANETARY REGULATION OF SECULAR AND SUPERSECULAR SUNSPOT CYCLES

Since the middle seventies attention has been focused on special phases in the Sun's revolution about CM that proved to be the hallmark of all kinds of cycles of solar activity.[56] The Sun reaches extreme positions relative to CM when the giant planets form special constellations. The Sun's centre (CS) and CM come very near to each other when Jupiter on one side of the Sun is in opposition to Saturn, Uranus, and Neptune on the other side, whereas CS and CM reach their greatest distance when all of the giant planets form a conjunction. Conspicuously, just in 1951, when the Sun's centre CS was very near CM and the Sun changed from approaching it to receding from it, the secular sunspot cycle of about 80 years reached a maximum. This was no fortuitous fit. Further analysis showed that such phases of spectacular change in the Sun's orbital motion coincide with relatively strong impulses of the torque (IOT).[57]

The torque T acting on the Sun is defined by $T = dL/dt$, which is the first derivative of the angular momentum L of the Sun's orbital motion. Impulses of the torque, measured by the time integral $\Delta L = \int_{t_0}^{t_1} T(t)dt$, occur when T approaches zero, changes sign, and shows a more or less sharp increase in the new direction measured in the relatively short time interval $t_1 - t_0 = 300$ days. L, the Sun's orbital momentum, can vary from about -0.1×10^{47} g cm^2 s^{-1} to about 4.3×10^{47} g cm^2 s^{-1}, which is an increase by a factor of up to 40 and more. The maximum value of the Sun's orbital momentum reaches 25% of the Sun's rotational momentum which is 1.7×10^{48} g cm^2 s^{-1}. If there were spin-orbit coupling, a transfer of angular momentum from the Sun's orbit to the Sun's spin on its axis or vice versa, this could make a difference of more than 5% in the Sun's equatorial rotational velocity,[58] which is actually observed.

When consecutive IOT are taken and smoothed to constitute a new time series, a wave pattern emerges that bears information as to the epochs of extrema in the secular Gleissberg-cycle. Figure 19 shows this wave for the years 1100 to 2100 A.D. It has a mean length of 166 years, but each extremum, whether positive or negative, is correlated to a maximum in the secular sunspot cycle, while minima occur when the curve reaches zero values. The mean interval between consecutive extrema is 83 years and varies within 47 to 118 years. Wolfgang Gleissberg found corresponding variations in the secular cycle that range from 40 to 120 years. The cycle length of 83 years conforms with results elaborated by G. W. Brier. He found a prominent period of 83 years in the unsmoothed cosine transform of 2148 autocorrelations of 2628 monthly sunspot numbers.[59] The assessment of the mean length of the secular torque cycle of 83 years is based on calculations covering the period 5259 B.C. to 2347 A.D.[60] The fat arrows in Figure 19 indicate the epochs of maxima in the secular sunspot cycle assessed by Wolfgang Gleissberg making use of data by D. J. Schove.[61] These epochs are in phase with the computed secular torque cycle. The wave in Figure 19 reveals that there is an excess of positive or negative impulses of the torque for many decades. This is an indication of a cumulative effect.

The plot in Figure 20 covers the years 300 to 1100 A.D. The smoothed curve, elaborated by W. Gleissberg, is based on detailed data by J. D. Schove.[62] D_M

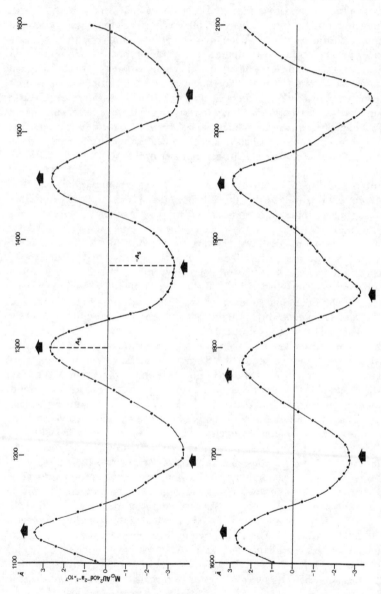

Figure 19: Smoothed time series of consecutive impulses of the torque (IOT), the epochs of which are indicated by dots. The resulting wave pattern is related to the secular cycle of sunspot activity. The average wave-length is 166 years. Each extremum at mean intervals of 83 years is connected with a maximum in the secular sunspot cycle. These maxima, as assessed by W. Gleissberg, are marked by fat arrows. Minima occur when the wave is near zero values. The wave reflects the effect of solar system configurations that cause impulses of the torque.

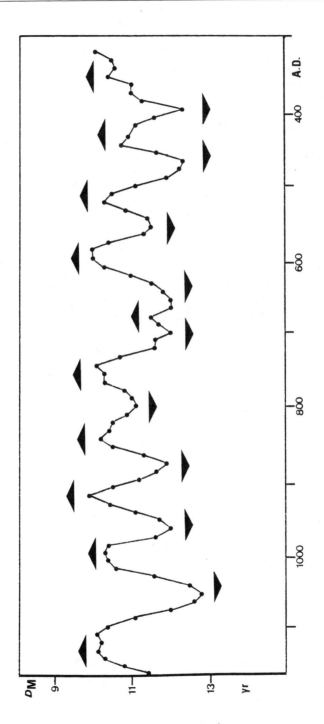

Figure 20: Secular cycle of sunspots for 300 to 1100 A.D. after W. Gleissberg and D. J. Schove. Flat triangles indicate epochs of secular maxima and minima derived from calculated IOT-data. The extrema of the two data sets are in phase.

represents intervals between consecutive 11-year maxima that reflect the secular cycle. Minima of D_M correspond to strong sunspot maxima and inversely. The flat triangles indicate the calculated epochs of secular maxima and minima based on the secular torque cycle. The data sets are in phase. An evaluation of the total result for the years 300 to 1980 confirms the high degree of synchronism of the Gleissberg-data and the calculated torque epochs. A Pearson-test yields the value 54.5 (1 degree of freedom; $P \ll 0.00001$) for the maxima, and 22.3 (1 degree of freedom; $P < 0.00001$) for the minima. When subsets are formed, the results prove to be homogeneous. The torque wave points to a secular sunspot minimum past 1990.

The extrema in the secular wave of IOT can be taken to constitute a smoothed supersecular wave with a quasi-period of 391 years. This long wave points to an imminent supersecular sunspot minimum about 2030.[63] There are indications that secular and supersecular sunspot minima are related to variations in climate. Thus a prolonged period of colder climate is about to be initiated by the secular minimum past 1990, will reach its deepest point around the supersecular minimum in 2030, and come to an end about 2070. A shorter torque cycle of 31 years, based on an analysis of a cross-correlation function of sunspots and IOT, made it possible to predict the end of the Sahelian drought three years in advance. The forecast: "The next drought maximum is to be expected about 2010. A humid period should already begin within 2 yr and reach a first maximum about 1986", was published in 1983.[64] There was enough rain in the Sahelian countries in 1985 and still more in 1986. Geoffrey Dean, whose negative review of forecasts based on planetary constellations has been mentioned above, had received a preprint of this paper that also contained the evaluation of the positive result of the forecasts of energetic flares for the years 1979 to 1981 as well as the successful prediction of X-ray bursts $> X9$ in 1982. He nevertheless declared that successful predictions based on planetary configurations did not exist.

VII. PLANETARY FORCING AND FLARE CYCLES

Cycles of solar activity of medium wavelength, like the 11-year sunspot cycle, are also related to IOT.[65] But even such short cycles as those that emerged from the spectral analysis of the distribution of energetic flares are connected with IOT. Strong impulses of the torque are initiated when the planet Jupiter, the centre of mass CM, and the Sun's centre CS are in line (JU-CM-CS). There are two types of JU-CM-CS events: those that are accompanied by a sharp increase in orbital momentum and centrifugal motion of the Sun away from CM (JU-CM-CSc), and those that coincide with a decrease in orbital momentum and centripetal motion of the Sun toward CM due to prevailing gravitation (JU-CM-CSg). These two different types can have different effects on the Sun and solar-terrestrial interaction. JU-CM-CSg events that can be related to the investigated time series of energetic flares, covering the period 1970 to 1982, occurred during 1970.02 and 1982.83. They formed a cycle with a period of 153.7 months.

Just this cycle and harmonics of it represent most of the variance in the flare spectra discussed above.[66] The most prominent amplitudes in Figures 16 and 17 point to the torque cycle itself, to the exact harmonics 4.8 months and 1.2 months with a neighbouring peak at 1.1 months, and to a strong amplitude at 2.8 months, that seems out of sequence, since 2.4 months would be the fitting harmonic between 4.8 and 1.2 months. But the shift to 2.8 months seems to be the result of the interference with another flare cycle in this range, regulated by tidal planets. Its mean period is 3.36 months. This value, when combined with the 2.4 month harmonic of the torque cycle, yields a mean value of 2.88 months which properly matches the strong amplitude at 2.8 months in the flare spectrum.[67]

This combination is consistent in so far as the torque harmonic of 2.4 months is nearer to the interfering period of 3.36 months than the torque harmonic of 4.8 months. But this latter harmonic is also connected with the interfering cycle. Calculation shows that the period of the 3.36-month cycle has a range of variation of ± 1.6 months. If it gets in phase with the torque harmonic of 4.8 months, which occurs at irregular intervals, as a rule highly energetic X-ray bursts are released. This connection is of practical importance in assessing the category of expected X-ray bursts in predictions. There is a gap between the prominent amplitude related to the torque cycle of 154 months itself and its higher harmonics of 4.8 months and beyond. This could be due to resonance with the interfering oscillator, the period of which varies about 3.36 months. Only the higher harmonics of the torque cycle are then expected to respond.

There is a wealth of papers that try to establish a relation between tidal planets and sunspots. Critical authors stress that all tidal planets, when in conjunction, could only raise a tide of a few millimeters on the Sun. But it should be taken into consideration that the horizontal component of the tidal forces could be of interest, as the Sun's gravity acceleration is 28 times that of the Earth's. E. Oepik[68] has shown that the mean velocity of tidal currents on the Sun can reach about one-third of tidal currents generated by the Moon on Earth. This is not negligible as the plasma in the Sun is subject to magnetohydrodynamic instabilities and turbulence. There are only few papers

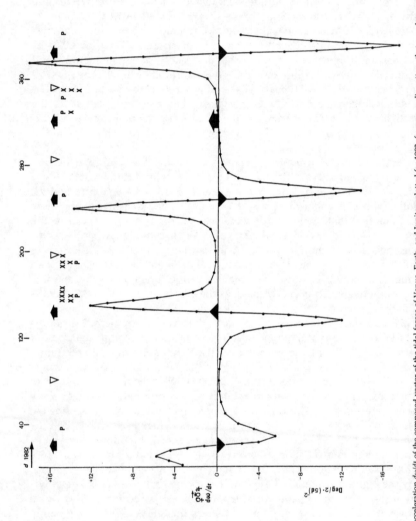

Figure 21: The angular acceleration $d\omega/dt$ of the composed vector of the tidal forces of Venus, Earth, and Jupiter, plotted for 1982, forms a cyclic pattern that correlates with observed proton events (P) and X-ray burst equal to or greater than class X3 (X). Active phases in the related flare cycle, displayed on top, begin when $d\omega/dt$ changes from positive to negative values, or inversely. These crucial zero phases that coincide with a boundary transition are indicated by fat marks. Lulls in flare activity begin in the middle between consecutive zero phases; these lull starts are marked by white triangles.

that deal with relations of tidal planets with flares.[69] This is difficult to understand, as it is known from Skylab observations that flares are set off by initial disruptions in hot coronal loops over active regions. It is easier to imagine that weak tidal disturbances may trigger such events in an unstable zone of the Sun's atmosphere than to concede that the tide-generating forces could act on the strong magnetic fields that are contained in sunspots.

Calculations of the relative tidal forces of the planets Mercury to Saturn show that the latter is as negligible as that of Mars. Comparison of the composed vector of the tidal forces of Venus, Earth, and Jupiter, excluding or including Mercury, shows that the vector including Mercury oscillates around the vector of Venus, Earth, and Jupiter. Therefore, only the latter was investigated in its relation to energetic flares marked by X-ray bursts equal to or greater than class X2 ($\geq X2$). Figure 21 presents the result. Unexpectedly, no cardinal correlations with the magnitude of the vector emerged. But the change in direction proved to be crucial. The angular acceleration $d\omega/dt = d^2\varphi/dt^2$ of the vector forms a cyclic pattern which shows a strong relation with X-ray bursts observed since 1970. Figure 21 reflects the course of the cycle in 1982. The abscissa axis designates the days of 1982. The ordinate represents the time rate of change of the angular velocity of the vector. The active phase of the related flare cycle begins when the curve crosses the time axis. This is again a boundary phenomenon, a transition from the domain of one quality into the realm of the opposite quality, which is together the transgression of a borderline; $d\omega/dt$ changes from positive to negative acceleration, or inversely. These crucial zero phases are indicated in Figure 21 by fat triangles, and in one case by a fat arrow. The effect on flares is stronger when the curve ascends then when it descends. Furthermore, the strength of the effect is inversely proportional to the steepness of the ascent or descent. Slow ascent releases prolonged flare activity reaching a high level of energy display. Cases of less steep ascent occur when the magnitude of the vector reaches maximum values. The fat arrow on the time axis designates such a situation.

Lull phases in the flare cycle always begin in the middle between two zero values of $d\omega/dt$. Their start is marked by the second harmonic of the respective cycle. On top of Figure 21 the active and the lull phases of the tidal flare cycle are marked by arrows pointing upwards, and by white triangles pointing downwards. Observed proton events and X-ray bursts $\geq X3$ are indicated by P and X. They match the phases of activity without exception. In 1982 the steep ascent marked by a triangle pointing upwards had as strong effects as the slow ascent marked by a fat arrow; but the latter category showed a stronger overall effect since 1970. When all 118 X-ray bursts $\geq X2$ observed since 1970 are tested, 96 of them fit active phases in the tidal cycle, and only 22 inactive ones. A Pearson-test yields the value 47 for 1 degree of freedom ($P < 0.00001$). All events $\geq X6$ fell into the active periods. As the sample covers more than 40 cycles, the result seems to indicate a dependable relationship.

In the spectra of energetic X-ray flares presented in Figures 16 and 17, the two prominent peaks in the range of higher frequencies at 1.1 and 1.2 months are clearly set off though they are close together. The 1.2-month amplitude has been explained to be a harmonic of the torque cycle. The tidal cycle is involved too. The exact period of the neighbouring amplitude in the spectra is 1.12 months, precisely the third harmonic of the period 3.36 of the tidal cycle.

The change in the length of the tidal cycle and the torque cycle is very irregular. The length of the $d\omega/dt$ cycle varies between 40 and 134 days. The current torque cycle marked by JU-CM-CSg events 1982.83 and 1998.56 will have a length of 15.7 years, compared with 12.8 years of the former cycle. So the former 4.8-month cycle changes to 5.9 months, the former harmonic at 2.4 months will be at 2.9 months, and the combined cycle at 2.8 months will shift to 3.2 months. These variations affect forecast techniques that make use of the interference effects of the torque cycle and the tidal cycle. The complex results show how difficult it would be to predict solar flares and their terrestrial effects without knowledge of the intricate regulation of solar activity by both the giant planets and the tidal planets, the effects of which are coupled by Jupiter, the main factor in both groups. The new forecast issued in January 1983, discussed in the beginning, was based on the current torque cycle with a period of 15.7 years. The strongly varied periods of its harmonics in comparison with those of the former cycle and the tidal cycle were allowed for. The change in the pattern offered a chance to test the reliability of the connections in question. As has been shown above, this test yielded a distinct confirmation.

VIII. MODULATION OF THE SUN'S ROTATION BY PLANETARY CONFIGURATIONS

The successful forecast of highly energetic events greater than class X9 in 1982 was directly founded on the JU- CM-CS event in 1982.83. Such constellations are nearly always accompanied by very energetic eruptional activity.[70] They seem to affect such activity via the Sun's rotation rate. The Sun, rotating on its axis, and the Sun, revolving around CM, could be looked at as coupled oscillators capable of internal resonance resulting in slight positive or negative accelerations in the Sun's spin. Such accelerations are actually observed. Speeding up or slowing down of the Sun's rotation rate is liable to influence the Sun's activity. Slower rotation seems to be linked to enhanced activity and faster rotation to weak activity. According to investigations by John E. Eddy,[71] based on historical observations by Scheiner and Hevelius, the rotation of the Sun's equator sped up just before the Maunder Minimum, a protracted period of very weak sunspot activity in the 17th century, whereas its rotation rate about 1620, near a secular maximum of sunspots, was much the same as it is today. Modern data confirm this relation. Mt. Wilson observations[72] show two striking jumps in the Sun's rate of rotation in 1967 and in 1970. These jumps into deceleration concurred with the epochs of IOT, as can be seen in Fig. 22. The arrows indicate heliocentric conjunctions of Jupiter and CM (JU-CM-CS) that initiate IOT. A further deceleration was observed in 1974, the epoch of the following JU-CM-CS event.

The planet Jupiter that is involved in these constellations plays a dominant role even among the giant planets that regulate the Sun's oscillations about CM. Jupiter holds 71% of the total mass of the planets and 61% of the total angular momentum of the system, whereas the Sun governs less than 1% of the angular momentum. This seems to be indicative of a case of spin-orbit coupling of the spinning Sun and the Sun revolving about CM, involving transfer of angular momentum from Jupiter to the revolving Sun and eventually to the spinning Sun. With respect to the angular momentum conservation law it makes sense that the observed slowing down in the Sun's spin coincides with an increase in the Sun's orbital angular momentum. Coupling could result from the Sun's motion through its own electric and magnetic fields that are relatively strong near the Sun's body. Even at a height of one solar diameter above the Sun's surface the electron density is still about 1 million electrons per cm^3. The Sun's average distance from CM is 1.1 solar radii. Thus, the low corona can act as a brake on the Sun's surface.[73]

The older Mount Wilson data were not corrected for scattered light. Meanwhile corrected rotation data are available that are based on a single reduction method for the entire interval 1967 to 1982. This time series elaborated by R. Howard[74] covers Carrington rotation numbers 1516 to 1726. They are displayed on the x-axis of Figure 23 and correspond to the period December 29, 1966, to September 4, 1982. The rotation values represent the equatorial angular sidereal rotation rate averaged over respective rotations. The plot is based on the running variance of these data. Running means are a well known feature in statistics. Variance, the square of the standard deviation, can be subjected to a similar process. The respective moving values

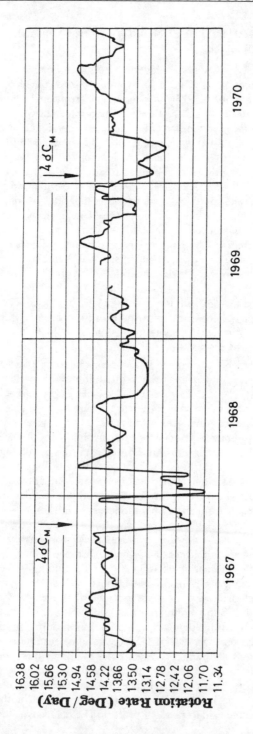

Figure 22:   Sudden decrease in the Sun's rate of rotation (Mount Wilson data) related to heliocentric conjunctions of Jupiter with the centre of mass CM.

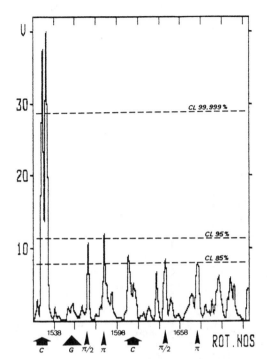

Figure 23: Smoothed running variance V of the Sun's equatorial angular sidereal rotation rate (Mount Wilson data) covering Carrington rotations 1516 (December 29, 1966) to 1726 (September 4, 1982). Fat arrows point to JU-CM-CSc epochs (C), while a triangle marks the epoch of a JU-CM-CSg event (G). Arrow-heads designate harmonics of quasi-cycles formed by consecutive JU-CM-CS events.

of the variance cover two consecutive rotations, thus measuring the variation in variability from one rotation to the next one. These results have been subjected to a Gaussian low-pass filter eliminating short range features covering less than five rotations. The ordinate axis measures this smoothed running variance. The epochs of JU-CM-CS events in 1967.8 and 1974.48 are marked by fat arrows and the letter C, whereas the epoch of the event in 1970.02 is indicated by a fat triangle and the letter G. This makes allowance for the two types of JU-CM-CS events mentioned already: those that go along with an increase in orbital momentum and resulting centrifugal motion of the Sun (C), and those that initiate a decrease in orbital momentum and centripetal motion due to prevailing gravitation (G).

The two C-conjunctions are related to prominent variance peaks significant at the 85% confidence level (CL) and far beyond. If the running variance is not subjected to smoothing, the second C-peak in 1974 reaches the 95% confidence level. There is only a relatively small variance peak connected with the G-conjunction in 1970. This points to a different quality of this kind of events, which was to be expected, as the orbital momentum does not increase, but is diminished. Nevertheless, G-conjunctions, too, have an impact on the Sun's differential rotation. The Mount Wilson rotation data do not cover the following G-conjunction in 1982.8. It is beyond the frame of the plot. If consecutive conjunctions are thought to form quasi-cycles initiated by the

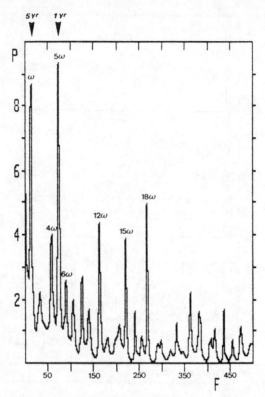

Figure 24: Maximum entropy spectrum of the running variance of the Sun's equatorial rotation rate (Mount Wilson data). The prominent peaks represent the mean period (ω) of the JU-CM-CS cycles involved and its harmonics 4ω, 5ω, 6ω, or simple multiples of these frequencies.

respective foregoing event, there should emerge subcyclic effects in the rotation data, provided that these are connected with the fundamental cycle. The quasi-cycle initiated by the second C-conjunction in 1974.5 had a period of 8.3 years as the following conjunction occurred in 1982.8. It can be seen in Figure 23 that the phases $\pi/2$ and π radians (90° and 180°), indicated by small pointers, coincide with variance peaks that are significant at the 85% confidence level. In the unsmoothed data these peaks reach the 95% level. The corresponding phases are outstanding, too, in the foregoing quasicycle initiated by the G-event indicated by a triangle. The peaks reach the 99% confidence level in the unsmoothed data. So far only the equatorial rotation rate has been investigated. As the Sun's differential rotation is rather complex, decelerations or accelerations in other latitudes may be involved.

As shown in Figure 23, subcyclic features like the second and fourth harmonic of cycles of JU-CM-CS events can be identified by their mark on the Sun's rotation. Fig. 24 is a confirmation of this connection. It presents the maximum entropy spectrum of the rotation data. It covers 211 data points (Carrington rotations No. 1516 – 29 December 1966 – to No. 1727 – 4 September 1982) and is based on 70 filter coefficients. The frequency f is measured in millicycles per sampling interval of a Carrington rotation. The ordinate axis

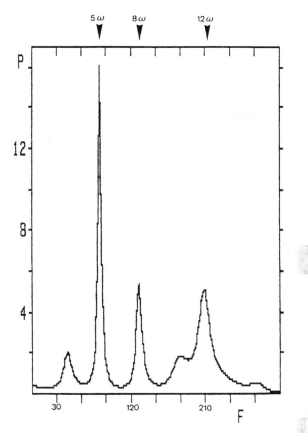

Figure 25: Maximum entropy spectrum of the running variance of Mount Wilson rotation data covering the JU-CM-CS quasi-cycle 1970 to 1974.5. The prominent peaks point to the frequency 5ω and the double value of 4ω and 6ω.

designates the relative power P of the respective frequencies. The spectrum is stable. A change in the number of filter coefficients does not generate spectral shifts. The prominent low frequency peak, the fundamental ω, has a period of 66.67 Carrington rotations or 5 years. This is exactly the mean interval of the JU-CM-CS events involved (1967.8, 1970, 1974.5, 1982.8; (2.2yr + 4.45yr + 8.35yr)/3 = 5yr). The outstanding harmonic is 5ω with the period 1 year. It is known in the physics of vibrating systems, especially that of vibrating strings, that the 5th harmonic is in a central position. An indication of this is the fact that in musical harmony the three major chords F-A-C, C-E-G, and G-B-D each represent fundamental tone sequences with the frequency ratio 4 : 5 : 6.[75] The neighbouring harmonics 4ω and 6ω are exactly represented in the spectrum, too, and in addition the peaks 12ω, 15ω, and 18ω, which are simple multiples of the 4th, 5th, and 6th harmonic. Figure 25 corroborates the weight of these harmonics. It shows the maximum entropy spectrum of the rotation data of the single JU-CM-CS-cycle 1970 to 1974.5. The 5th harmonic again stands out from the other frequencies, and the prominent peaks 8ω and 12ω are simple multiples of the 4th and 6th harmonic.

IX. HARMONICS OF SOLAR SYSTEM CYCLES, THE MAJOR PERFECT CHORD, AND HIGHLY ENERGETIC SOLAR ACTIVITY

These results beg for an experimental synthesis of the 4th, 5th, and 6th harmonic such that corresponding cosine waves are superimposed to form a resultant wave with the frequency of the fundamental which is the cycle of JU-CM-CS events. The amplitudes of the single cosine waves were chosen to form the inverse ratio 6 : 5 : 4. Figure 26 presents the prototypal pattern of the composite wave. The time units 0 to 100 on the x-axis represent normalized centesimal fractions of the period of JU-CM-CS cycles of any length. Thus events that occur in the same phase of cycles of different periods coincide in the prototypal pattern. Phase coincidence becomes immediately apparent. This is important as JU-CM- CS cycles show very different periods from 2 to 16 years.

Solar cosmic ray events, that are accompanied by very energetic X-ray bursts, were observed since 1942. As they are rare events, only 21 of them were listed through 1969. The epochs of these highly energetic proton events are marked in Figure 26 by the letter P. Out of 21 events, 17 match positive phases of the composite wave that are marked at the top by lines bounded by bars. The two phases that show a less steep descent, cycle fractions 20/100 to 26/100 and 50/100 to 55/100, seem to show a prolonged effect; thus three negative percentiles were added to the respective positive phases as indicated by those lines bounded by bars. A Pearson-test of the distribution of these 21 solar cosmic ray events yields $\chi^2 = 8.1$ for 1 degree of freedom ($P < 0.005$).

Since 1970 X-ray bursts have· been continually observed by satellite instrumentation and listed in Ursigrams of IUWDS and in Solar- Geophysical Data, published by the National Oceanic and Atmospheric Administratrion (NOAA), in Boulder, Colorado. From 1970 through 1986 altogether 46 flare-generated X-ray bursts $\geq X4$ were recorded. The epochs of these bursts are indicated in Figure 26 by arrow heads. Out of 46 bursts 41 fit the defined positive phases of the composite wave; only 5 hit negative phases. A Pearson-test yields $\chi^2 = 28.2$ for 1 degree of freedom; $P = 1.1 \times 10^{-7}$. When only very energetic X-ray bursts $\geq X7$ are selected, all of 18 observed events fit the positive phases. A combination of cosmic ray events and bursts $\geq X4$ gives a sample of 67 events, 58 of which meet the positive phases of the superposition. A Pearson-test yields $\chi^2 = 35.8$ for 1 degree of freedom; $P = 7 \times 10^{-10}$.

This highly significant result was tested by predictions. According to a long-range forecast issued January 15, 1983, during respective positive phases of the JU- CM-CS cycle 1982.83 to 1990.3 – 15 Jan. to 1 April 1983, 1 Jan. 1984 to 1 Febr. 1985, and 1 Jan. 1986 to 9 Jan. 1987 – the incidence and weight of energetic X-ray bursts, proton flares, and geomagnetic storms were expected to reach 2.5 times that of less active intervening periods. Meanwhile, this forecast has turned out to be correct. All bursts $\geq X4$, the most energetic proton events, and all severe magnetic disturbances fit the predicted phases of stronger activity: 3 Febr. 1983: $X4$; 4 Febr. 1983: proton event 340 particles (cm² ster s)$^{-1}$ at 10 MeV; 5 Febr. 1983: $A\kappa = 110$; 16 Febr. 1984: proton event 660 particles; 24 April 1984: $X13$; 26 April 1984: proton event 2500 particles; 19 May 1984: $X4$; 20 May 1984: $X10$; 11 Nov. 1984: $A\kappa = 87$; 22 Jan. 1985: $X4$; 8 Febr.

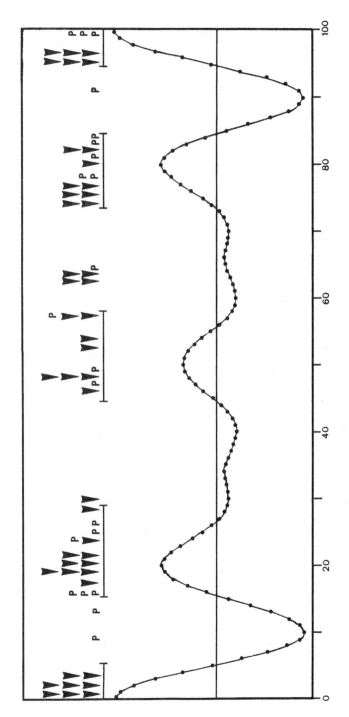

Figure 26: Prototypal pattern of a composite wave formed by the superimposition of harmonics with the frequency ratio 4 : 5 : 6. The time units 0 to 100 represent normalized centesimal fractions of JU-CM-CS cycles of any length. The positive phases of the composite wave coincide with clusters of solar cosmic ray events (P), observed from 1942 to 1969 and flare-generated X-ray bursts equal to or greater than class X4 (marked by pointers) registered 1970 through 1986.

1986: $A\kappa = 230$. These successful forecasts were again checked by astronomers and the Space Environment Services Center, Boulder.

The periods of predicted events $> X9$ in 1982 met a positive phase in the preceding JU-CM-CS cycle; this was one of the clues pointing to eruptional activity rising above the usual level. This shows how different cycles, that can all be derived from impulses of the torque initiated by JU-CM-CS events, can be used to develop a long range forecast of solar activity that covers most of the energetic events which are important in solar-terrestrial interaction. The cycles involved are often related to all kinds of JU-CM-CS events, and sometimes only to JU-CM-CSc or JU-CM-CSg events. It will be a difficult task to find out in detail how special IOT events are connected with special time series of solar-terrestrial data. The results presented here are only a first step in a new direction. It is intriguing that the ratio of the superimposed harmonics 4 : 5 : 6 is that of the major perfect chord in musical harmony. Kepler had found just this chord C – E – G when he analyzed the ratios of the velocities of different planets at aphelion and perihelion. Kepler's finding is also valid for the outer planets Uranus to Pluto.[76] Thus, the major perfect chord turns out to be a fundamental structural element of the planetary system. The results presented here are a new substantiation of the Pythagorean harmony of the spheres at a complex level that relates planetary configurations to the Sun's oscillations about CM, solar rotation, the Sun's activity, and solar-terrestrial interaction.

There is still another confirmation of harmonical relations. In Figure 26 one larger aggregation of 5 events at 63/100 on the horizontal axis is outside the positive phases. This position represents exactly the ratio 5 : 8 of the minor sixth in musical harmony, and together that of the golden section (61.8 : 38.2), key to aesthetic proportions in art. When allowance is made for this ratio, too, 63 out of 67 very energetic solar eruptions of the last 4 decades could have been forecast by means of JU-CM-CS cycles, their harmonics, and harmonical and aesthetic ratios. As has been shown, an actual forecast covering a period of seven years has proved successful since 1983. Such "composition" of dependable predictions based on key chords of the Sun's energetic music of the spheres is by no means an isolated feature. It will be shown in the final chapters that cosmic harmony expressed in precise consonant ratios is a paramount phenomenon that regulates the most important cycles of the Sun's energy display and their terrestrial response.

X.   SOLAR SYSTEM CONSTELLATIONS AND GEOMAGNETIC DISTURBANCES

Geomagnetic storms, which are released by energetic solar eruptions, are important geophysical events. Newer results indicate that there is a connection with weather. Figure 27, after V. Bucha,[77] shows zonal type of atmospheric circulation (at top) as a result of geomagnetic disturbances caused by the Sun's eruptional activity, and meridional circulation (at the bottom) related to a lull in geomagnetic activity. This is a permanent feature that regulates the prevalence of warm westerly flow or cool arctic air over Europe and North America. A statistical analysis covering the years 1955 to 1974 yields a correlation coefficient $r = 0.65$. Bucha has tried to give a geophysical explanation of this correlation.

The bulk flow speed of the solar wind, that is indicative of the energy of eruptional mass ejections and resultant shock waves caused by solar eruptions, is strongly coupled to geomagnetic activity,[78] which in turn seems to be the common factor of a wide variety of terrestrial phenomena. Many authors including Sazonov,[79] Mustel,[80] Beynon and Winstanley,[81] Stolov and Shapiro,[82] and Sidorenkov,[83] have reported various connections between geomagnetic disturbances and features of the troposphere. Cobb[84] has shown that the monthly variation of the air- earth current from mean values at Mauna Loa, Hawaii, is correlated with Bartel's magnetic character index Cp.

According to Mustel[85] surface pressure increases in anticyclones and decreases in cyclones after isolated geomagnetic storms. King[86] has reported similar results. In a study that covers the years 1964 to 1971, Roberts and Olson[87] have found that troughs that enter the Gulf of Alaska or are formed there two to four days after a sharp increase in geomagnetic activity, tend to be larger than average size. Prohaska and Willett[88] applied Eigen-analysis technique to a matrix of cross-correlation coefficients between the geomagnetic aa-index and the monthly mean temperature at 32 United States stations, and isolated temperature anomaly patterns that are highly correlated with the aa-index. As this index is considered to be a strong descriptor of the solar wind, Prohaska and Willett hold that the source of the effect influencing the local temperature field through the atmospheric circulation is also driving the solar wind and disturbing the geomagnetic field.

Sazonov[89] and King[90] have drawn attention to the similarity between meteorological and geomagnetic contour maps. Neubauer[91] has discovered that sudden commencements of geomagnetic storms, released by solar eruptions, are related to displacements in the 70 mb polar vortex in the lower stratosphere which in turn influence the polar vortex in the troposphere. The shift in the 70 mb polar vortex is caused by a localized sudden stratospheric warming. Of 66 magnetic storms observed during the winters 1978/1979 and 1979/1980, as much as 61 were accompanied by such stratospheric warming. According to Neubauer this effect can be explained in detail by geophysical processes. There are indications that explosive volcanic activity is related to changes in weather and climate.[92] It is not out of the question that variations in the torque exerted by the solar wind on the Earth's magnetosphere have an

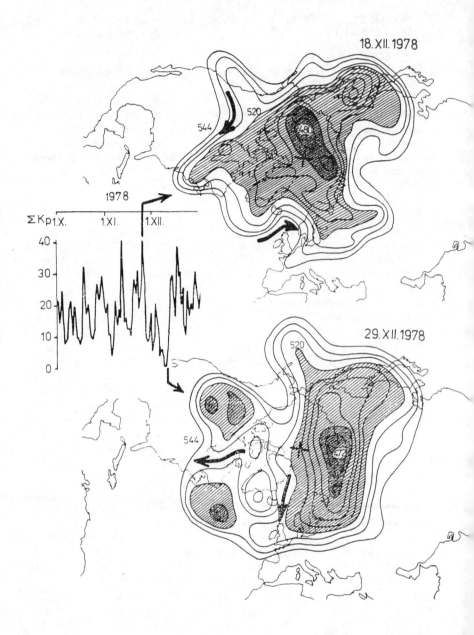

Figure 27:   The plot by V. Bucha shows zonal type of atmospheric circulation, parallel to the equator (at top) as a result of geomagnetic disturbances caused by the Sun's eruptional activity, and meridional circulation (at the bottom) related to a lull in geomagnetic activity. The *Kp*-scale (in the middle) measures the degree of geomagnetic activity.

influence on volcanic activity via changes in the Earth's rotational velocity and the motion of continental plates with respect to one another.[93] Some of these results may be spurious. Nevertheless, one of the few common threads that appear so widely in the otherwise disparate literature as to suggest that they probably have some validity, is the link between geomagnetic storms and meteorological or geophysical responses.[94] The Executive Committee of the International Working Group on Magnetic Field Satellites holds that there is an apparent relationship in the geomagnetic secular change to the length of the day and average global temperature on a decade time scale, suggesting that several of the major physical forces on the Earth may be interrelated[95]. Thus, long-term prediction of geomagnetic activity seems to be important, both for space mission planning and testing empirical understanding of the impact of the fast solar wind on the Earth's magnetosphere and possible meteorological responses.

Long range forecasts of geomagnetic activity were thought to be impossible, though there is a general correlation with the sunspot number R. In detail, however, the data do not correspond as well. This can be seen in Figure 28 after P. N. Mayaud[96] which presents yearly means of the Mayaud-index aa that measures the observed geomagnetic activity. The data run from 1868 to 1984. Upward arrow heads at the bottom of the plot mark the epochs of 11-year sunspot maxima. They do not match the highest peaks in the plot and sometimes even coincide with minima, as for instance in 1979. The arrows pointing downwards, however, fit the most prominent peaks in geomagnetic activity in nearly all cases. They mark the epochs of JU-CM-CS events that occurred 1868 to 1984.

There were only two striking exceptions to the fit: the conjunctions in 1901 and 1912. But they coincided with deep protracted 11-year sunspot minima; there was no potential of activity to draw on. No other such coincidence occurred in the investigated period. The deficit in conjunction effects seems to have depressed the general level of activity in the decades from 1900 to 1920; it reached the deepest point in the period of observation of more than a hundred years. In 1967 and 1970 the related peaks were low. This could be due to a disturbance of the rhythm in the pattern. The interval between the two JU-CM-CS events involved was unusually short, only 2.2 years. The depression in geomagnetic activity, however, could also be a special expression of the major solar instability event in 1968.

A Pearson-test of the goodness of fit of outstanding aa-peaks, going beyond defined thresholds, and JU-CM-CS epochs yields the value 17.1 for 1 degree of freedom ($P = 0.00004$). The strong enhancement of geomagnetic activity in 1982 was forecast with regard to these results in January 1982. The prediction was controlled by the astronomers W. Gleissberg, J. Pfleiderer, and H. Woehl. A new peak in geomagnetic activity is to be expected around the next conjunction in 1990.3. Its height depends on the activity potential of the 11-year cycle No. 22.

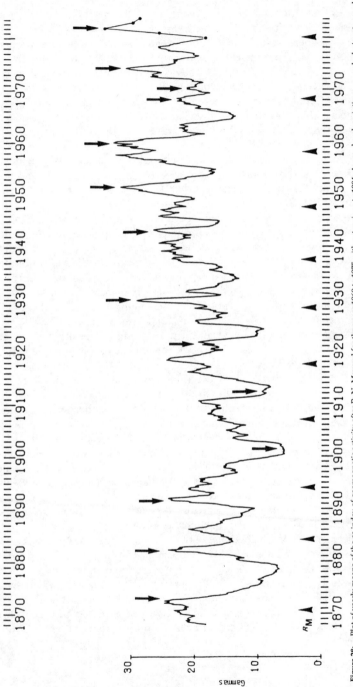

Figure 28: Plot of yearly means of the *aa*-index of geomagnetic activity after P. N. Mayaud for the years 1868 to 1975 with extensions to 1984. Arrow-heads pointing upwards designate epochs of 11-year sunspot maxima that show a poor conformity with *aa*-peaks. Large arrows mark epochs of JU-CM conjunctions that match the most prominent crests in geomagnetic activity. The peak in 1982 was predicted on the basis of this relationship.

XI. JUPITER, CENTER OF MASS, AND THE OZONE COLUMN

There is an abundance of papers speculating about the response of atmospheric ozone to solar activity and its effects on tropospheric climate. R. Reiter[97] has launched a series of radiosonde flights immediately after energetic solar flares. These observations revealed lowering of the tropopause, intrusion of warm stratospheric air from higher levels, formation of a sharply defined secondary ozone maximum immediately above the tropopause, perforation of the tropopause, emerging of jet streams, and change from zonal to meridional circulation. This development, involving ozone profile, was observed to occur within a few days after energetic flares. Intriguingly, JU-CM-CS events seem also to be related to variations in the ozone concentration. Modern U.S. and Canadian records of such data extend back only to about 1960. But continuous ozone monitoring at Arosa in the Swiss Alps since 1926 provides a rare long-term record of ozone levels.[98]

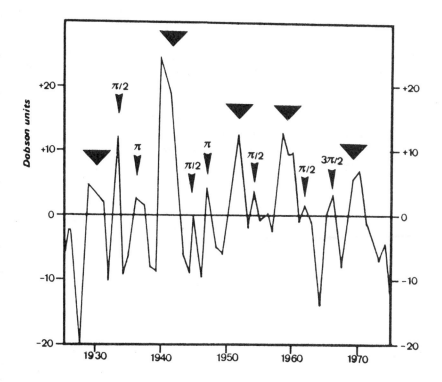

Figure 29:   Arosa record of ozone levels since 1926 after H. U. Duetsch. The curve plots the deviation of annual mean values from the 50-year mean of 337 Dobson units. Triangles mark epochs of JU-CM-CS events. Arrow heads point to harmonics of cycles formed by consecutive Jupiter-CM conjunctions. The respective epochs meet peaks in the ozone column.

Figure 29 presents the deviation of annual mean values from the 50- year mean of 337 Dobson units. A change of about 17 Dobson units corresponds to a 5% change in ozone concentration. The epochs of JU-CM-CS constellations are marked by flat triangles. As to the events 1967.8 and 1970, which are only separated by an interval of 2.2 years, the mean of both epochs is indicated. It is together the epoch of the major solar instability event that started in 1968. The JU-CM-CS epochs, which are related to periods of energetic flare activity, also fit the strongest ozone deviations, as can be seen in Figure 29. In addition, the phases $\pi/2$ and π radians (90° and 180°), that were conspicuous in the Sun's rotation data, concur with secondary peaks. Small arrow heads point to these phases. After the instability event starting in 1968 the pattern seems to have changed. The epoch of JU-CM-CS in 1974 coincided with a minimum. If the new pattern proves to be stable, the next minimum is to be expected in 1990.

XII.   COSMIC INFLUENCE ON WEATHER

There has been a lot of controversy over whether or not the Sun's activity influences weather on Earth. Simple relationships discovered in the 1870's and 1880's vanished when examined more critically, or faded in the light of longer records. A classical example is a marked correlation between the 11-year sunspot cycle and the water level in Lake Victoria that seemed to imply a direct connection between solar activity and rainfall in Africa. After the middle 1920's, however, the pattern that included two sunspot cycles vanished and did not appear again. In addition, such ephemeral relationships were limited to special regions and did not cover larger areas subjected to the same or a similar climate. These discussions will perhaps enter a new stage now. The following results cover more than a century and large parts of the Northern Hemisphere in a consistent way.

Figure 30 provides evidence of a strong connection of rainfall over central Europe with JU-CM-CS epochs. The investigation is based on the mean of yearly rainfall totals in mm derived from observations of 14 German stations by Baur.[99] This homogeneous time series, supplemented by data from "Berliner Wetterkarte", published by the Meteorological Institute of the Free University of Berlin, covers the period 1851 to 1983. The 2-year running variance s^2 of these data was subjected to a Gaussian low-pass filter. Peaks in the plot point to a strong contrast in the rainfall of consecutive years. Very wet years are followed by very dry years or very dry years by very wet years, whereas minima go along with little contrast in this respect. The x-axis indicates the years of observation and the y-axis the smoothed variance $v = s^2$. It is obvious that the epochs of JU-CM-CS events marked by pointers show a good correlation with peaks in the plot, whereas minima, designated by open circles, coincide with phases π radians (180°) in the middle between two epochs that also can be looked at as second harmonics of cycles of consecutive JU-CM-CS events. Only at the secular minimum in sunspot activity around 1900 the respective maxima are quite weak or even disappear.

This correlation is corroborated by a statistical analysis of the unsmoothed 2-year running variance of the German rainfall data presented in Figure 31. The JU-CM-CS epochs are marked by flat triangles and the phases π radians (180°), the second harmonics, by open circles. The analysis evaluates the significance of the difference between means of the running variance of two groups: Group 1 composed of the variance of years coinciding with JU-CM-CS epochs and of the respective preceding year and following year; Group 2 comprising the variance of the years that concur with phases π radians (180°) and the respective preceding year and following year. The rainfall distribution is Gaussian and free from Markov type persistence. Daily or monthly data show some persistence patterns. These were eliminated, however, by the formation of yearly means. Thus, the t-test may be applied. The Fisher-Behrens formula, described in the glossary, is to be used, as the variance in the test groups shows a significant difference.

Group 1 yielded: number of data points $n_1 = 46$; mean $\bar{x}_1 = 13.46$; standard deviation $s_1 = 15.25$. The corresponding values in Group 2 are: $n_2 = 48$, $\bar{x}_2 =$

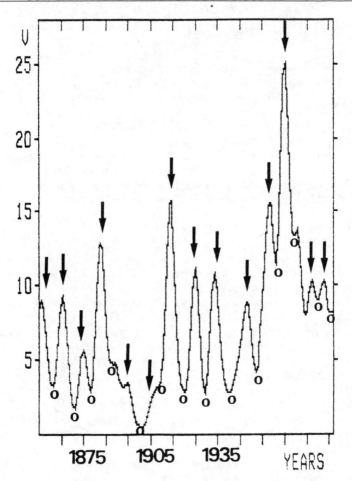

Figure 30:   Smoothed running variance of yearly rainfall totals (mm) derived from observations of 14 German stations by F. Baur. The time series covers the period 1851 to 1983. Arrows mark epochs of Jupiter- CM conjunctions which coincide with maxima in the running variance. Open circles designate second harmonics of respective cycles created by consecutive heliocentric conjunctions of Jupiter and the centre of mass CM that match minima in the variance of rainfall.

3.48; s_2 = 7.65. The corresponding test value t (df=67) = 3.98. Considering that the variance generates positive values only and Group 1 is known to have a higher mean than Group 2, the rules valid for single-sided distributions apply: $P < 0.0002$. The null hypothesis of no significant difference between the means involved can be rejected at a high level of significance. The same procedure applied to the same data set, but based on a 3-year running variance, gives the results: n_1 = 46; $\bar{x}_1$ = 12.19; s_1 = 8.76. n_2 = 48; $\bar{x}_2$ = 4.38; s_2 = 6.8. t (df=87) = 4.82; $P < 0.00003$. 4-year and higher running variance shows deteriorating results. Nonparametric tests confirm the established connections. The Mann-Whitney-test yields: z = 3.84; $P < 0.0001$.

Another approach contributes to these corroborations. The complete data set is characterized by $n = 132$; $\bar{x} = 7.5$; $s = 11.85$. In a group that comprises only the variance data of the years of phases π radians (180°), the corresponding values are $n_3 = 16$; $\bar{x}_3 = 1.15$; $s_3 = 1.3$. The t-test yields t (df=147) $= 5.87$; $P < 0.000002$. This connection relating the phase π radians (180°) in the middle between consecutive JU-CM-CS events, the second harmonics, to low variance values, seems to be rather dependable. This means in practice that around phases π radians (180°) there is little contrast as to wetness and drought in consecutive years, whereas change of flood years to drought years or inversely occurs frequently around JU-CM-CS events, at least in central Europe since the middle of the 19th century.

A replication was made by means of yearly rainfall averages in England and Wales for the years 1850 – 1976.[100] The same procedure based on 2-year running means yielded: $n_1 = 47$; $\bar{x}_1 = 2.67$; $s_1 = 3.55$. $n_2 = 45$; $\bar{x}_2 = 1.06$; $s_2 = 1.62$. t (df=66) $= 2.83$; $P < 0.004$. The null hypothesis of no real difference between the means of the two groups is disproved again.

When the groups of three years each around the epochs in question are replaced by groups allotted to a sine wave that comprises all data available, the tests continue to indicate highly significant results. The JU-CM-CS epoch is assigned to the sine wave such that it coincides with the phase $\pi/2$ radians (90°) at the crest, while the epoch in the middle between JU-CM-CS concurs with the phase $3/2 \pi$ radians (270°) at the trough. All years matching positive phases of the sine wave including the phases 0 and π radians (180°) fall in Group 1, and all years coinciding with negative phases are assigned to Group 2. As to the rainfall over Germany, this new procedure, when based on a 2-year running variance, yields t (df=109) $= 3.9$. The corresponding probability $P<$ 0.0002 justifies the dismissal of the null hypothesis at a high level of significance. The rainfall averages in England and Wales subjected to the new procedure give t (df=104) $= 3$; $P < 0.002$. Another replication makes use of the yearly total rainfall (mm) in the eastern United States, reduced to Philadelphia equivalent values, covering the period 1850 – 1967.[101] The sine wave procedure yields: $n_1 = 66$; $\bar{x}_1 = 1.72$; $s_1 = 1.91$. $n_2 = 51$. $\bar{x}_2 = 1.01$; $s_2 =$ 1.14. t (df=110) $= 2.48$; $P = 0.009$. The null hypothesis can be rejected. This points to a real difference of the two groups as to rainfall in the northern hemisphere, but so far only as to mid- latitudes.

The next replication makes use of data from the equatorial region: yearly monsoon season (June – September) rainfall (mm) at Bombay for the years 1850 to 1960.[102] The difference of both groups is still evident, but the sine wave procedure reveals a phase shift: the effect begins and ends $\pi/2$ radians (90°) earlier. If allowance is made for this shift, the results are: $n_1 = 65$; $\bar{x}_1 = 2.54$; s_1 $= 3.09$. $n_2 = 45$; $\bar{x}_2 = 1.45$; $s_2 = 2$. t (df=109) $= 2.24$; $P = 0.014$. The phase shift by $\pi/2$ (90°) emerging in low latitudes is no ephemeral feature. It is confirmed by the analysis of All-India summer monsoon (June to September) rainfall (mm) for the period 1871 – 1978.[103] Sine wave processing yields: $n_1 = 68$; $\bar{x}_1 =$ 9.84; $s_1 = 13.4$. $n_2 = 44$; $\bar{x}_2 = 4.88$; $s_2 = 6.47$. t (df=104) $= 2.62$; $P = 0.005$. This result is again a dismission of the null hypothesis at a high level of significance. Therefore, a two-phase system with relation to the geographic latitude seems to be a promising approach.

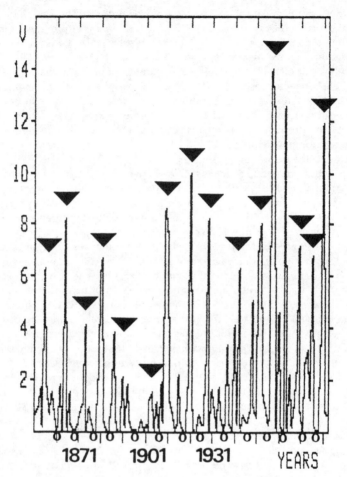

Figure 31: Unsmoothed values of the data presented in Figure 30. Epochs of Jupiter-CM conjunctions are indicated by black triangles. Open circles mark second harmonics of conjunction cycles. The respective epochs coincide with extrema in the rainfall variation.

The JU-CM-CS effects seem to have left their mark still in other climatic features. The longest records of ice in the western North Atlantic are derived from the yearly counts of the number of icebergs that pass south of latitude 48° N to affect the shipping lanes.[104] These counts are quoted in terms of the Smith-index which provides a scale from −5 to +5. The time series covers the period 1880 to 1976. As the counts refer to higher latitudes, the position of the crucial epochs in the sine wave should show no phase shift. This turns out to be true. The test of both groups, processed in the same way as the German, England and Wales, and U.S. rainfall data, yields the following result: $n_1 = 56$; $\bar{x}_1 = 5.32$; $s_1 = 7.17$. $n_2 = 40$; $\bar{x}_2 = 2.68$; $s_2 = 3.37$. t (df=84) = 2.41; P = 0.009. The rejection of the null hypothesis is again justified at a high level of significance.

Temperature opens a further field of replication. F. Baur[105] established a time series of yearly temperature averages (°C) based on the respective means of the stations Utrecht-de Bilt, Potsdam, Basle, and Vienna. With extensions taken from the "Berliner Wetterkarte", the series covers the period 1851–1983. The sine wave method, as applied to the central European rainfall data, gives the following values: $n_1 = 77$; $\bar{x}_1 = 0.463$; $s_1 = 0.619$. $n_2 = 55$; $\bar{x}_2 = 0.217$; $s_2 = 0.3$. t (df=118) = 3; $P < 0.002$. This result is again highly significant. Yearly mean temperatures in central England for the period 1851 – 1976[106] offer occasion for another replication. The result is significant, but less striking: $n_1 = 69$; $\bar{x}_1 = 0.293$; $s_1 = 0.382$. $n_2 = 56$; $\bar{x}_2 = 0.196$; $s_2 = 0.274$. t (df=123) = 1.65; $P = 0.05$. As was to be expected, there are no indications of a phase shift. Phases π radians (180°) point to series of years showing little contrast in temperature, whereas JU-CM-CS epochs are characterized by sequences of alternately hot and cold years. An analysis of annual average temperatures of the Northern Hemisphere for the period 1850 — 1978 yielded no significant difference of the means of groups formed with respect to epochs of JU- CM-CS events. This may be due to phase differences in different geographical latitudes that cancel out.

These are the first results in the field of solar-terrestrial relations regarding weather which cover large areas and long periods consistently. Moreover, they are accessible to prediction because they are based on configurations of cosmic bodies in the solar system that can be computed. The results of this new kind of interdisciplinary approach, which integrates astrological views and modern science, should be intriguing enough to induce experts in the different fields involved to follow the trace outlined in this study.

XIII. PYTHAGOREAN HARMONY

One of the first interdisciplinary approaches to a holistic understanding of our world was that of Pythagoras and his disciples. They created the theory of the functional significance of numbers in the objective world and in music. Their famed dictum "all is number" meant that all existing entities can be ultimately reduced to number relationships that do not only link mathematics to music theory, but also to acoustics, geometry, and astronomy. Even the dependence of the dynamics of world structure on the interaction of pairs of opposites, the first of which is the even-odd polarity essential to numbers, emerges from these number relationships.[107] Pythagoras would have been happy to learn of attractors opposite in character that are created by simple feed back cycles of numbers and form tenuous boundaries, dynamic sites of instability and creativity.

Pythagorean thinking deeply influenced the development of classical Greek philosophy and medieval European thought, especially the astrological belief that the number harmony of the universe affects everything including terrestrial affairs in their relation to space-time configurations of cosmic bodies. Men were intrigued by the precision of those number relationships between musical harmonies, that deeply touch man's soul, and prosaic arithmetical ratios of integers. This connection was first demonstrated by Pythagoras himself in the sixth century B.C. In his famous experiment a stretched string on a monochord was divided by simple arithmetical ratios as 1/2, 2/3, 3/4, 4/5, 5/6 and plucked. It was a Eureka moment when he discovered that the respective partitions of the string create the consonant intervals in harmony.

One tone is not yet music. One might say it is only a promise of music. The promise is fulfilled, and music comes into being, only when tone follows upon tone. Strictly speaking, therefore, the basic elements of music are not the individual tones, but the individual tone to tone moves. Each of these moves spans a certain pitch distance. The pitch distance between two tones is called an interval. If the basic elements of a melody are the individual moves, melody is a succession of intervals rather than of tones.[108] Intervals can be consonant or dissonant. It was Pythagoras' great discovery to see that the ratios of the first small integers up to six give birth to consonant intervals; the smaller these integers, the more complete the resonance. A string divided in the ratio 1 : 2 yields the octave (C-C') of its fundamental note, an equisonance. The ratio 2 : 3 – the entire length of the string to two thirds of its length – yields the fifth (C-G), 3 : 4 the fourth (C-F), 4 : 5 the major third (C-E), 5 : 6 the minor third (E-G), and 3 : 5 the major sixth (C-A). The pairs of notes given in brackets are examples of the respective consonances.

The minor sixth created by the ratio 5 : 8 seems to go beyond the limit six. But eight, the only integer greater than 6, is only the third power of 2 which is a member of the senarius of consonant numbers; eight is created by an octave operation which gives birth to absolutely equisonant tones. All authorities agree that besides the equisonant octave there are no other consonant intervals than the third, the fourth, the fifth and the sixth.[109] If more than two notes are to be consonant, each pair of them must also be consonant. As mentioned already, the most complete consonance within the range of an octave is the major perfect chord C-E-G = 4:5:6 that unites the major third and the fifth to the fundamental note. These concepts of harmony, harmonic intervals and chords are not an arbitrary invention. The consonant intervals are formed in nature by the first terms in the series of overtones or harmonics. The harmonic series was unknown in the age of Pythagoras. It was discovered by Marin Mersenne in 1636, and the inherent law of nature was found by Joseph Sauveur in 1702. When there is a musical sound, there is always in addition a series of harmonics that relate the fundamental tone to an infinity of overtones which influence the quality of the fundamental. The overtones up to the sixth harmonic represent the consonant intervals: the octave, the fifth, the fourth, the major third, the minor third, and the sixth.

XIV. ENERGY DISPLAY IN SOLAR ERUPTIONS "SET TO MUSIC"

Now we are prepared to focus again and with more attention to detail on the art of "composing" predictions of energetic solar eruptions. Most features of Figure 32 are known to the reader already. They were presented in Figure 21 that shows the angular acceleration $d\omega/dt$ of the vector of the tidal forces of Venus, Earth, and Jupiter. The cyclic pattern created by boundary transitions from positive to negative values, or inversely, correlates with proton events (*P*) and X-ray bursts $\geq X3$ (*X*) observed in 1982. This year was only an example of the general pattern of this kind of cycles. 1982 was, however, a year with exceptionally intense eruptional activity. In the preceding years the Sun produced less intense eruptions, even though there were active phases in the $d\omega/dt$ cycles as well as in 1982 and in spite of the fact that the 11-year sunspot cycle reached a high maximum in 1979/1980.

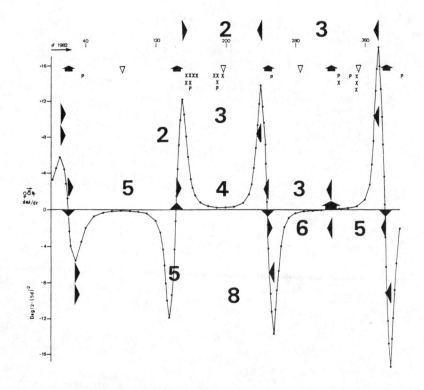

Figure 32: Role of Pythagorean harmony in "composing" predictions of energetic solar eruptions. A wealth of consonant intervals (2 : 3, fifth; 3 : 4, fourth; 4 : 5, major third; 5 : 6, minor third; 5 : 8, minor sixth), designated by vertical triangles and large numbers, points to eruptions of exceptional intensity. Flares that emerge in active phases of cycles related to the angular acceleration of the composed vector of the tidal forces of Venus, Earth, and Jupiter, as explained with respect to Figure 21, display unusual energy when the extrema of the angular acceleration appear at intervals that are together consonant intervals in musical harmony.

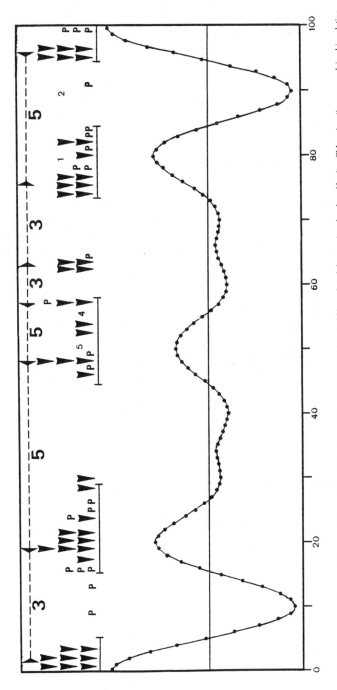

Figure 33: The prototypal pattern of a composite wave formed by the superimpositions of the fourth, fifth, and sixth harmonics of cycles of Jupiter-CM conjunctions, as explained in relation to Figure 26. The distribution of highly energetic X-ray flares and proton events, as explained with respect to Figure 26, is not only related to the major perfect chord. It also follows the ratio of the major sixth (3 : 5), indicated by vertical triangles and large numbers, as well as the major third (4 : 5) and the octave (1 : 2) indicated by small numbers between groups of arrow-heads.

Figure 32 explains why in 1982 the active phases in the $d\omega/dt$ cycles displayed eruptions of such high intensity. Contrary to former years, zero phases and extrema of the curve of the angular acceleration of the composed vector of the tidal forces of Venus, Earth, and Jupiter formed just in 1982 a wealth of consonant intervals of musical harmony. Vertical flat triangles in Figure 32 indicate the limits of the respective intervals. At the top two fifths (2 : 3) are formed by the positive extrema in the curve. In the middle, around the time axis, the zero phases appear just at such distances that they represent a fourth (3 : 4), a major third (4 : 5), and a minor third (5 : 6). Eventually, three of the four negative extrema form a minor sixth (5 : 8). Such connection of an accumulation of consonant intervals and strong solar activity is a common feature. Only when the 11-year sunspot cycle is in its deepest valley, is there no effect because of the lack of an energy potential that could be tapped.

Figure 33 repeats the former presentation of the prototypal pattern of a composite wave formed by the superimposition of the fourth, fifth, and sixth harmonics of JU-CM-CS cycles of any length. The positive phases coincide with clusters of solar cosmic ray events (P), observed from 1942 to 1969, and flare-generated X-ray bursts $\geq X4$, indicated by arrow heads, registered from 1970 through 1987. It has been stressed in the explanation of Figure 26 that the ratio 4 : 5 : 6 of the composed harmonics is representative of the major perfect chord. Figure 33 shows in addition that the centroids of clusters of highly energetic events mark intervals of the major sixth (3 : 5) rather precisely. This is indicated by vertical flat triangles and large numbers on top of the plot. Furthermore, the octave (1 : 2) and the major third (4 : 5) form substructures that are indicated on the right of Figure 33 by small numbers between the arrow heads. As the prototypal pattern in Figure 33 presents a synopsis of the most energetic category of solar eruptions recorded for the past 45 years, it corroborates the hypothesis that consonant intervals play an important role with respect to the Sun's eruptional activity.

XV. HARMONICAL CONSONANCES IN SOLAR CYCLES COVERING THOUSANDS OF YEARS

Another confirmation of this hypothesis are the connections presented in Figure 34 that cover thousands of years. It has been shown in Figure 19 that consecutive impulses of the torque IOT in the Sun's motion about CM, when taken to constitute a smoothed time series, form a wave-pattern the positive and negative extrema ($\pm A_s$) of which coincide with maxima in the secular sunspot cycle. This Gleissberg cycle, with a mean period of 83 years, which modulates the intensity of the 11-year sunspot cycle, is in turn modulated by a supersecular sunspot cycle with a mean period of about 400 years. The Maunder Minimum of sunspot activity in the 17th century and a supersecular maximum in the 12th century are features of this supersecular cycle. It seems to be related to the energy in the secular wave presented in Figure 19.

This energy may be measured by squared values of the secular extrema $\pm A_s$. When these values are taken to form another smoothed time series, a supersecular wave emerges as plotted in Figure 34.[110] It runs parallel with the supersecular sunspot cycle. Its mean period is 391 years, but it varies from 166 to 665 years. Each dot in the plot indicates the epoch of a secular extremum ($\pm A_s$). These epochs are numbered from -64 to $+28$ and range from 5259 B.C. to 2347 A.D. Black triangles indicate maxima in the correlated supersecular sunspot curve and white triangles minima. The medieval maximum, which was together a climate optimum (O), the Spoerer Minimum (S), and the Maunder Minimum (M) are marked by respective abbreviations. The extrema in the supersecular wave properly reflect all marked peaks and troughs in the supersecular sunspot curve derived from radiocarbon data by Damon and Eddy.[111]

Phase jumps are a common feature of all kinds of cyclic time series observed in Nature. Diverse examples of phase jumps in series of short-term cycles have been presented above. The energy wave in Figure 34 is an intriguing example of phase change in series of long-term cycles. The dashed horizontal lines mark two quantitative thresholds. When the energy in the wave transgresses the upper line, or falls beneath the lower line, a phase jump emerges in the correlated supersecular cycle of sunspot activity. At the crucial phases, set off in Figure 34 by dotted vertical lines, the extrema change sign; a preceding supersecular maximum is not followed by a minimum, but by another maximum, or a minimum by a further minimum. More details of these connections have been given in special publications. One of the consequences that can be derived from the energy wave is the forecast of an imminent supersecular sunspot minimum around 2030 A.D. The dotted vertical line quite on the right of Figure 34 points to the epoch of a phase change such that the supersecular Maunder Minimum (M) will be followed by another supersecular minimum about 2030.

Intriguingly, the intervals in the energy wave that separate consecutive phase jumps, too, show a relationship with consonant intervals. These intervals, marked by the vertical dotted lines and vertical flat triangles, represent the major sixth (3 : 5) and the minor sixth (5 : 8). The pattern that combines the major with the minor sixth seems to be a permanent feature, a

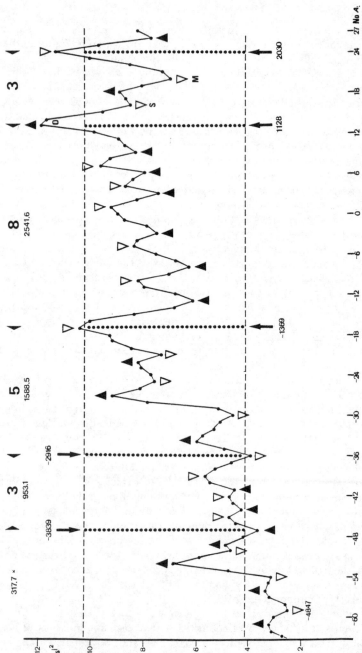

Figure 34: Combination of the consonant intervals major sixth (3 : 5) and minor sixth (5 : 8) emerging in solar system processes covering thousands of years. The intervals are indicated by vertical triangles and great numbers. The curve represents the supersecular variation of the energy in the secular torque wave, part of which was shown in Figure 19. The energy is proportional to squared values of the extrema in the secular torque wave ($\bar{A}_s^2$). Points in the curve represent epochs of extrema A_s numbers −64 to +28 (5259 B.C. to A.D 2347). The mean length of the cycle is 391 years. Black triangles point at maxima in the corresponding supersecular sunspot cycle; open triangles indicate minima. When the energy goes beyond quantitative thresholds, indicated by hatched horizontal lines, a phase jump occurs in the correlated supersecular sunspot cycle. These critical phases are marked by vertical dotted lines. A new phase jump is imminent about 2030. It points to a supersecular minimum, comparable with the Egyptian minimum (E) around 1369 B.C., a prolonged period of distinct cooling and glacier advance. The proportion 3 : 5 : 8, representing the major and minor sixth, just marks the intervals that separate those rare phase jumps set off by vertical dotted lines. The 317.7-year period of the triple conjunction of Jupiter, Saturn and Uranus is too involved in this connection as indicated by small numbers beneath the great numbers at the top.

new start of which can be identified beyond the phase jump in 1128, the epoch of the medieval optimum (O). The consonant intervals are designated by large numbers on top of Figure 34. The smaller numbers underneath point to a connection with the period of the triple conjunction of Jupiter, Saturn, and Uranus, mentioned in the introductory part. This period of 317.7 years, which is related to the Sun's activity and terrestrial climate in Precambrium, also shows a connection with the consonant intervals investigated here. The threefold, fivefold, and eightfold values of the period of the triple conjunction, namely 953, 1589, and 2542 years, properly reflect the actual intervals between consecutive phase jumps. These actual values seem to oscillate about the values derived from multiples of the period of the triple conjunction of Jupiter, Saturn, and Uranus. As has been pointed out in the beginning with respect to the Elatina cycle, the period of conjunctions of Jupiter and Saturn and important torque cycles are involved, too, because they are commensurable with the period of the triple conjunction. Reference is made to the corresponding details.

XVI REALISATIONS OF MUSICAL CONSONANCES IN TERRESTIAL CYCLES

Just that interval of the sixth (5 : 8) as defined in Figure 34 by the phase jumps in 2916 B.C., 1369 B.C, and 1128 A.D, is reflected, too, in terrestrial data that show a relation to the supersecular sunspot cycle. Figure 35, after H. H. Lamb,[112] shows 20-year averages in the growth rings of Bristlecone pine trees near the upper tree line in the White Mountains, California, from 3431 B.C. The variations in the ring widths at this height may be taken as indicating variations of summer warmth or its seasonal duration. The data were supplied by V. C. La Marche at the Laboratory of Tree Ring Research, University of Arizona. The arrows point to the respective epochs of phase jumps in the supersecular energy wave. It is obvious that just the periods around these epochs are characterized by the greatest variations in the ring widths that reach 34/100 mm to 39/100 mm, whereas in the long periods between these three phases of exceptional change the ring widths vary by less than half of this range. This coincidence of outstanding features in the supersecular energy wave and the time series of growth rings of trees, matching the consonant interval of the minor sixth (5 : 8) in both cases, is a solid indication that we are dealing with a real relationship.

Figure 36 after Rhodes W. Fairbridge[113] contributes to this growing body of circumstantial evidence. In the Hudson Bay, Canada, beach ridge formations have been preserved as a long series of almost continuous "staircases" from top to bottom of ancient strandlines in an area of maximum postglacial uplift. As Fairbridge put it, "we have been able to walk back so-to-speak through time, ascending the stair-treads, a few meters at a time, from the present beach to the level dated about 8300 years B.P., the marine limit, the time of the postglacial marine invasion of the Hudson Bay." Fairbridge assumes that critical periods of storminess, when local sea level was raised above its usual average stand, may have been an important factor in the building of beach ridges. The irregular curve in Figure 36 is a plot of the moving average of the measured beach de-levelings. Each dot represents one of the individual beach ridge formations. The measured data cover more than 8000 years before the period 1975 (B.P.).

In the plot of Figure 36 only the data back to about 6000 B.P. are given, because the calculation of phase jumps in the supersecular energy wave does not go beyond this range. The fat arrows mark the epochs of phase jumps in the energy wave that are indicated by vertical dotted lines in Figure 34. If these epochs coincide with supersecular maxima in Figure 34, the respective arrows in Figure 36 point upwards, while they point downwards when the epochs indicate supersecular minima in sunspot activity. The respective arrows properly fit the most prominent ups and downs in the curve that reflect the differences in the beach de-levelings measured on the ordinate axis by rates of emergence in cm/yr. The trend is designated by a dashed line. Both of the two greatest negative deviations from the trend properly fit the phase jump minima in 2916 B.C (4892 B.P.) and 1369 B.C (3345 B.P.) while the most

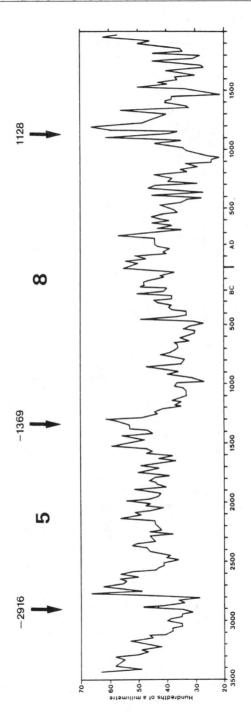

Figure 35: This plot after H. H. Lamb shows 20-year averages in the growth rings of Bristlecone pine trees near the upper tree line in White Mountains, California, from 3431 B.C. Arrows point at the respective epochs of phase jumps in the supersecular energy wave. These epochs, separated by intervals conforming with the ratio 5 : 8 of the minor sixth, coincide with the greatest variations in the tree ring widths.

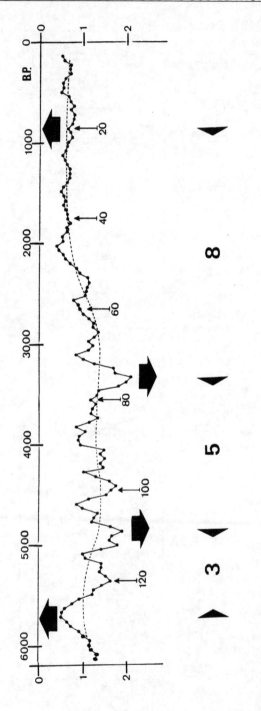

Figure 36: Beach ridge formations in the Hudson Bay, Canada, after R. W. Fairbridge, a long series of almost continuous "staircases" from top to bottom of ancient strand lines in an area of maximum postglacial uplift, covering more than 6000 years before the period 1975 (B.P.). The pattern of this series seems to reflect critical periods of storminess. The figures beneath small pointers indicate the numbering of individual "staircases". Fat arrows mark the epochs of phase jumps in the energy wave indicated in Figure 34 by vertical dotted lines. They properly fit the most prominent ups and downs in the curve which repeat the proportions of the major and minor sixths (3 : 5 : 8), also present in the energy wave and the related supersecular sunspot cycle.

prominent positive deviations coincide with the phase jump maxima in the secular wave about 3839 B.C. (5815 B.P.) and 1128 A.D. (847 B.P.). In the period of rather flat oscillations around the trend about 847 B.P. on the right of the plot this is not as clearly visible as in the period about 5815 B.P with its strong positive deviation from the trend. It is obvious, however, that all of the fat arrows in Figure 36 point to maxima of curvature or turning points in the trend line. The arrow at the phase jump epoch 1128 A.D. (847 B.P.) is no exception; it indicates a crest turning point as well as the other arrow pointing upwards at the epoch 3839 B.C. (5815 B.P.). Consistently, the major and minor sixths (3 : 5 and 5 : 8) appear as well as with respect to the phase jumps in the supersecular energy wave. These consonant intervals are set off in Figure 36 by vertical flat triangles and numbers designating the respective ratios of the intervals.

XVII.   EPILOGUE

Cycles are at the core of all connections presented here. So let us complete a cycle in returning to the beginning where it has been shown that a simple mathematical feed-back cycle, a model of the fundamental functions of cycles, creates pre-images of polar tension, called attractors, and instable, but creative boundaries between the domains of competing attractors of opposite quality. These boundaries give birth to a wealth of explicit structures, an incredible variety of Julia sets, one of which was presented in Figure 3. Adrien Douady[114] has given an apt description of their various forms: "Some are a fatty cloud, others are a skinny bush of brambles, some look like the sparks which float in the air after a firework has gone off. One has the shape of a rabbit, lots of them have sea-horse tails. . .".

But from the mathematical feed-back cycles also emerges a core entity called Mandelbrot set M which regulates the incidence of the different forms of Julia sets. Peitgen and Richter[115] compare its function with that of the genome, the entire set of hereditary factors contained in a haploid number of chromosomes of an individual: "There is one constant in the diversity of motives and their variation in the morphology of the Julia sets: the Mandelbrot set itself, which appears again and again in different sizes but always in the same form. One has to think of the genetic organisation in higher organisms: each cell contains the complete genome, the totality of all forms of expression, but at any point in the organism only a small selection actually is expressed."

Similar thoughts occurred to Adrien Douady,[116] an authority on the analysis of the Mandelbrot set: "We can think of the iteration process defined by the formula $z_{n+1}=z_n^2+c$ as an extraordinary efficient way to develop the information contained in the data (the value of c for a Julia set, and the window for a detail of the Mandelbrot set), acting as a key. This phenomenon of developing information is also striking in biology: a transcription of all the genetic DNA of a human being (or any vertebrate) would take a hundred pages or so. Compare this with a treatise on anatomy, to which you should add one on endocrinology and one on innate behaviour! Imagine scientists faced with the collections of Julia sets without knowing where they come from; would they not do just what zoologists did in the 19th century: define phyla, classes, orders and genera, give a description of the specific features attached to each term of classification, and so on? Let us be clear: I am not claiming that Julia sets can provide a model for any biological phenomenon, but they are a striking example of how a very simple dynamical system can develop the small information contained in a key, and produce various highly organized structures."

According to J. H. Hubbard, the Mandelbrot set is "the most complicated object in mathematics."[117] It can be defined as the set of all complex numbers of c for which the size of z^2+c is finite even after an indefinitely number of iterations. The mathematical feed-back cycle, described by words in the introductory part and defined by a formula in the Douady quotation ($z_{n+1}=z_n^2+c$; given a number z_0 take its square and add a constant c to get z_1; then repeat to get z_2, z_3, and so on), produces the Mandelbrot set when the complex number z is always made zero and different values of c are selected.

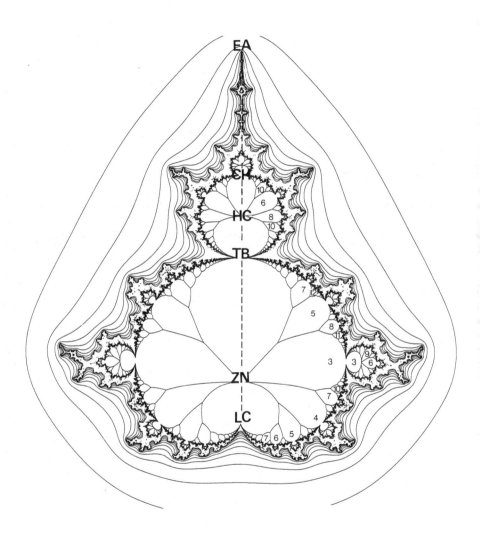

Figure 37: Representation of the Mandelbrot set after Peitgen and Richter. The impression that it rests on harmony, even better conveyed by Figure 4, is confirmed by rational analysis. It reflects in double version all known consonant intervals, the major perfect chord, and also the combination of the major and minor sixth 3 : 5 : 8 found in the supersecular torque- and sunspot cycle, as well as in tree ring widths and beach de-levelings. The intervals are measured along the "spine", marked by a dashed line, ranging from the libido centre (LC) to the end of antenna (EA). The zero navel (ZN), top of body (TB), head centre (HC) and crown of head (CH), are distributed such that respective intervals form all acknowledged harmonical proportions. The acronyms allude to Peitgen and Richter's "apple man anatomy" and might stimulate imagination beyond the number relationships involved.

Figure 4 is the result of such process. Julia sets are created when c remains fixed and z varies beginning with a special initial value z_0. Julia sets are legion; for each fixed value of c used in the iteration formula, a new and different Julia set develops. Here the control function of the Mandelbrot set comes in. The position of c in the complex plane relative to the Mandelbrot set M decides on the form of the Julia sets. They are connected structures if c is from within M, and broken into infinitely many pieces if c lies outside M. Most interesting is the boundary of M. When c crosses the boundary, associated Julia sets will be subject to an explosion that decomposes them into a cloud of points, called Fatou dust. This fractal dust gets thinner and thinner the farther c is from the Mandelbrot set M. Thus, crossing the boundary of M functions like a mathematical phase transition for Julia sets, as Peitgen and Richter[118] put it.

The reader should hold in mind that all these fascinating qualities emerge from simple feed-back cycles that can be found, too, in the relative motion of cosmic bodies in the solar system. Beyond the mathematical complexity of the Mandelbrot set its aesthetic appeal should not be forgotten. The mathematicians Philip J. Davis and Reuben Hersh[119] have stated: "Blindness to the aesthetic element in mathematics is widespread and can account for a feeling that mathematics is as dry as dust, as exciting as a telephone book, as remote as the laws of infangthief of fifteenth century Scotland. Contrariwise, appreciation of this element makes the subject live in a wonderful manner and burn as no other creation of the human mind seems to do."

This is the proper attitude to look at Figure 4 again. The picture, when looked at in a holistic way, conveys the impression of harmony and creativity. It could serve as a powerful emblem of these fundamental qualities. Even the self-collectedness and sitting posture of meditating man seems to be embodied in the pictorial representation of M. This impression is deepened by the antenna above the "head" of the "apple man". It is seen on close inspection that it carries many little copies of the larger M. They sit there like pearls on a string, and further smaller ones sit between the larger ones, and so on and on forever. One relatively large miniature Mandelbrot on the antenna is visible in Figure 4. This productive abundance which contributes to the impression of creativity is not limited to the antenna. There is a wealth of sprouting miniature Mandelbrots everywhere; they grow out of the cardioid-shaped main body as well as out of the head disk and satellite disks. Buds give birth to buds that give birth to buds and so on without end. This image applies to the growth of ideas as well as to bodily propagation.

The pictorial impression that the Mandelbrot set rests on harmony is confirmed by rational analysis. As shown at the Sixth London Astrology Research Conference in 1987, [120] the proportions of the pictorial representation of the Mandelbrot set reflect all known consonant intervals, the major perfect chord, and also the combination of major and minor sixth 3 : 5 : 8 which has been found in the energy wave related to the supersecular sunspot cycle as well as in tree ring widths and beach de-levelings. The harmonic ratios of the intervals in question may be taken from Figure 37 after Peitgen and Richter.[121] Its original destination was to present results from some ongoing research on M. The numbers on the right of the plot are related to this research and may be neglected in our context though they attest to the deep interest mathematicians have in bringing to light structures hidden in M.

The intervals are measured along the spine of the "apple man" that is marked in Figure 37 by a dashed line. This ranges from the cusp of the cardioid-shaped main body to the end point of the antenna. According to a theorem by A. Douady and J. H. Hubbard, the Mandelbrot set is connected, and the antenna, too, is contained in M.[122] The spine is no arbitrary choice. In the complex plane that the Mandelbrot set inhabits, the real part of complex numbers is represented by an axis of coordinates, a section of which is the spine. The origin of the complex plane is that point in Figure 37 where those fine lines in the main body intersect. This zero point, the natural centre of the cardioid-shaped main body, is marked by ZN (zero navel). This acronym alludes to the "apple man anatomy", as well as five others. Interestingly, ZN coincides with the Hara point of spiritual tradition in Japan.

The cusp below the zero point, designated by LC (libido centre), is at the point 0.25 on the real part axis. In the large disc, tangent to the cardioid body, the fine lines, a result of mathematical analysis as well as those in the main body, intersect at the centre HC (head centre) at the point – 1 on the axis designating the real parts. The points TB (top of body) at – 0.75 and CH (crown of head) at – 1.25 designate boundary positions the structural importance of which is evident. EA (end of antenna) indicates the upper point reached by the representation of the Mandelbrot set in Figure 4. The overall distance LC – EA is 2.25. Unity on the real part axis is equal to ZN – HC, the interval that separates head centre and zero navel. LC – TB, the height of the main body, too, is equal to 1. The third distance that is equal to unity is HC – EA, the interval that separates head centre and end of antenna. All of the three distances LC – ZN, TB – HC, and HC – CH are equal to 0.25, and both ZN – TB and CH – EA equal three times 0.25. Thus, it is no surprise that the "apple man's" proportions, measured along the spine, show a wealth of consonant intervals and harmonies:

Octave (1:2)	→	(TB1–CH)	:	(LC–TB)	and (HC–EA)	:	(ZN–EA)
Fifth (2:3)	→	(TB–CH)	:	(ZN–TB)	and (TB–CH)	:	(CH–EA)
Fourth (3:4)	→	(ZN–TB)	:	(LC–TB)	and (ZN–TB)	:	(ZN–HC)
Major third (4:5)	→	(LC–TB)	:	(LC–HC)	and (HC–EA)	:	(LC–HC)
Minor third (5:6)	→	(ZN–CH)	:	(LC–CH)	and (LC–HC)	:	(LC–CH)
Major sixth (3:5)	→	(ZN–TB)	:	(ZN–CH)	and (CH–EA)	:	(TB–EA)
Minor sixth (5:8)	→	(ZN–CH)	:	(ZN–EA)	and (TB–EA)	:	(ZN–EA)

There are always at least two forms of the respective interval that visually, too, make sense and appeal to imagination. The first realisation of the octave, for instance, relates the height of the "head" to that of the main body. The reader may delve into these appealing relationships by himself with the aid of Figure 37. The most harmonious chord is also present in two forms:

Major perfect chord   (4 : 5 : 6)   →   (LC – TB) : (LC – HC) : (LC – CH)
                                                        (ZN – HC) : (ZN – CH) : (LC – CH)

The visualisation of these proportions again yields intriguing relationships that stimulate imagination. The best way to tune in, however, is to listen to the major perfect chord struck on a monochord or another instrument. The combination of the major and minor sixth is, as announced above, also related to the proportions of the "apple man":

$$3 : 5 : 8 \rightarrow \quad (ZN - TB) : (ZN - CH) : (ZN - EA)$$

This is all the more important as the Mandelbrot set is no arbitrary invention of the human mind, but a structure found in Nature, as the physicist and mathematician Gert Eilenberger[123] put it: "It is not our sensory and perceptual activity that forces Nature into a strait-jacket of mathematics, it is Nature, which, in the process of our evolutionary development, has impressed mathematics into our reason as a real, existing structure, inherent to herself. Less abstractly: the ape, from which we are descended, had to have a very accurate idea of the geometry of space actually existing if he were not to fall out of his tree and break his neck. Similarly, one can argue that the evolution of our abilities for abstraction and manipulation of logical symbols must be oriented on actually existent structures in the real world."

The Mandelbrot set, seen as a pre-image, embraces a wide range of phenomena that seem to be the common morphological root of most diverse processes in microcosmos and macrocosmos: control of the growth of highly organized structures by the development of relatively simple key information; realization of consonances, resonances, and harmony in accordance with balanced harmonious proportions inherent in the set; expression of primordial cyclic functions that create polar tension and instability and conditions favourable to creativity in boundary regions between the realms of attractors of different quality. The most fundamental morphological features, however, seem to be those feed-back cycles that create polarities, conditions of instability and creativity, Mandelbrot- and Julia sets, and that mesh of harmonically interwoven oscillations which connects the revolutions of the giant planets with the Sun's irregular swing about the centre of mass, the Sun's rotation, secular and supersecular sunspot cycles, energetic solar eruptions, geomagnetic storms, climatic change, rainfall and temperature, abundance in wildlife, economic cycles, and human creativity.

Thus, our new multidisciplinary approach, together based on wide astrological views and on recent scientific knowledge from so diverse fields as mathematics, astronomy, geophysics, climatology, meteorology, biology, economy, and psychology, has yielded unexpected holistic results that confirm in detail the unity of the universe which is generally proven by the violation of Bell's inequality. As Peitgen and Richter[124] aptly say: "It is no longer sufficient to discover basic laws and understand how the world works "in principle". It becomes more and more important to figure out the patterns through which these principles show themselves in reality. More than just fundamental laws are operating in what actually is."

TABLE   89

TABLE
Epochs of JU-CM-CS events   1800 – 2000:1998.56

(g)	22	July	1998	1998.56		(c)	20	April	1990	1990.30
(g)	31	Oct.	1982	1982.83		(c)	24	June	1974	1974.48
(g)	9	Jan.	1970	1970.02		(c)	20	Oct.	1967	1967.80
(g)	13	Aug.	1959	1959.62		(c)	16	May	1951	1951.37
(g)	15	April	1942	1942.29		(c)	1	May	1930	1930.33
(g)	25	Oct.	1920	1920.82		(c)	18	Jan.	1912	1912.05
(g)	8	Oct.	1901	1901.77		(c)	2	March	1891	1891.17
(g)	20	Nov.	1881	1881.89		(c)	11	April	1873	1873.28
(g)	16	March	1859	1859.21		(c)	26	Nov.	1850	1850.90
(g)	5	March	1843	1843.18		(c)	22	Nov.	1834	1834.89
(g)	9	Sept.	1819	1819.69		(c)	3	June	1811	1811.42
(g)	14	Sept.	1803	1803.70						

Epochs of second harmonics of JU-CM-CS cycles:

1994.43	1986.57	1978.66	1972.25
1968.91	1963.71	1955.50	1946.83
1936.31	1925.58	1916.44	1906.91
1896.47	1886.53	1877.59	1866.25
1855.06	1847.04	1839.04	1827.29
1815.56	1807.56		

REFERENCES

1) Einstein, Podolsky, and Rosen (1935); Bell (1965; 1976); d' Espagnat (1979); Jammer (1980); Aspect *et al.* (1981); Zukav (1979); Selleri (1984); Krueger (1984); Gardner (1986) (*See Glossary*)

2) d'Espagnat (1979) p.140; Stapp (1975; 1977; 1979); Sarfatti (1977); Selleri (1984) pp. 139, 140 (*See Glossary*)

3) Landscheidt (1987 b)

4) Aspect *et al.* (1981); Freedman and Clauser (1972); Bruno *et al.* (1977); Bertolini *et al.* (1981); Jammer (1980) p. 516; d'Espagnat (1979) pp. 136, 137

5) Gingerich (1982) p. 124

6) Brewster (1855) Vol. 2, pp. 371, 372

7) Rattensi (1972)

8) Jantsch (1984) pp 34–36

9) Prigogine *et al.* (1983); Glansdorff and Prigogine (1971)

10) Hofstadter (1979) p. 27

11) Peitgen and Richter (1986) p. 84

12) Peitgen and Richter (1986) p. 10

13) Colour picture of the Mandelbrot set created by Peitgen and Richter; a black and white version is to be found in Peitgen and Richter (1986) p. 78

14) Poincaré (1889); Poincaré (1892) Vol. 1, p.253 and Chapter V, entitled "Nonexistence of Uniform Integrals"; see also Ekeland (1984)

15) Haken (1978) Preface to the First Edition

16) Krueger (1984) p. 144

17) Landscheidt (1976; 1980; 1981 a; 1981 b; 1983; 1984 a; 1984 b; 1984 c; 1984 d; 1986 a; 1986 b; 1986 c; 1987 a; 1987 c; 1988)

18) Dewey (1973) p. 25

19) Haken (1981) p. 127

20) Dewey (1973) p. 27

21) McLeod (1985) p. 4599

22) Dewey (1973) p. 95

23) Dewey (1973) p. 119

23a) The forecast of the top turning point 1987.3 and the bottom epoch 1990 in the course of international stock prices was first published January 9, 1986, in a lecture presented at the astronomical Olbers-Gesellschaft, Bremen: Zyklen solarer Energieausbrüche: Entdeckung, irdische Auswirkungen, Vorhersage

24) Dewey (1973) p. 71

25) Williams *et al.* (1985); Williams (1986)

25a) Eysenck (1981) pp. 11–14

26) Dean (1986) p. 170

26a) Correlation (1981) p. 3

27) Landscheidt (1976; 1980; 1981 a; 1981 b; 1983; 1984 a; 1984 b; 1984 c; 1984 d; 1986 a; 1986 b; 1986 c; 1987 a; 1987 c; 1988)

28) Dean (1977) p. 508

29) Dean (1983)

30) Woehl *et al.* (1986)

31) Woehl (1986) p. 585

32) Recely *et al.* (1984)

33) EOS (1986) p. 537

34) Landscheidt (1984 b) pp. 105–114

35) Landscheidt (1987 b) pp. 113–118

36) Burton *et al.* (1973)

36a) Armstrong *et al.* (1983) p. 75

37) Landscheidt (1986 c) p. 195; Kreplin *et al.* (1977)
38) Mayaud (1973); Mayaud *et al.* (1977)
39) Krishna (1967)
40) Bucke (1969) pp. 332, 351
41) Kollerstrom (1986)
42) Personal communication by Suitbert Ertel
42a) Seymour (1986) pp. 2–3, 10–13
43) Koestler (1967) pp. 216, 217
44) Segrè (1984) p. 190
45) von Klitzing (1985); Halperin (1986)
46) Landscheidt (1984 a; 1986 c)
47) Blackman and Tukey (1959)
48) Mitchell (1966)
49) Panofsky and Brier (1958)
50) Burg (1968, 1972, 1975)
51) Junk (1982) p. 39
52) Stuart *et al.* (1971)
53) Cajori (1934)
54) Zehnder (1923)
55) Jose (1965)
56) Landscheidt (1976; 1980; 1981 a; 1981 b; 1983; 1984 a; 1984 b; 1984 c; 1984 d; 1986 a; 1986 b; 1986 c; 1986 d; 1987 a; 1987 c; 1988)
57) Landscheidt (1981 a) p. 8; (1983) p. 294
58) Blizard (1982) p. 896
59) Brier (1979)
60) Landscheidt (1983) p. 298
61) Gleissberg (1975)
62) Gleissberg (1958)
63) Landscheidt (1983) p. 302
64) Landscheidt (1983) p. 304
65) Landscheidt (1986 b) pp. 54–56
66) Landscheidt (1984 c) p. 28; (1986 a) p. 83
67) Landscheidt (1984 c) p. 29; (1986 a) pp. 83–85
68) Oepik (1972)
69) Blizard (1965); Švestka (1968); Landscheidt (1983; 1984 a; 1984 b; 1984 c; 1986 a; 1988)
70) Landscheidt (1976) pp. 12–13
71) Eddy *et al.* (1977)
72) Howard (1975)
73) Dicke (1964)
74) Howard (1984); Howard *et al.* (1983)
75) Feynman *et al.* (1966) pp. 50-4
76) Warrain (1942) p. 79; Haase (1976) pp. 38, 39
77) Bucha (1983) p. 21
78) Gosling *et al.* (1977)
79) Sazonov (1965)
80) Mustel (1966)
81) Beynon and Winstanley (1969)
82) Stolov and Shapiro (1974)
83) Sidorenkov (1974)
84) Cobb (1967)
85) Mustel (1977)
86) King (1974)
87) Roberts and Olson (1973)

88) Prohaska and Willett (1983)
89) Sazonov (1974)
90) King (1974)
91) Neubauer (1983)
92) Schneider and Mass (1975)
93) Landscheidt (1987 c)
94) Wilcox (1975)
95) EOS (1985) p. 441
96) Mayaud (1977) p. 102
97) Reiter (1983)
98) Duetsch (1974). Figure 29 was adapted from a plot by H. U. Duetsch. Eidgenoessische Technische Hochschule, Zuerich, in Rowland (1978)
99) Baur (1975)
100) Lamb (1977) pp. 621–625
101) Lamb (1977) pp. 625–628
102) Lamb (1977) p. 631
103) Mooley and Parthasarathy (1984)
104) Lamb (1977) pp. 580–581
105) Baur (1975)
106) Manley (1974) pp. 389–405; Lamb (1977) pp. 574–576
107) Thesleff (1977)
108) Zuckerkandl (1971) p. 64
109) Rameau (1971) p. XLI
110) Landscheidt (1983) pp. 300–303
111) Damon (1977); Eddy (1977) p. 67
112) Lamb (1982) p. 133
113) Fairbridge (1981) p. 134
114) Douady (1986) p. 161
115) Peitgen and Richter (1986) p. 17
116) Douady (1986) pp. 172, 173
117) Dewdney (1985) p. 12
118) Peitgen and Richter (1986) p. 12
119) Peitgen and Richter (1986) p. 21
120) Landscheidt (1987 a)
121) Peitgen and Richter (1986) p. 61
122) Peitgen and Richter (1986) p. 15; Douady (1986) p. 162
123) Eilenberger (1986) p. 178
124) Peitgen and Richter (1986) p. 1

Bibliography of quoted authors

Armstrong, T. P., Brungardt, C., and Meyer, J. E. (1983): Satellite Observations of Interplanetary and Polar Cap Solar Particle Fluxes from 1963 to the Present, in McCormac (1983) pp. 71 – 79.

Aspect, A., Grangier, P., and Roger, G. (1981): Experimental Test of Realistic Local Theories via Bell's Theorem, Phys. Rev. Lett. 47, 460.

Baur, F. (1975): Abweichungen der Monatsmittel der Temperatur Mitteleuropas und des Niederschlags in Deutschland, Beilage zur Berliner Wetterkarte des Instituts fuer Meteorologie der Freien Universitaet Berlin vom 24. 6. 1975.

Bell, J. S. (1965): Physics 1, 195.

Bell, J. S. (1976): Epistemological Letters (March 1976).

Bertolini, G., Diana, E., and Scotti, A. (1981): Nuovo Cim. 63 B, 651.

Beynon, W. J. G. and Winstanley, E. H. (1969): Geomagnetic Disturbance and the Troposphere, Nature 222, 1262 – 1263.

Blackman, R. B. and Tukey, J. W. (1959): The Measurement of Power Spectra, Dover Publications, New York.

Blizard, J. B. (1965): Predictions of Solar Flares Months in Advance, Astron. J. 70, 667.

Blizard, J. B. (1982): Solar Motion and Solar Activity, Bull. Am. Astron. Soc. 13, 896.

Brewster, D. (1855): Memoirs of the Life, Writings, and Discoveries of Sir Isaac Newton, Vol. 2, 371 – 372, Boston.

Brier, G. W. (1979): Use of Difference Equation Methods for Predicting Sunspot Numbers, in McCormac and Seliga (1979) pp. 209 – 214.

Bruno, M., d'Agostino, M., and Maroni, C. (1977): Nuovo Cim. 40 B, 142.

Bucha, V. (1983): Direct Relations between Solar Activity and Atmospheric Circulation, its Effect on Changes of Weather and Climate, Studia Geoph. et Geod. 27, 19 – 45.

Bucke, R. M. (1969): Cosmic Consciousness, Dutton, New York.

Burg, J. P. (1968): A New Analysis Technique for Time Series Data, paper presented at NATO Advanced Institute for Signal Processing, Enschede.

Burg, J. P. (1972): The Relationship between Maximum Entropy and Maximum Likelihood Spectra, Geophysics 37, 375 –376.

Burg, J. P. (1975): Maximum Entropy Analysis, Ph.D. thesis, Stanford University, Palo Alto.

Burton, N., Hart, P., and Laughlin, J., eds. (1973) The Asian Journal of Thomas Merton, New York.

Cajori, F. (1934): Newton's Principia, University of California Press, San Francisco, Book III, Proposition XIII.

Cobb, W. E. (1967): Evidence of Solar Influence on the Atmosphere Electric Elements at Mauna Loa Observatory, Mon. Weather Rev. 95, 905 – 911.

Damon, P. E. (1977): Solar Induced Variations of Energetic Particles at One AU, in White (1977) pp. 429 – 445.

Dean, G. (1977): Recent Advances in Natal Astrology, Analogic, Subiaco.

Dean, G. (1983): Shortwave Radio Propagation: Non–Correlation with Planetary Positions, Correlation Vol. 3, No. 1, 4 – 36.

Dean, G. (1986): Does Astrology Need to Be True?, The Skeptical Inquirer 11, 166 – 184.

d'Espagnat, B. (1979): The Quantum Theory and Reality, Scient. American 241, 128 – 140.

Dewdney, A. K. (1985): A Computer Microscope Zooms in for a Look at the Most Complex Object in Mathematics, Scient. American 253, 8 – 12.

Dewey, E. R. (1973): Cycles, Manor Books, New York.

Dicke, R. H. (1964): The Sun's Rotation and Relativity, Nature, 202, 432 – 435.

Douady, A. (1986): Julia Sets and the Mandelbrot Set, in Peitgen and Richter (1986), pp. 161 – 173.

Drodzdov, O. A. and Vorob'eva, eds. (1974): General and Synoptic Climatology, Trudy, Vyp. 316, Leningrad, Glavnaja Geofiziceskaja Observatorija, pp. 35 – 42.

Duetsch, H. U. (1974): The Ozone Distribution in the Atmosphere, Can. J. Chem. 52, 1491 – 1504.

Eddy, J. A. (1977): Historical Evidence for the Existence of the Solar Cycle, in White (1977) pp. 51 – 71.

Eddy, J. A., Gilman, P. A., and Trotter, D. E. (1977): Anomalous Solar Rotation in the Early 17th Century, Science 198, 824 – 829.

Eilenberger, G. (1986): Freedom, Science, and Aesthetics, in Peitgen and Richter (1986) pp. 175 – 180.

Einstein, A., Podolsky, B., and Rosen, N. (1935): Can Quantum Mechanical Description of Reality be Considered Complete? Phys. Rev. 47, 777.

Ekeland, I. (1984): Le calcul, l'imprévu, Editions du Seuil, Paris.

EOS (1985): Transactions, American Geophysical Union.

EOS (1986): Transactions, American Geophysical Union.

Eysenck, H. (1981): The Importance of Methodology in Astrological Research, Correlation 1, 1, 11 – 14.

Fairbridge, R. W. (1981): Holocene Sea–Level Oscillations, in: Koenigsson, L. K. and Paabo, K., eds., In Florilegium Florinis Dedicatum, Striae 14, 131 – 139, Uppsala.

Feynman, R. P., Leighton, R. B., and Sands, M. (1966): The Feynman Lectures on Physics, Vol. 1, Addison–Wesley, Reading.

Freedman, S. J. and Clauser, J. F. (1972): Phys. Rev. Lett. 28, 938.

Gardner, M. (1986): The EPR Paradox and Rupert Sheldrake, The Skeptical Inquirer 11, 128 – 131.

Gingerich, O. (1982): The Galileo Affair, Scient. American 247, 118 – 128.

Glansdorff, P. and Prigogine, I. (1971): Thermodynamic Theory of Structure, Stability, and Fluctuations, New York.

Gleissberg, W. (1958) The 80–Year Sunspot Cycle, J. Brit. Astron. Ass. 68, 150.

Gleissberg, W. (1975) Gibt es in der Sonnenfleckenhaeufigkeit eine 179–jaehrige Wiederholungstendenz, Veroeffentlichungen des Astronomischen Instituts der Universitaet Frankfurt, No. 57.

Gosling, J. T., Asbridge, J. R., and Bame, S. J. (1977): An Unusual Aspect of Solar Wind Speed Variations during Solar Cycle 20, J. Geophys. Res. 82, 3311 – 3314.

Haase, R. (1976): Der messbare Einklang – Grundzuege einer empirischen Weltharmonik, Ernst Klett Verlag, Stuttgart.

Haken, H. (1978): Synergetics, Springer Verlag, Berlin, Heidelberg, New York.

Haken, H. (1981): Erfolgsgeheimnisse der Natur, Deutsche Verlagsanstalt, Stuttgart.

Halperin, B. I. (1986): The Quantized Hall Effect, Scient. American 254, 40 – 47.

Hofstadter, D. R. (1979): Goedel, Escher, Bach: an Eternal Golden Braid, Basic Books, New York.

Howard, R. (1975): The Rotation of the Sun, Scient. American 232, 106 – 114.

Howard, R. (1984): Solar Rotation, Ann. Rev. Astron. Astrophys. 22, 131 – 155.

Howard, R., Adkins, J. M., Boyden, T. A., Cragg, T. A., Gregory, T. S., LaBonte B. J., Padilla, S. P., and Webster, L. (1983): Solar Rotation Results at Mount Wilson, Solar Physics, 321 – 338.

Jammer, M. (1980): Le paradoxe d'Einstein–Podolsky–Rosen, La Recherche 11, 510 – 519.

Jantsch, E. (1984): Die Selbstorganisation des Universums, Deutscher Taschenbuch Verlag, Carl Hanser Verlag, Muenchen. Edition in English: The Self–Organizing Universe, New York 1980.

Jose, P. D. (1965): Sun's Motion and Sunspots, Astron. J. 70, 193 – 200.

Junk, H. P. (1982): Die Maximum–Entropie–Spektral–Analyse (MESA) und ihre Anwendung auf meteorologische Zeitreihen, Diplomarbeit des meteorologischen Instituts der Universitaet Bonn.

King, J. W. (1974): Weather and the Earth's Magnetic Field, Nature 247, 131 – 134.

Koestler, A. (1967): The Act of Creation, Laurel Edition, New York.

Kollerstrom, N. (1986): The Eureka Moment, paper presented at the 5th International Astrological Research Conference, London, November 22 – 23, 1986.

Kreplin, R. W., Dere, K. P., Horan, D. M., and Meekins, J. F (1977): The Solar Spectrum Below 10 Å, in White (1977) pp. 287 – 312.

Krishna, G. (1967): Kundalini, The Evolutionary Energy in Man, Ramadhar and Hopman, New Delhi and Zuerich.

Krueger, F. R. (1984): Physik und Evolution, Verlag Paul Parey, Berlin and Hamburg.

Lamb, H. H. (1977): Climate Present, Past, and Future, Vol. 2: Climatic History and the Future, Methuen, London.

Lamb, H. H. (1982): Climate History and the Modern World, Methuen, London and New York.

Landscheidt, T. (1976): Beziehungen zwischen der Sonnenaktivitaet und dem Massenzentrum des Sonnensystems, Nachrichten der Olbers–Gesellschaft 100, 2 – 19.

Landscheidt, T. (1980): Saekularer Tiefpunkt der Sonnenaktivitaet, Ursache einer Kaelteperiode um das Jahr 2000?, Jahrb. d. Wittheit zu Bremen 24, 189 – 220.

Landscheidt, T. (1981 a): Swinging Sun, 79–Year Cycle, and Climatic Change, J. interdisc. Cycle Res. 12, 3 – 19.

Landscheidt, T. (1981 b): Long Range Prediction of Energetic Solar Eruptions and their Terrestrial Effects, paper presented at the Second International Astrological Research Conference, London, November 28 – 29, 1981 (Correlation 1, 2, 3).

Landscheidt, T. (1983): Solar Oscillations, Sunspot Cycles, and Climatic Change, in McCormac (1983) pp. 293 –308.

Landscheidt, T. (1984 a): Cycles of Solar Flares and Weather, in Moerner and Karlèn (1984) pp. 473 – 481.

Landscheidt, T. (1984 b): Funktionen kosmischer Organismen: Schwingungen der Sonne und irdische Resonanzen, in Resch (1984) pp. 37 – 130.

Landscheidt, T. (1984 c): Prediction of Energetic Solar Eruptions and their Terrestrial Effects by Constellations of Planets, Astrology'84, The National Astrological Society, New York, pp. 25 – 35.

Landscheidt, T. (1984 d): Decipherment of the Rosetta Stone of Planetary Functions in the Solar System, paper presented at the 4th International Astrological Research Conference, London, October 27 – 28, 1984.

Landscheidt, T. (1986 a): Long Range Forecast of Energetic X-Ray Bursts Based on Cycles of Flares, in Simon, Heckman, and Shea (1986) pp. 81 – 89.

Landscheidt, T. (1986 b): Long Range Forecast of Sunspot Cycles, in Simon, Heckman, and Shea (1986) pp. 48 – 57.

Landscheidt, T. (1986 c): Cyclic Distribution of Energetic X–Ray Flares, Solar Physics 107, 195 – 199.

Landscheidt, T. (1986 d): Modulation of the Sun's Rotation, Energetic Solar Eruptions, Geomagnetic Storms, Weather, Abundance of Wild Life, and Economic Cycles by Conjunctions of Sun, Jupiter, and the Center of Mass of the Solar System, paper presented at the 5th International Astrological Research Conference, London, November 22 – 23, 1986.

Landscheidt, T. (1987 a): Foundations of Astrology in the Third Millenium, paper presented at the 6th International Astrological Research Conference, London, November 20 – 22, 1987.

Landscheidt, T. (1987 b): Wir sind Kinder des Lichts – Kosmisches Bewusstsein als Quelle der Lebensbejahung, Verlag Herder Freiburg, Basel, Wien.

Landscheidt, T. (1987c): Long Range Forecasts of Solar Cycles and Climatic Change, in Rampino, Sanders, Newman, and Koenigsson (1987) pp. 421 – 445.

Landscheidt, T. (1988): Solar Rotation, Impulses of the Torque in the Sun's Motion, and Climatic Variation, Climatic Change 12, 265–295.

Manley, G. (1974): Central England Temperatures, Monthly Means 1659 to 1973, Quart. J. Roy. Met. Soc. 100, 389 – 405.

Mayaud, P. N. (1973): A Hundred Year Series of Geomagnetic Data 1868 – 1967, IAGA Bulletin No. 33, IUGG Publication Office, Paris.

Mayaud, P. N. and Romana A. (1977): Supplementary Geomagnetic Data 1957 – 1975, IAGA Bulletin No. 39, IUGG Publication Office, Paris.

McCormac, B. M., ed. (1983): Weather and Climate Responses to Solar Variations, Colorado Associated University Press, Boulder, Colorado.

McCormac, B. M. and Seliga, T. A., eds. (1979): Solar–Terrestrial Influences on Weather and Climate, Reidel, Dordrecht, Boston, London.

Moerner, N. A. and Karlèn, W., eds. (1984): Climatic Changes on a Yearly to Millenial Basis, Reidel, Dordrecht, Boston, London.

McLeod, M. G. (1985): On the Geomagnetic Jerk of 1969, J. Geophys. Res. 90, 4597 – 4610.

Mitchell, J. M. (1966): Climatic Change, World Meteorolog. Org. Publ. No. 195, Geneva.

Mooley, D. A. and Parthasarathy, B. (1984): Fluctuations in All-India Summer Monsoon Rainfall 1871 – 1978, Climatic Change 6, 287 – 301.

Mustel, E. R. (1966): The Influence of Solar Activity on the Troposphere in the Polar Cap Regions, Soviet Astronomy – AJ 10, 288 – 294.

Mustel, E. R. (1977): Solar Activity and the Troposphere, Translation from Russian, available from NTIS, Springfield, VA 22151, 25 – 52.

Neubauer, L. (1983): The Sun–Weather Connection – Sudden Stratospheric Warmings Correlated with Sudden Commencements and Solar Proton Events, in McCormac (1983) pp. 395 – 397.

Oepik, E. (1972): Planetary Tides and Sunspots, Irish Astron. J. 10, 298.

Panofsky, H. A. and Brier, G. W. (1958): Some Applications of Statistics of Meteorology, The Pennsylvania State University, University Park, Pennsylvania.

Peitgen, H. O. and Richter, P. H. (1986): The Beauty of Fractals – Images of Complex Dynamical Systems, Springer Verlag Berlin, Heidelberg, New York, Tokyo.

Poincaré, H. (1889): Sur le problème des trois corps et les équations de la dynamique.

Poincaré, H. (1892): Méthodes nouvelles de la mécanique céleste, Vol. 1, Chapter 5, G. Villars, Paris, and Dover Publications, New York.

Prigogine, I. and Stengers, I. (1983): Dialog mit der Natur, Piper Verlag, Muenchen and Zuerich.

Prohaska, J. T. and Willett, H. C. (1983): Dominant Modes of Relationships between U.S. Temperature and Geomagnetic Activity, in McCormac (1983) pp. 489 – 494.

Rameau, J. P. (1971): Treatise on Harmony, Dover Publications, New York.

Rampino, M. R., Sanders, J. E., Newman, W. S., and Koenigsson, L. K., eds. (1987): Climate History, Periodicity, and Predictability, van Nostrand Reinhold Company, New York.

Rattensi, P. M. (1972): Science, Medicine, and Society in the Renaissance, London.

Recely, F. and Harvey, K. L. (1986): He I 10830 Observations of Flare Generated Coronal Holes, in Simon, Heckman, and Shea (1986) pp. 204 – 211.

Reiter, R. (1983): Modification of the Stratospheric Ozone Profile after Acute Solar Events, in McCormac (1983) pp. 95 – 116.

Resch, A., ed. (1984): Geheime Maechte, Resch Verlag Innsbruck.

Roberts, W. and Olson, R. H. (1973): J. atmos. Sci. 30, 135.

Rowland, F. S. (1978): Stratospheric Ozone – Earth's Fragile Shield, 1979 Yearbook of Science and the Future, Encyclopaedia Britannica, University of Chicago.

Sarfatti, J. (1977): The Case for Superluminal Information Transfer, MIT Technology Review, No. 5.

Sazonov, B. I. (1965): On the Solar–Troposphere Relation, Astron. Zhurnal 42, 653 – 655.

Sazonov, B. I. (1974): Circulation in the Troposphere and Anomaly in the Terrestrial Magnetic Field, in Drodzdov and Vorob'eva (1974) pp. 35 – 42.

Schneider, S. H. and Mass, C. (1975): Volcanic Dust, Sunspots, and Temperature Trends, Science 180, 741 – 746.

Segrè, E. (1984): Die grossen Physiker und ihre Entdeckungen, Piper Verlag, Muenchen, Zuerich.

Selleri, F. (1984): Die Debatte um die Quantentheorie, Verlag Vieweg, Braunschweig, Wiesbaden.

Seymour, P. A. H. (1986): A Causal Mechanism for Gauquelin's Planetary Effect, published by the author, Mannamead, Plymouth.

Sidorenkov, N. S. (1974): Solar Corpuscular Fluxes and Weather on Earth, Moscow Akademija Nauk, Priroda 3, 14 – 23.

Simon, P. A., Heckman, G., and Shea, M. A., eds. (1986): Solar–Terrestrial Predictions: Proceedings of a Workshop at Meudon, France, June 18 – 22, 1984, National Oceanic and Atmospheric Administration, Boulder, Colorado.

Stapp, H. P. (1975): Bell's Theorem and World Process, Nuovo Cimento, No. 29 B.

Stapp, H. P. (1977): Theory of Reality, Foundations of Physics 7, 317.

Stapp, H. P. (1979): Foundations of Physics 9, 1.

Stolov, H. L. and Shapiro, R. (1974): Investigation of the Responses of the General Circulation at 700 mb to Solar Geomagnetic Disturbance, J. Geophys. Res. 79, 2161 – 2170.

Stuart, W. F., Sherwood, V., and MacIntosh, S. M. (1971): Pure Appl. Geophys. 92, 150.

Švestka, Z. (1968): On Long–Term Forecasting of Proton Flares, Solar Physics 4, 18 – 29.

Thesleff, H. (1977): Pythagoreanism, Encyclopaedia Britannica, Macropaedia 15, 322 – 326.

von Klitzing, K. (1985): Mit Kurven im Kopf das Unerwartete gefunden, Bild der Wissenschaft No. 12, 124 – 134.

Warrain, F. (1942): Essai sur Harmonices mundi ou musique du monde de Johann Kepler, Vol. 2, Paris.

White, O. R., ed. (1977): The Solar Output and its Variation, Colorado Associated University Press, Boulder, Colorado.

Wilcox, J. M. (1975): Solar Activity and the Weather, J. Atmosph. Terr. Phys. 37, 237 – 256.

Williams, G. E. (1986): The Solar Cycle in Precambrian Time, Scient. American 255, 80 – 89.

Williams, G. E. and Sonett, C. P. (1985): Solar Signature in Sedimentary Cycles from the Late Precambrian Elatina Formation, Australia, Nature 318, 523 – 527.

Woehl, H. and Landscheidt, T. (1986): Solares Aktivitaetsminimum erst 1989/90?, Sterne und Weltraum 25, 584 – 585.

Zehnder, L. (1923): Die zyklische Sonnenbahn als Ursache der Sonnenfleckenperiode, Halle an der Saale.

Zuckerkandl, V. (1971): The Sense of Music, Princeton University Press, Princeton.

Zukav, G. (1979): The Dancing Wu Li Masters – An Overview of the New Physics, William Morrow, New York.

Glossary:

am: Annual mean of Mayaud's index *aa* of geomagnetic activity.

Å: Unit of wavelength for electromagnetic radiation covering visible light and X-rays, named after the Swedish physicist A. J. **Ångström:** 10^{-10} m.

Angular acceleration: Time rate of change of the angular velocity, the angular displacement of an object or a vector.

Angular momentum: Property that characterizes the rotary motion of an object. The Earth has orbital angular momentum by reason of its annual revolution about the Sun and spin angular momentum because of its daily rotation on its axis. Angular momentum is a vector quantity that requires the specification of both a magnitude and a direction. This quantity measures the intensity of rotational motion and is equal to the product of the angular velocity of a rotating object and its moment of inertia with respect to the rotation axis.

Autocorrelation function: The plot of the autocorrelation coefficient as a function of different lags in a time series. The autocorrelation coefficient measures the correlation between successive data of the time series. The statistical autocorrelation analysis can be used as a means to detect cyclic features within a time series.

Bell's theorem: In 1964 John S. Bell showed mathetically that the tenets of theories based on separability impose a limit on the extent of correlation of a pait of distant particles (see Einstein-Rosen-Podolsky paradox). The limit is expressed in the form of an inequality that can be proved by means of the mathematical theory of sets. This Bell inequality constitutes a precise prediction of the outcome of an experiment on condition that Einstein separability is valid. The rules of quantum mechanics can be employed to predict the quantum results of the same experiment which differ by 40%. Actual experiments carried out from 1972 violate the Bell inequality based on the principle of separability. They precisely confirm the prediction of quantum mechanics, a comprehensive theory describing a universe governed by the principle of inseparability and nonlocality (for details see references 1–2, especially B. d'Espagnat, 1979: The Quantum Theory and Reality, Scient. American 241, 128–140).

Carrington rotation: R. C. Carrington, who is famous for his discovery that the Sun rotates faster at the equator than near the poles, defined the heliographic longitude of the central point of the solar disk. This longitude is measured from the solar meridian that passed through the ascending node of the solar equator on the ecliptic on January 1, 1854, at Greenwich mean noon. Carrington's zero meridian passed the ascending node 12 hours earlier. Carrington rotations are numbered in relation to these coordinates. No. 1 commenced on November 9, 1853. The dates of commencement of current rotation numbers are given in astronomical yearbooks and ephemerides.

C-conjunctions: JU-CM-CSc events.

Chi-square test: see Pearson-test.

CM: Center of mass of the solar system, also called barycentre. Forces external to the solar system produce an acceleration of this centre just as though the whole mass of Sun and planets were concentrated there. The Sun's position relative to CM depends practically on the masses and the varying distances and directions of the giant planets Jupiter, Saturn, Uranus, and Neptune; the effect of the inner planets and of Pluto's tiny mass is negligible. Constellations of the outer planets regulate the Sun's orbital motion about CM. The Sun's centre CS and CM nearly coincide when Jupiter is in opposition to Saturn, Uranus, and Neptune, whereas the two centres reach their greatest distance when all of the giant planets are conjunct. Most of the time CM is outside the Sun's body.

Cosine wave: A curve described by the equation $y = cos\ x$, the ordinate being equal to the cosine of the abscissa. The cosine wave reaches its maximum at $0°$, its minimum at $180°$ (π radians), and zero values at $90°$ ($\pi/2$ radians) and $270°$ ($3\pi/2$ radians).

Cross correlation function: Statistical analysis of the correlation of two time series involving lags as applied in autocorrelation analysis.

CS: The Sun's geometric centre.

dB: Decibel, a unit of power ratio, proportional to the common logarithm of the intensities of two sources.

Dobson unit: Unit measuring the level of ozone concentration in the atmosphere.

$d\omega/dt$-cycle: 3.36-month cycle in energetic solar flares related to cyclic variations in the angular acceleration of the vector of the tidal forces of Venus, Earth, and Jupiter.

Einstein-Rosen-Podolsky paradox: Albert Einstein throughout his life remained dissatisfied with the probabilistic nature of the interpretations, generally given to quantum mechanics, which he thought incompatible with the locality principle, also called separability, inherent in his theory of relativity. In 1935 he and two young colleagues, Boris Podolsky and Nathan Rosen, devised a thought experiment, aimed to cast special doubt on quantum mechanics. They argued that this theory, based on nonlocality and inseparability, was incomplete because it does not explain how two particles, once related by interaction, can remain correlated over vast distances without being causally connected.

Filter coefficient: Determines the length of a prediction-error filter of the estimate of covariances in an autoregressive process related to informational entropy. It shows a vague resemblance to the function of lags in the autocorrelation function (Vide N. Andersen, On the calculation of filter coefficients for maximum entropy spectral analysis, Geophysics 39 (1974), 69 - 72).

Fisher-Behrens formula: This algorithm has to be applied in the *t*-test of the difference between means if the variance in the test groups shows a significant difference:

$$t = \frac{\bar{x}_1 - \bar{x}_2}{\sqrt{\dfrac{s_1^2}{n_1} + \dfrac{s_2^2}{n_2}}}$$

The number of the degrees of freedom (df) results from:

$$df = \frac{\left(\dfrac{s_1^2}{n_1} + \dfrac{s_2^2}{n_2}\right)^2}{\dfrac{\left(\dfrac{s_1^2}{n_1}\right)^2}{n_1 + 1} + \dfrac{\left(\dfrac{s_2^2}{n_2}\right)^2}{n_2 + 1}} - 2$$

Forbush decrease: A decrease in the level of galactic cosmic ray reception on Earth caused by major solar flares.

Gaussian low pass filter: A special technique of data smoothing related to the Gaussian distribution (Vide H. A. Panofsky and G. W. Brier, Some applications of statistics to meteorology, Pennsylvania State University, University Park, 1958).

G-conjunctions: JU-CM-CSg events.

Gleissberg-cycle: Secular cycle of sunspot activity that exhibits an average periodicity of about 80 years.

IOT: Impulse of the torque in the Sun's orbital motion about the centre of mass CM of the planetary system. The intensity of IOT is measured by the change in angular momentum effected by the impulse. This is why IOT are also called time integral of the torque. Strong IOT are initiated by JU-CM-CS events that occur when the centre of mass CM, the Sun's centre CS, and Jupiter are in line.

IUWDS: International Ursigram and World Days Service founded in 1962 by the International Astronomical Union (IAU), the Union Radio Scientifique Internationale (URSI), and the International Union of Geodesy and Geophysics (IUGG). Ursigrams spread diverse solar-terrestrial data gathered by more than 140 institutes all over the world.

JU-CM-CS: Heliocentric constellation that is formed when the centre of mass of the solar system (CM), the Sun's centre (CS), and the planet Jupiter are in line. JU-CM-CS events initiate impulses of the torque (IOT) in the Sun's orbital motion about CM that release energetic solar eruptions and connected terrestrial events.

JU-CM-CSc: JU-CM-CS event that is accompanied with a sharp increase in orbital angular momentum and centrifugal motion of the Sun away from CM.

JU-CM-CSg: JU-CM-CS event that goes along with a steep decrease in orbital angular momentum and centripetal motion of the Sun toward CM due to prevailing gravitation.

Major instability event: The centre of mass of the solar system keeps staying in or near the Sun's surface for several years; a phase of instability in solar activity and its terrestrial response ensues from this solar system constellation.

Markov type persistence: Distribution of data that reflects the pattern of a Markov chain, named after the Russian mathematician A. A. Markov. Markov chains appear in sequences of random events in which the probability of each event depends on the distribution of previous data.

Maunder Minimum: A period of very weak sunspot activity in the 17th century that seems to be connected with the climatic period of the so-called Little Ice Age.

MEM: Maximum entropy method of spectral variance analysis which shows much higher resolution than earlier methods, especially at lower frequencies. It is based on the density of informational entropy related to the autocovariance function of a time series.

MeV: Million electron-volt.

Minor instability event: Term that points to the boundary quality of JU-CM-CS events.

Orbital momentum: Angular momentum of the Sun's motion about CM.

Pearson-test: Chi-square test for the significance of the deviation of observed frequencies from expected frequencies.

Pi radians: Phase angle of 180° expressed in radians.

Pi/2 radians: Phase angle of 90° expressed in radians.

Polar cap absorption (PCA):   An ionospheric phenomenon evidenced by enhanced absorption of radio waves in the polar regions. PCA are released by solar proton events.

Proton event: A sudden increase in the number of solar protons of very high energy detected at the Earth after an energetic solar eruption.

Radiosonde flights: Sounding balloon which ascends to high altitudes, carrying meteorological equipment which modulates radio signals transmitted back to equipment on Earth.

Running variance: The well-known smoothing technique of running means over two, three, or more consecutive readings with equal or different weights is applied to variance, the square of the standard deviation.

Secular cycle of sunspot activity: Vide Gleissberg-cycle.

Secular torque cycle: Torque cycle in the Sun's motion about CM that is related to the secular sunspot cycle.

Spectral analysis: Statistical methods (Fourier analysis, autocorrelation function, cross correlation function, power spectrum, maximum entropy spectrum) for disclosing cyclic patterns in time series of data. The results of such analysis are presented in the form of spectra in the frequency or time domain.

Spectral peak: Peak in a spectrum resulting from spectral analysis that points to the frequency or the period of a cycle hidden in the data.

Supersecular sunspot cycle: Cycle of sunspot activity that exhibits an average periodicity of about 400 years.

Tidal cycle: Vide $d\omega/dt$-cycle.

Torque: Torque bears the same relationship to rotation as force does to linear movement. It could be called "rotary force" because it is the tendency of a force to rotate the body to which it is applied about a point or an axis. Torque produces rotation or revolution the effectiveness of which is measured by the vector product of the force and the perpendicular distance from the line of action of the force to the axis of rotation. The time rate of change of the angular momentum of a rotating body is equal to the torque of the force applied to it.

Torque cycles: Quasi cycles of different periods that are related to impulses of the torque (IOT) in the Sun's revolution about the centre of mass of the solar system (CM).

***t*-test:**   Student's test of the significance of experimental data.

Variance: Average of the squares of the deviations of a number of observations of a quantity from their mean value.

***X*-ray bursts:**   Flare-generated emission of energetic *X*-rays. The *X*-ray classification of solar flares is a better index of the geophysical significance of flares than the older optical groups of importance 1 to 4.

INDEX

Essex County Council

Many libraries in Essex
have videos for loan —

enquire at your local library
for details

THE ROYAL FLYING CORPS
BOY SERVICE

Boy J. Ross No 83445 May/June, 1917
Age 16½ years, a recruit

The Royal Flying Corps Boy Service RFC – RNAS – RAF

The Link is Forged

by

John Ross, RFC, RAF

With a foreword by
Air Chief Marshal Sir Hugh P. Lloyd,
GBE, KCB, MC, DFC, LID

Regency Press (London & New York) Ltd.
125 High Holborn, London WC1V 6QA

By the same author
The RFC to the RAF, India 1919

ISBN 0 7212 0830 4

Printed and bound in Great Britain by
Buckland Press Ltd., Dover, Kent.

CONTENTS

PART ONE

CONTENTS

PART TWO

LIST OF ILLUSTRATIONS

At the end of this book will be found a collection of illustrations of historic interest.

Four RFC Boys in uniform. Wearing "Cadet" (officers) white band. On leave.

Leave or Duty Ration book, 1918.

A. V. Roe, standing beside the wreck of one of his early machines.

Kapitan Leutnant Martin Dietrich. Commander of Zeppelin L22 which raided Sheffield.

B. C. Hucks. Pioneer Aviator, pre 1914.

Boy George Watson and another at Cranwell RAF.

Ten ex. RFC boys in main service aged over 18 years.

Handley-Page 0/400 Bomber A/C

George Fleming, the boy from Sheffield, we enlisted together.

Miles Martlet aeroplane.

Herbert Latham, Brooklands 1911.

Roland Garros, french aviator, Hendon 1913.

Graham White, ten seater aircraft, one engine 100 hp "green".

ACKNOWLEDGEMENTS

In appreciation, I am pleased to acknowledge the kindness of:
My late parents and family for saving my letters and photographs.
Flight International incorporating the Magazine *The Aeroplane* 1916, 1917 and later.
The *Morning Telegraph, Sheffield. The Star. Sheffield Telegraph. Sheffield Independent.* All taken over by Sheffield Newspapers Ltd.
The late Mrs M. Arzt. Mr Chaz Bowyer. Mr M. G. E. Bryne of British Aerospace, Brough. Mr H. H. Edmunds. Wing Commander S. Townson, RAF (Retd), ex-RFC. Mr J. Whitting. Some ex-boys. Extracts from the Cranwell RNAS. The magazine *The Piloteer* 1918. To my wife, Lucy for her complete understanding and a splendid thank you.
There is nothing in other publications for research about the Royal Flying Corps Boy Service. This cannot claim to tell the whole story as sadly so few are left to complete it.

My other book, *The RFC to the RAF, India 1919* follows on from this story. It is available from the same publishers priced £4.95.

FOREWORD

It is a pleasure to write a foreword to this interesting book which records the creation and growth of Boy Service in the Royal Flying Corps way back in 1917.

It was a service founded by Marshal of the Royal Air Force, Lord Trenchard, whose intention was to build and create a powerful, safe and lasting foundation of technical knowledge and leadership for the new Royal Air Force when it was formed in April 1918. Lord Trenchard wanted to be sure of a knowledgeable nucleus of young airmen. In this he wholly succeeded.

When I went to India in 1919 practically all the junior airmen were original boys of the Royal Flying Corps and the Royal Naval Air Service. It was these young men who built up and created the excellent maintenance and technical services, which were to serve us so well, not only between the wars, but to face up to and win that dreadful struggle in the air with the German Air Force.

It has been my pleasure to have known dozens of these excellent young men. One is the author of this book who sometimes occupied my back seat in a Bristol fighter as we flew our security patrols over that wild and troublesome area of the then North Western Frontier of India.

Air Chief Marshal Sir Hugh P. Lloyd,
GBE, KCB, MC, DFC, LID.

PREFACE

Much of this is an autobiography, but my intention is to describe the events of the young and older generations as I saw them before, during and after the terrible war of 1914-18.

From the placid life before 1914 great respect for families and neighbours was predominant. Ordinary people, if not with plenty of money and little in the way of mechanical labour-saving devices, lived a spartan life during the war, with its turmoil in every way on the Home Front. Afterwards came the dreadful feeling of the war not fully settled and unemployment was added to life's complexities.

The Royal Flying Corps was only two years old in 1914 when war started and was built up from scratch. The late Lord Trenchard saw a difficult future for the continuous strength of the RFC, because the enlistment of mechanics had drained the nation. His idea resulted in the Royal Flying Corps Boy Service being formed to train hundreds of apprentices. I was in the original 400.

What a catastrophe it would have been when hostilities ceased with "Duration of war" men leaving. This calamity was averted. The trained RFC Boys were ready for action on regular service. Many squadrons were disbanded and emptied of all ranks. The necessary stations and squadrons were manned by the few retained officers, NCOs, not many men and the hundreds of ex-boys. The ex-boys on squadrons had to learn the handling of different aircraft, but we mastered the complete maintenance programme.

A few boys were engaged on a longer regular engagement; in large numbers we were placed on reserve and immediately unemployed. The three armed forces were drastically reduced by the "Geddes axe". For our services the RFC Boys received no recognition in the 1914-18 war. We had done what they needed us for; then they forgot all about us.

People on the "Home Front" were still enduring the shortages and the colossal losses in families, coupled with unemployment on a huge scale, yet carried on steadfastly with the determination to create a better future. And as a body of the general public they did not fail. As in the second world war, our nation did not seek to go to war and, for that reason alone, we must be proud of ourselves for setting an example to the whole world. Our ancestors were great people.

John Ross

PART ONE

CHAPTER ONE

EARLY DAYS. REMINISCENCES. 1914 WAR, AND AT SCHOOL. WOODSEATS. APPRENTICE ENGINEER. THE PIONEER AVIATORS. I SEE AEROPLANE FLY FOR THE FIRST TIME. ZEPPELIN RAID ON SHEFFIELD. INTEREST IN THE ROYAL FLYING CORPS.

When war broke out in August 1914 I was at school. It was a village school at Greenhill under the Derbyshire Education Authority, then outside Sheffield. Previous to living in Woodseats, my parents opened a new confectionery shop at the corner of Scarborough Road and Main Road (No 52), Darnall, around 1903, moving to Harbord Road, Woodseats around 1906.

At this village school in Greenhill the only lighting was by means of oil lamps hanging from the ceiling. I remember the headmaster, Mr Beddows going through the ritual of lighting these huge lamps. He was an upright man and had served in the old volunteers. In addition to being a fine schoolmaster, Mr Beddows was a man of high principles, devoted to his King and country. He was every inch a soldier and a gentleman.

Being near to the school leaving age of 14 and in the top class of standard eight, which only a few attained, we were drawn, as elders, to the war by the various activities the school undertook. Maps of the front were posted up with flags of the combating nations pinned to their relative positions. I was one of the map tactitions. The girls were busy sewing up materials for sandbags and making first aid slings. The lads helped to parcel the goods, all of us doing many other jobs.

The school sold coloured silk Union Jacks, in aid of the local Relief Fund. These were priced one penny. Collections made by the scholars bought "comforts", taking them from school to a temporary hospital near Dore and Totley railway station for Belgian and British wounded soldiers brought from the front.

My elder brother, a Territorial, was in France with the "Old Contemptibles" in the Lincolnshire Regiment. Father was very patriotic, taking a keen interest in the progress of the war. There was no radio: newspapers were the only means of general communication of information. Therefore, the conversations about the war were the main topics between my father, neighbours, relatives and friends. Thus the young ones were drawn into the atmosphere of this great war. Those of military age discussed the units they would join, because the forces were calling for recruits. We young ones were constantly reminded of it. Our talks were about the battles, serving relations and the war heroics.

In this same year, November 1914, I left school at 14 years of age. As I was interested in steam locomotives, my father, knowing Mr Kerry, the foreman engineer, got me in to the Midland Railway locomotive sheds at Millhouses, Sheffield, now demolished, as an apprentice engineer. I got on well under the training of a good man – old Mr Hollis – who taught me so much about the use of tools and the workings of steam locomotives and engineering.

The engine numbers were 260 on the small engines, and the range of 350 up to 400 on the express engines, each engine having its own driver, fireman and the cleaner. The names of Hill, Jacques, Ronksley, Scott and Wood are those of a few of the express drivers I remember. Their engines were turned out in spotless condition.

At times the work was heavy, but interesting. I was trained to be smart, exact and clean in my work, a lesson I never forgot, serving me well later in the RFC and the RAF.

Only a little was known by the public about aeroplanes and those who flew them. I was interested in reading about the famous airmen: Bleriot, B. C. Hucks, Cody, Graham-White, Gustav Hamel (who demonstrated the loop the loop before HM King George V and Queen Mary), A. V. Roe, Farman Sopwith, Martinsyde, Handley-Page, Paulham, Raynham and other pioneers.

It was rumoured that aeroplanes had been seen near Sheffield. My father cycled to Doncaster where the first aviation meeting in England was held from October 15, 1909. There was no flying on that day, as the weather was not clear enough. It was held for a week, finishing on October 22, 1909.

In July 1911 an aeroplane landed in a field at Tinsley, Sheffield and, after a few repairs, took off again. I understand it was piloted by C. F. Cody. In 1912 three airmen flew in to Sheffield. On August 3, H. Slack dropped in during a tour, while on August 29, Gustav Hamel flew in for three days, demonstrating at Niagara Grounds. On November 22, J. L. Hall, a Sheffield airman, flew at Redmires, but crashed on a very windy day. These visits did not receive a great deal of publicity.

The first big aviation display in Sheffield was organised by the Sheffield *Daily Independent*, called "Sheffield Aviation Week 1914" from March 29 to April 4, 1914.

My sister, Clara, took me as a boy to see Mr Harold Blackburn fly his Blackburn Type I monoplane where the Sheffield sports stadium is at Owlerton. I was thrilled at this first sight of flying and bought five different postcard photographs of him.

When Gustav Hamel came to Sheffield, he flew his Morane monoplane at the Niagara Grounds, Wadsley Bridge, but I missed seeing him. Later, the first Sheffield-born airman to announce his visit to fly, Mr Marcus D. Manton, came to Sheffield to give his own flying display in a Bleriot monoplane. It was well advertised. This was extraordinary – a local airman was to give a demonstration of his skills in the air, this marvel of aviation, and loop the loop and perform other feats. He later became a qualified and well-known instructor at the Hendon Flying School.

It was Whit Tuesday and the following Wednesday and Thursday in June 1914 when he came, using the Redmires old racecourse as his airfield.

This I could not resist. Mother packed sandwiches and also provided me with some tea in a medicine bottle, as thermos flasks were unknown. I was not yet 14 years old, but I set off down the old Abbey Lane, then a narrow, winding lane and on to Redmires, about three miles away. It was a lovely day.

I sat on a bank overlooking the airfield and this wonderful monoplane. Manton climbed into his Bleriot. It was started up and he "took off", circled above us, climbed and performed a great feat of evolution in flying by looping the loop. Then came steep turns and low flying; the whole exhibition of flight lasted just about 15 minutes.

I was absolutely thrilled and marvelled at his wonderful and dashing display of expert flying – at times right over my head and so close it

Harold Blackburn
Sheffield Aviation Week
(Blackburn Monoplane)
1914

Marcus. D. Manton 1914

seemed I could touch him.

When he finished, I set off for home and no doubt ran part of the journey, because I got there so quickly. Breathlessly I told the family of the thrills and excitement of the display. I remember my father being so pleased at me going all that way on my own to watch this Sheffield aviator fly: he awarded me with a silver threepenny bit, which was good money in those days for a boy. I proudly kept the reported cuttings of Marcus Manton and his photograph from the local paper.

Marcus Manton's father was a well-known doctor in the Park district of Sheffield. In later years I knew his sister, Mrs M. Arzt, who resided in Germany. She told me much about Marcus and flew with him sometimes. We corresponded regularly until her death, which was soon after Marcus died, being killed crossing the road outside his home. Mrs Arzt gave me the postcard photograph of him and many treasured newspaper cuttings.

Before 1914 there were only a few private owners of motor cars in the district and their constant winding at the front caused much amusement. The quaint motor coaches ran out to certain villages by private owners, perhaps one a day but, in some cases, only once a week. Many were open "charabancs" with high seats, each seat the width of the coach, the rear seat being higher than the one in front, with five or six persons to one seat. They had a large, bulb-squeezing horn, no windscreen and solid tyres which ran on a road surface of stone and grit flattened by a steam-roller. The timetable, if any, was unreliable. Steam-driven waggons did long-distance haulage. Vamplews of Woodseats had a lot of them and large works had some.

The horse-drawn vehicle was dominant, with a trap for business and pleasure, the delivery van, street salesmen, taxis, haulage, weddings, funerals and general "carting". If a horse fell down on the roadway, there was a cry of "Horse down". Men rushed to help; one sat on its head, whilst others unfastened the harness, allowing the horse to free itself and get up. Certain men, expert at this, were often fetched out to a fallen horse. It was not easy if the horses were in pairs. Some had to be killed.

Boys climbed on the back of vehicles. On horse-drawn ones people called to the driver, "Whip behind!" The driver then leaned over and, with his long whip, whipped us off.

Until 1914 Woodseats was a nice community with not many houses and a limited number of shops. The terminus for the tramcars was at

Chantrey Road shopping area; a few mostly small-windowed shop⹁
extended as far as Cobnar Road. There were a few shops on t⹁
opposite side of the road, then a gap to the Big Tree public hou⹁
From the mortar mill at Cobnar Road corner, the whole length ᴏɪ
Chesterfield Road on that side comprised fields up to the rifle-range
opposite the brickworks, then trees to Meadow Head. Opposite the
mortar mill was a little sweet shop with steps leading up on either side
of the door, then up past the "Poplars" to the Abbey Hotel and the
blacksmiths' open area and cottages.

At the back of our house was an open space to the post office.
(Doctor Chandler's house was built later.) Then up to the tin Roman
Catholic Church and on to Meadow Head, where Mr Newbould had a
wooden hut, repairing bicycles and selling cups of tea. The whole area
of Meadow Head was open fields down to the hamlet of Low Edges,
opposite being the hamlet of Coal Aston. Here my father was turned
away from the fields for trespassing on Government property. The RFC
came. Woodseats was peaceful until hundreds of Royal Flying Corps
men arrived and were billeted there, transforming it into a busy place.
Two well-known locals, Mr Birtles and Mr Hunt were RFC men who
married Woodseats girls.

The Royal Flying Corps took over the fields opposite at Coal Aston,
up to Norton Lane. I saw a BE2C come down over the hedges
bordering the narrow fields along Norton Lane. It burst into flames, but
the pilot crawled out of the wreckage and walked away.

As a result of working on steam locomotives, I became interested in
motor cars. My father said that the petrol engine would soon be
providing the most popular means of transport and liked the idea of his
son learning about it. I had the chance of an apprenticeship at one of
the few Sheffield motor car dealers, which was still busy building
horse-drawn carriage vehicles. The company was known as William
Wilson and Sons Ltd. It was owned by a Mr Fretwell Downing and a
Mr Fields. Situated near to the top of Cambridge Street, with a large
doctor's house opposite, where Cole Bros' large shop now stands, at
the rear it backed on to a narrow lane called Backfields. Afterwards
Wilsons changed ownership, becoming a large billiard saloon, which
was eventually destroyed by fire.

I was given permission by letter to leave the Midland Railway
apprenticeship in March 1916. It was signed by the Superintendent of
the locomotive section, a Mr Buckley.

I commenced my apprenticeship with Wilsons at six shillings a week. I was put to work with one of the best motor mechanics in Sheffield, a Mr Tom Carrol. He was very good at his work, and under his guidance I soon got down to the workings of the internal combustion engine. Having previous experience of the use of tools, I settled down to what was much lighter work than that on the steam locomotives, but with a similar principle of action of the piston type of engine. I practised backing cars and some lorries and chassis in and out of the garage and became good enough to take over the wheel and drive outside. You did not require a driving licence in those days.

I worked the entire period with this mechanic, working on every type of motor car available at the time – small ones to the big lorries and charabancs which were becoming popular. The chassis were fetched by a driver from the makers. We erected the body and interior and had our own painters. Sign-writers finished off the complete new outfit and then the vehicle was ready for our final outside test run.

Wigmores of Dinnington had a number of charabancs from us. Warriners had some, together with a few lorries. We did a great deal of work for Kennings of Clay Cross, a company which was starting to deal in motor cars. I remember a Mr Kenning, founder of the huge Kennings business.

We undertook all the work that came in, doing complete overhauls and repairs. This wide range of work proved of great value to the keen apprentice, who not only took parts away and replaced them with new ones, but often had to make up new ones. When engines were stripped, the crankshaft would be sent away to have the journals re-turned and set. We would run out the old metal from the big end and re-mould them with new white metal. After turning them on the lathe, we would scrape them until they were a perfect fit on the journal. After the complete re-fitting and timing came the great thrill of the test, which was the usual run of West Street and up the hill to Glossop Road, Sheffield.

Road surfaces were not so good as they are today. We knew where to find each other if some failure occurred; there were no snack bars in those days to pop into.

The main big vehicle at this place was the Commer, which had a pre-selected gear change. It was chain driven, with a hand-brake applied to the two rear wheels; it had solid tyres, no windscreen and a foot-brake on the shaft. Paraffin lamps provided the means of lighting.

There was a bulb horn and no heating system. We did a great deal of work on this type of vehicle, the gearbox demanding meticulous workmanship.

Other motor cars were the American "Liberty", Vulcan, General Motors, Studebaker, Chevrolet, Dennis, Alvis, Sunbeam, Renault, and the Albion.

The war was expanding. The Royal Flying Corps had taken over some farmland just outside Sheffield near the village of Coal Aston. There were a few canvas hangars and a few aircraft, mainly the BE2C. My father, a builder by trade, started erecting the buildings for the RFC. He used to tell me about the aeroplanes and those who flew them.

The Commanding Officer's motor car, a Studebaker, used to be brought to the garage where I worked. I would see the driver dressed in the uniform of the RFC and try to talk to him. I somewhat envied him and his uniform; he was very aloof and looked down upon me with an air of superiority.

In my spare time, if the weather was good, I would walk towards Coal Aston, peer over the hedges and wait for the aircraft to be flown. Often the hangars were never opened. Sometimes men would open a hangar and out would be dragged an aircraft, a BE2C. They would start up the engine and run it up to full throttle. However, my hopes of witnessing the thrill of a good display of flying would soon be thwarted, for more often than not they simply pushed it back into the hangar again.

My interest in aircraft, flying and the Royal Flying Corps was increasing. As the sailors, soldiers and airmen in uniform were idolized by all at home, I was anxious to join them. Troops were expected to wear their uniform at all times, even when they were away from their unit.

There were very few local fellows in the Royal Flying Corps. A pilot was regarded as someone special, a "dasher" with a devil-may-care flying spirit.

Young RFC officer pilots at Coal Aston would be seen and heard tearing up and down Meadow Head and Woodseats like madmen on their solo motor cycles, causing quite a stir and alarm to many people. With the arrival of the Leyland lorries, the Crossley tenders and other vehicles, Woodseats was awakened and soon totally transformed.

Zeppelins had already attacked the north-east, east, south-east coast and the London area and were now venturing further inland to the Midlands.

People in Sheffield had heard the air-raid sirens, the cry of "The buzzers are going!", whistles blowing and hooters being blasted. The banging of doors awoke those who did not hear them. Otherwise they would be awoken by the cries of "Put that light out!". Warnings came to be regarded as false alarms, with the "All clear" sounding without anything happening.

Upon the "alert", my father always went out, walked down Abbey Lane with one or two neighbours and me, passing the football and cricket grounds belonging to Woodseats Friends Adult School, a popular winter sledging slope, to the old stone wall where the Abbey Lane School is now situated. Fields extended right down to Bocking Lane, which was bordered by hedgerows. Opposite were houses to Linden Avenue, where St Chad's Church now stands. Next came a few old cottages, then some big houses at the point where Abbey Lane became very narrow. There were stone walls and fields to Crawshaw's Farm, opposite the cart-track known as Bocking Lane. Here was our "listening post" on this adventurous vigil. In the stillness of the night we could hear dogs barking miles away. From our "observation post" we heard the drone of Zeppelins far away, a long time before Sheffield was first bombed. They had already attacked parts of the Midlands.

Newspapers gave very brief news of the raids. Many people began to regard the warnings and sirens as nonsense and took little notice when the "alert" was sounded. There was a stupid complacency among many, who boasted that the Zeppelins would never reach Sheffield.

My father, constantly alert, was not so sure about this and was convinced that as Sheffield was a great industrial city making munitions, the enemy would make a big effort to try to reach a target of such importance. He prepared for such an emergency by strengthening the cellar walls and storing rations, water and other daily requirements there. This was his own idea and a prelude to the cellar-type shelter that was introduced by the Government twenty or so years later.

There was no organised ARP service in those days and no shelters were provided. The police formed the main body responsible for giving out instructions from the Government as to what the public was required to do after the air-raid warnings had been sounded. Notices headed "Zeppelin raids, Special instructions for the protection of the public", were posted on walls, with regulations framed for turning off the gas supply and all electric lights.

Once the "alert" was sounded, volunteers, mainly boy scouts, patrolled the streets on bicycles, calling "Put that light out!". In the dark they also helped on the ambulances, blowing whistles throughout the journey. The police, some on foot and others on bicycles, gave shrill blasts on their whistles and reported offenders for disobeying the "Black out" regulations.

On September 25, 1916, at about 10.45pm, the air-raid sirens had sounded. I was at my usual quiet observation spot on Abbey Lane, Woodseats, with my father and a few neighbours. My father said, "Quiet, hark, listen to that."

We all looked up into the dark sky towards Chesterfield; we saw nothing, but could hear in the darkness above us a distant, dull drone, drone, drone approaching. It was not too loud, as if it was creeping along over Norton Woodseats. This was a Zeppelin all right. It was the L22 commanded by Kapitan Leutnant Martin Dietrich. It sounded as though the engines were running at slow speed. It travelled over to the area near Redmires.

At this time we heard an express train roar into Sheffield down by Heeley and towards the Sheffield Midland Railway Station. Minutes passed; the quietness had a doubtful appeal, with an eerie silence above which seemed to convey to this small group of men that something terrible, something they had never known before, was about to happen. They felt sure that the Zeppelin had not left the district.

My father said, "I don't like it." Pointing his stick in the direction of the Redmires area, he announced in measured words and with a grave tone: "He is floating in the air over there somewhere." The others in the group agreed.

The feeling of fear of the Zeppelin and bombs was within all of us. Had any one of the party said, "Let's get away from here and go home", I think my father would have been the only one to have stayed behind.

Rumour had it that a man was lowered by cable in a small gondola from the Zeppelin to make observations. This was proved to be true by the Germans after the war. It was known as an observation car, which was able to carry one man. Instruments and a telephone were fitted, so that he could give the commander in the Zeppelin above much valuable information. The gondola could be lowered by winch to a depth of about 800 metres, approximately half a mile below the level of the airship. It was a lonely and often cold trailing "basket".

All eyes were peering up into the darkness of the sky when suddenly we heard the powerful drone of the engines of the Zeppelin approaching the city from the Redmires area. We saw nothing in the air.

My father insisted that it was a Zepplin and that the Germans on board had seen the train entering Sheffield station. It was having a free passage, because there were no aircraft up from the nearby RFC aerodrome. We were a sitting target. There were no searchlights, only the strong, dull drone, drone, drone.

It was approaching midnight when suddenly, towards the centre of Sheffield, we heard a swishing noise which sounded to me like slates sliding quickly down a roof. There was a flash and a yellowish glare that lit up the whole of the city centre in the valley of Sheffield.

The thunderous roar of an explosion came up towards us. This was constantly repeated, as if all hell was let loose and some dreadful catastrophe was taking place. It certainly was. I remember the sudden cry of great fear among the gathered group of men: "It's the Zepps! They are here!"

While the flashes and the thud of explosions were taking place, our legs were carrying us as fast as they could manage back to our homes. There was no anti-aircraft attack from the Sheffield battery. It was later established that those who were supposedly manning the battery were all at the Hippodrome Theatre enjoying a night out.

This Zeppelin raid on Sheffield was the first. It killed 29 people and either destroyed or damaged 100 houses and property away to the east following the Great Central Railway. One of the last incendiary bombs set fire to a house in Britannia Road, Darnall – the spot where the Darnall Library now stands. Yet during the raid, some people living on the outskirts of Sheffield slept right through it, completely unawares.

The public had never heard explosions like this before, only the crack at a rifle range. But the tremendous explosions of the bombs, destruction and loss of life were a new and terrifying experience, an ordeal of modern warfare brought home to us all. It was a rude awakening.

The names of the places bombed by the Zeppelins were never published in the press for two reasons. One, it was better that the public should not be too greatly upset. Secondly, the enemy would not be informed by us as to where the Zeppelins had been. The Germans were always making incorrect claims about their raids. The report of this raid merely stated that it was, "an attack on a North Midlands town, which had no military importance."

All these incidents were not conducive to the peaceful outlook of young people. It was something new to all of us, both young and old alike. It was a war in which everyone had an active part. Soldiers were not leaving with a farewell parting to go to a far distant land to fight battles only they knew about, until the survivors triumphantly returned home again.This was a great war on land, on the sea and in the air. It involved everyone in our cities and towns. The terrific conflict of European armies engaged in deadly combat in Flanders and other places abroad was widespread knowledge. There were naval battles which resulted in the sinking of every type of ship and the new pattern of the nation's aircraft engaged in aviational warfare. Now we had something we had never known before, a truly exciting innovation to talk about and wonder at; it was both important and terrifying, gradually increasing in pace and approaching our doorsteps.

Boys and girls of 14-17 had nothing to offer the nation by way of support, except to join in the war effort in whatever way they could. Nearly all the new songs of the day had a patriotic theme. London shows were very musical, but there were no groups of music-makers and certainly no pop or rock and roll. There was no organisation of youth services by the local councils as there is today and rebel groups were unheard of. The only associations in existence for youngsters were the Boy Scouts, the Boys Brigade, the St John Ambulance Brigade, Church and Chapel Institutes and Bible classes and the YMCA evening classes at local schools.

We invented keenly competitive games involving cigarette cards, buttons, peg tops, "peggy", running and hitting an iron rim with a stick, marbles and imaginary horses and trains and diabolo – a game at which one of my sisters was quite an expert.

Then there was the local Woodseats Picture Palace. Mr O'Neil was the manager. Admission for children at Saturday matinées was one old penny. William S. Hart was one of the heroes of the silver screen at that time, rescuing damsels in distress, such as the famous actress, Mary Pickford.

We young lads formed our own football and cricket teams. The team sheet was posted in a local shop window. Our playing field was usually on Crawshaw's Farm, which now forms the Abbey Lane Cemetery. We provided our own limited gear, which the youth of today would despise. Sometimes we would see our results published in the local sports paper, the "Green-Un".

The Ministry of Munitions was created. Many men, youths and women entered the factories and, with overtime, were paid well. Females were doing the type of work women had never previously done in the large steelworks.

Being interested in aeroplanes, I was making models of biplanes and the like from photographs which appeared in the weekly magazine, *The Aeroplane*, which was priced at one old penny. There were no model kits available at that time.

I soon became engrossed in this magazine. It contained photographs, drawings and details of aircraft being built by the different nations. It also contained details of certain aero engines, information from all the fighting Air Forces, reports from private flying schools and pupils' progress. Articles and discussions with extracts from Parliamentary debates also appeared.

I was fascinated by the accounts of the activities of the Royal Naval Air Service and the Royal Flying Corps, under the headings "Naval and Military Aeronautics" from the *London Gazette*, the Admiralty and the War Office.

These supplements gave details of promotions, attainments and personal matters, including awards for bravery of all ranks from the Victoria Cross to the Military Medal.

The Royal Flying Corps was built up by and contained hundreds of officers seconded from Army regiments coming for flying duties. Many would read like this: "Highland Light Infantry. 2nd Lieut G. T. Wilcox is seconded for duty with the Royal Flying Corp dated . . .". Casualty lists were reported. Under this "Personal Notice" information was given about the life of a young airman and how he had lost his life.

The Honours list, awards and special promotions in the RNAS and the RFC fascinated me. They gave me a youthful appetite for the thrills of the air. The accounts of conspicuous gallantry, bravery, devotion to duty, etc, of awards from the Victoria Cross downwards greatly impressed us young lads. These accounts were so vivid, it was no wonder that at the time these fellows were the idols of an impressionable young boy such as I then was. Instead of indulging in hooliganism, vandalism, attacking elderly people and scribbling on other people's property as is the wont of much of today's youth, we deeply admired the courage of these men, their uniform and their splendid feats of daring against the enemy.

One simple entry was the award of the Victoria Cross. It stated: "On September 5, 1916, Lt Wm Leafe Robinson, Worcester Regt and RFC for most conspicuous bravery. He attacked an enemy airship under circumstances of great difficulty and damaged and sent it crashing to the ground as a flaming wreck. He had been in the air for more than two hours and had previously attacked another airship during this flight."

There were the promotions from the ranks to Commissioned Officers in the RFC from Sgt-Major down to 2nd Class Air Mechanic. Also in the lists were the NCOs and Privates from Army units, one example being "NCOs, men, one, to be Temp Sec Lts (on probation) for duty with the RFC." Private Crewe, from the London Regt TF and dated.

Some of the promotions and awards of medals for officers and men of the RFC flying against the enemy were for gallantry and devotion to duty and service in the field.

This shows the great influence held upon the RFC by the War Office, which regulated air operations from a purely military basis deeply entrenched even to the retention of military ranks of Generals, Brigadier-Generals, Colonels, Majors, Captains and 2nd Lieutenants. The "other ranks" were a mixture of military NCO ranks, private or mechanic.

In our youthful minds one could imagine and believe that promotion was good. Details of air engagements which brought airmen on to the honours list formed most exciting reading. The thrill rested deep in our minds and our imagination was greater than anything before which could have been of naval or military history we learned at school, or even the Boer war, which many of the servicemen of 1914-18 had served in and their experiences recorded. These deeds of daring in the air were something new, something our parents had never known – and, in many cases, thought impossible.

We young ones had to read and find out for ourselves about aeronautics, as I did to the best of my limited ability. I admit that, in my case, it was intense hero worship, coupled with the quest for knowledge. I simply could not get hold of enough reading material about the mechanics of flight.

There were so few books on aeronautics available. The intricate knowledge of flying was contained mainly within the realms of those actually actively engaged in flying and the confidential manuals of the Service. No one other than those few engaged in flying could instructively converse on this new science.

There was even a brand of cigarettes which issued cards depicting aeroplanes. I collected these rare cards; they are still very interesting.

From the few books printed, the one I selected was *The Aeroplane Speaks*, by Captain H. Barber, RFC. I bought a copy out of my savings and found I could understand it. The drawings were so well defined and most informative, whilst the diagrams were illustrated with a simplicity and clarity, so that I quickly began to teach myself the "Principles of Flight".

This book did not contain any information about aero engines, but helped to teach the ordinary man to understand the aeroplane. I found it invaluable. I do not remember any books at the time printed on aero engines.

Young men of 18 were being called up in large numbers. My brother, Fred, two years my senior, had attested and been called to the forces and entered the KOYLIs. When on leave during his training, he looked fit and well, transformed from a clerk in an office to the outdoor life of a soldier. He changed to a fine, tall figure of a man, bronzed and robust, of whom the family was extremely proud.

I was restless. My parents knew about my deep interest in aeroplanes and the Royal Flying Corps, I had often spoken about my desire to enter the Forces, as I felt left out of it and wanted to get into uniform and do "my bit" with my elders. I was proud of them and their uniforms.

My father did not try to discourage me; he certainly approved of me being interested in the mechanics of the aeroplane, combustion engine and the Royal Flying Corps, since he too was enthusiastic about flying and aircraft in general.

I knew there were boys in the Navy and some in the Army and thought that if I applied to the Royal Flying Corps and offered myself for service, at my age, they might take me on as a boy learner.

My father agreed and so I decided to try to enter. On February 28, 1917, I wrote to the Recruiting Officer at the Royal Flying Corps, Farnborough, asking him if I could join as a boy learner (about which I had read in the magazine *Aeroplane*). I told them my correct age, which was then 16 years and three months.

Marcus Manton. 1914/15
His experimental bi-plane

Mr A.V. Roe. June 8th, 1908
Early Avro tri-plane

I received an official reply from the Acting Special Recruiting Officer, dated March 3, 1917, stating, "We beg to inform you that it is regretted your services cannot be accepted for the Royal Flying Corps." Signed H. G. Gould, Lieut.

That was it. I had offered myself and was rather disappointed to be turned down. However, it was not public knowledge but, at that time, a scheme for the purpose of forming a Royal Flying Corps Boy Service was being instigated to put to the authorities in order to start a school of apprentices.

This was to build up and provide a future supply of trained boy mechanics for the Royal Flying Corps, because adults were becoming in short supply at the recruiting offices. Therefore, the birth of the Royal Flying Corps Boy Service came about and we 400 were the originals. Others followed when, in later years, the Royal Air Force boy entrant scheme was introduced. There was no Air Training Corps. The ATC came into effect in 1941.

CHAPTER TWO

ENLISTMENT IN THE ROYAL FLYING CORPS BOY SERVICE. OFF TO
FARNBOROUGH. 400 BOY RECRUITS UNDER CANVAS. THE "INITIATION".
KITTED OUT. DRILL.

It was in the month of May 1917 when attention was drawn to me
about a small insertion in the Sheffield Telegraph. I cut it out. It read as
follows: "Sheffield boys for Air Service. The announcement is made
that there are vacancies in the Royal Air Service for boys 15 to 17½ to
be trained in the workshops. They must be fit for General Service and
have passed Standard VI in the Elementary School." Sheffield was
allotted 15 appointments.

Here was my chance. I was in good health, despite food rationing
and had finished Elementary School in Standard VIII. My father said
to me, "This seems to be just the thing you have been wanting." He
gave me his permission to apply. My mother, with her other two sons
already in the forces, knew my desire that I should be the next one to
be called to the ranks and quietly gave her consent. I decided to go to
the Sheffield Recruiting Office as soon as possible, in order to get in to
the first entries. So on the Bank Holiday of Whit Monday May 28,
1917, I presented myself at the Sheffield Recruiting Office, which was
then situated at the Corn Exchange, now demolished.

I remember that I spent most of this Bank Holiday in the recruiting
office, as men by the hundreds were being attested, medically
examined, sworn in and enlisted in to one of the three forces.

In the recruiting office I met another boy, George Fleming. We
became acquainted, because we were the only two boys present in
order to join up into the Boy Service of the Royal Flying Corps. All the
others were men, so we were something different, something special.
The staff dealt with us in their own good time and we were put through

the usual procedure of name, address, parents' consent, qualifications, age, birth certificate and so on. I produced a copy of my previous letter of application to join the RFC as a boy learner and the reply I received. This produced the unknown quantity of a nod and a grunt, although I had a feeling that the officer approved of my effort in that direction

After these preliminaries, we were sent into a separate room. The officer, wearing military uniform, took our papers and eyed us over his glasses as he closed the door. He read our documents and handed them to a soldier sat at a trestle table. Another soldier was in the room. The officer said to us, "So you wish to join the Air Service as Boys." We replied, "Yes." He looked at more papers and added, "You realise you will have to enlist for a period of four years in the Reserve of the Royal Flying Corps." We both agreed to that. He gave us a strict medical examination. I weighed in at eight stone five pounds, chest 30in, expanded 34in, height 5ft 5½in.

The officer told us that he was satisfied and accepted both our applications. These would be placed with the RFC Recruiting Centre at Farnborough and he would let us know the result.

We left for home rather tired, but very pleased with our arrangements and promised to meet again on the notified date. My parents appeared to view the matter with the reasoning that it was all right, as I would be called up within a year anyhow, probably with no choice of unit. This was something I wanted to do – join the Royal Flying Corps and to be with aircraft and learn the aero engine trade. I had prepared myself.

I went to work the next day and informed one of the directors of the motor garage, a Mr Fretwell Downing, of my intention to leave my employment if accepted into the Boy Service of the Royal Flying Corps, because already I had contacted the recruiting officer following an advertisement for boys in the newspaper. He was delighted and made quite a fuss of me.

The official letter came from the Sheffield Recruiting Officer, with the information that I had been accepted and was to report to him on June 5, 1917, when I would be enlisted into the Royal Flying Corps. At the garage I told Mr Downing, who took me into his office, paid me my wages and gave me some sound advice. He wrote on a piece of paper three maxims which, I am pleased to say, I never forgot. I carried them with me during my entire RFC and RAF service; they now are a very tattered possession.

I promised Mr Downing that I would always remember them. They are:

(1) Aim high.

(2) Do not be afraid of taking responsibility.

(3) Want of care does one far more harm than want of knowledge.
   Dated June 5, 1917. F.F.D.

Upon leaving his office, he wished me good luck and gave me half a crown (12½p) for pocket expenses on the way to the Royal Flying Corps.

As arranged, I met George Fleming, the other boy, who had also been accepted. We proceeded to the Sheffield Recruiting Office at the stated time. We were soon dealt with by the officer and signed on for four years from the age of 18 Regular Service and four years Reserve. He informed us that we had to travel on a morning train to St Pancras, London, on the Midland Railway, the next day.

I was entrusted with our documents in a sealed envelope to hand in upon our arrival at Farnborough. We were paid a ration allowance for the journey, the day's allowance being the grand total of sixpence (2½p) each. This is stated on the form given that ration allowance had been paid for the day's journey, filled in "Yes" in a separate entry.

It will be noted that here the Army was predominant, because this "Pass for Recruits" was Army Form B 216. It should have been handed in upon arrival at Farnborough. However, it is still in my possession.

I left home in the same manner as my brothers after a period of leave – all the "Good-byes" to be said indoors and then off with the minimum of farewells outside. We in the family had seen heart-rending scenes outside homes and at the railway stations by other families seeing off relatives at the end of their leave or on entering the forces and it could be very upsetting. I wanted my parents to see that I was not going to be upset or allow them to be upset, so I put on a brave show and acted with a calm assurance which pleased my father and gave my mother, with her natural motherly instincts, the easiest of departures. It must be understood that, in those days, young people did not travel as far from home as they do today and I and thousands of others at my age had never been as far away as London before.

My sister, Clara and Mrs Ward, a member of St Chad's Church, accompanied me to the Midland Railway Station in Sheffield, with me in civilian clothes and carrying a parcel with the required soap and towel, etc and a supply of sandwiches. I had some money in my pocket, the sealed envelope, two plain postcards addressed to my mother with a penny stamp affixed, one to fill in and post upon my arrival at Farnborough, the other to follow, giving her my address and my first impressions. We met the other boy, George Fleming, at the railway station. His mother and father were with him.

On the platform there were pitiful scenes between them, which my sister and I looked upon in sympathetic silence, the difference being, of course, that he was their only son and it was a great wrench for them, especially as it was their first such experience. My sister was used to it, with me being the third brother to be seen off to war, besides other relations. Other families were also upset.

Mr and Mrs Fleming pleaded with me to look after George, even though he was six months older than me. The documents were put in my care.

The steam train puffed out of the station and we settled down to the exciting adventure of going to London and further to the Royal Flying Corps. There were many troops on the train, which helped to make it pleasant. We spoke to an RFC man, who said he was going to St Pancras and travelling on the same tube as we needed to reach Waterloo, so we kept with him. He located the train and we boarded it, speeding us on our way to our destination.

It was mid-afternoon and quite hot and sunny when we arrived at Farnborough. We were a small party – all off the same train. Upon arrival at the camp, there were rows and rows of tents, the usual type of Army bell tents, in a huge field at the side of the hangars. This was to be our first home in the Royal Flying Corps.

At the first tent a corporal took charge of us – and he was a real scrounger. The first thing he told us was, "No smoking allowed to boys. Hand over all your fags to me. They will go to wounded soldiers." I did not smoke, so just watched. Fleming handed over a packet of twenty and the others turned out their pockets of fags. The corporal received a good supply. I noticed that this corporal had two gold-coloured stripes (chevrons) on his left sleeve, about two inches in length, sewn vertically about an inch apart, around three inches from the tunic sleeve bottom. This indicated that he had been wounded on two occasions. His tunic was not of the RFC, but a military one of khaki, with brass buttons.

I had learned much about "wangles" in the Army from my two brothers and relations when they were on leave, so quickly saw through this one. I said to one of the boys: "He can't force you to hand over your cigarettes. Can't you see, he is the wounded soldier, who is going to get a good free supply of your cigarettes!"

I soon got my first, "Stop talking you. You'll be for it." I shut up, but inwardly laughed at such simplicity and bluff and thought, "You would not get any off me so easily." His manner was crude; a small, ignorant man, who had not much qualification of reception. Even I, as a youth, noticed and he immediately impressed me as a transfer from the Army following war wounds, given two stripes and his job as a softener to any arrival who needed it. He was not polite, full of cheap importance and herded us together until more NCOs arrived.

We were ushered to a tent; our documents were taken and a few questions asked, and instructions given about, "You are in the Army now"; "Do as you are told"; "Do not leave the camp"; "NCOs are in charge and jump to it", etc. We were escorted to our tents, nine boys to a tent and given instructions on how to arrange our sleeping positions, heads at the outer side, feet to the middle pole. Three blankets were given to each boy. We had to sleep on the floorboards.

I thought this was awful, after leaving a nine-roomed house with all conveniences, bathroom, hot and cold water; this was too bad. I thought that as boys entering a "posh" RFC, we would be given a better official welcome than that which my brothers received on entering the ranks of the Army.

It was June. A hot sun was pouring down. As we settled in to this tent, the boys, including G. Fleming, seemed to be matey. We soon sorted things out. We were taken to a "buffet" and took tea and a fair amount of bread and jam. We hungry lads enjoyed it and I had a good "tuck in". I changed my opinion about the tent and thought: "It's not so bad. It'll be like camping out."

I filled in one of my stamped addressed postcards and I now see that I wrote upon it: "Have arrived at Farnborough. It is not six thirty. Am all right. Just been to buffet and had tea. Now going to aerodrome."

This was the field down by the lake, where we strolled to watch some daring flying. I posted my first postcard to home in a field post-box. I enjoyed the stroll and the flying, but we soon returned to our tent, talking and watching the aircraft flying from the nearby Royal Aircraft Factory.

We were becoming acquainted, preparing ourselves for our first night under canvas. A bugle awoke us next morning and we were

hounded up and out, a good cold wash, on to breakfast and then the
first parade. Instructions were shouted. We were jostled how to "fall
in", "number" and "form fours" in a manner strictly for raw recruits in
civilian clothes, some not knowing their right hand from their left, with
Flt Sgt Sainsbury – a very active senior NCO.

Tent inspections, teaching us how to fold blankets and general
tidiness followed. The morning wash was from buckets of cold water
provided near to the tents.

On parade we faced a trestle table in the open air, after being told
that we were soldiers (which many of us resented) and given details of
camp routine, "out of bounds" and so forth. We went through a tent in
single file. Each one was given a quick medical inspection, then
proceeded to the table in sharp progression, when the officer in
military uniform with staff at his side checked us and our RFC number.

My number was 83445, and George Fleming was given seniority of
number, his number being 83444. And so, for the sake of RFC RAF
history, we were the first two boys from Sheffield to join the Royal
Flying Corps Boys Service.

I posted my second postcard home and see that I told the family: "I
am all right. It seems rather strange, not like home, but I shall get used
to it. My next news will give you my address. Do not worry." Our
correspondence became regular after this.

George Fleming and I soon found out that it is better to bed down as
far away from the tent flap as possible because, in the dark, anyone
leaving the tent for any purpose was always likely to tread on your face
on leaving or entering, so we selected, and enforced, our two places
side by side at the far end and away from the entrance. This no one
objected to or dared to oppose!

Some of the boys seemed very timid and would weep about simple
things. I felt they would not settle so easily. This gave me some inward
urge to stand up to it and "be a man", because certain others were a
rough, tough lot whom we would have to face. Some were so dim and
crude that we wondered how on earth they had been selected in the
first place. As always in life, a mixed bunch of hard and soft, good and
bad, the strong and the weak.

Our weekly pay was four shillings and sixpence (22½p) and we were
paid at the rate of four shillings (20p) one week and five shillings (25p)
the next, in order to save paying out the odd sixpence (2½p).

Some boys were soon borrowing money, but I kept what spare

money I had in a place fastened by a safety pin. Some of us managed with money from our pay and let it be known to those wanting to borrow that there was nothing doing.

The kit issue was very much a biff and bash affair. White kit-bag first followed by the underwear, all given alike, with our number by the imprint from a large, indelible ink marker As each garment was thrown at you, you caught it and thrust it into your kit-bag. The fit did not matter. Then the boots, huge, heavy-looking army boots, known as "Ammo" boots, no delicate try to fit. Your number was hammered in at the upper inside top. Two pairs were allocated to each of us. These boots were out of the ordinary for many of us, heavy "clod hoppers" with thick soles and "hob-nails" hammered in. Around the heel was a formidable steel rim, a quarter of an inch thick. We were not allowed to wear any other boots. The drag of these hard, heavy boots from reveille to lights out was slog, slog and painful.

Our proud moment came with the issue of the walking out (No 1) Royal Flying Corps double-breasted tunic, with the emblem "Royal Flying Corps" on both sleeve shoulder tops.

This issue consisted of a similar short length greatcoat with the same emblem as on the tunic sleeves' top. The issue of four knee breeches was good; they had a front flap with a button at both top corners. Puttees too. The RFC service cap and RFC brass badge were also handed out. This was exactly the same uniform as supplied to the men, with nothing to indicate that we were the boys. The first issue was an infantryman's tunic, with brass buttons and slacks for daily routine. The issued shirts were thick army grey . . . and extremely rough.

A small, circular identity disc of red fibre the size of a shilling (5p piece) – with name and number hammered into it had to be carried by a cord permanently around your neck. All of us were issued with a poor type cut-throat razor, brushes for all needs, and a holdall known as "Mother's Friend", containing needles, cotton, a little grey darning wool and other odds and ends.

One important piece of RFC equipment we had to buy from the "Institute" was the regulation cane, complete with shiny, plated RFC crest on top.

Putting on the puttees was quite an art. Often we saw more than one boy on parade, or on a march with his puttees hanging off, trailing on the ground behind him. My brothers had shown me the knack of it, similar to applying a bandage, starting from inside the leg, below the top of the boot, keeping it fairly tight and rolling it over the boot and up the leg from the boot to the ankle, winding it, overlapping up the leg, exposing about an inch, not too tight, with the ribbon tucked under the last lap below the knee. I became good at this and helped new intakes who gave me a halfpenny at times for teaching them. It made a little extra money for me, helping to buy certain requisites like soap, boot and button polish from the Institute, now called the NAAFI. The camp barber and tailor had a list of fees and the replacement of any lost kit had to be paid for. The Regimental Military regulation cane could be bought in the Institute. It was two foot three inches in length and was a most important part of our equipment and drill which had to be carried when outside the station off duty.

I posted home a note of my number and address, The Depot, Royal Flying Corps, Farnborough, Hampshire. This depot was a huge field with 400 boy recruits, many men arriving and being posted overseas or on home duties, with a few of the newly formed RFC 17-year-old officer cadets for pilot training, all under canvas. The Royal Aircraft Factory and Royal Flying Corps personnel were also stationed here, but occupied a large area away from us. The only difference in their uniform was that the officer cadets had a white band around their service caps.

We soon learned the lesson to take care of our kit, because some boys lost all kinds of equipment, including personal belongings. We blamed the men camped alongside us, because they were arriving in numbers and posted out, moving so frequently in parties that we could be the easy victims of "scrounging".

We did what we could to maintain a guard on our tents. One or two fainted on certain parades and were carried to his tent. Practically all of us purchased a small lock from boys who got them in Farnborough for us; they fitted in our kit-bag steel thread fastener. Everything, except blankets, including personal belongings, was kept in the kit-bag.

It was obvious that the officers intended that we should look a smart outfit. On a clothing parade, officers, equipment officers, NCOs and the camp tailor, chalked our RFC and infantry tunics for alterations. Some were passed as a good fit. Mine were marked and taken away. Being hot, it was nice in short sleeves. Some smaller boys had badly fitting tunics, looking like potato sacks "chucked" on. After alteration my two tunics were a good fit and I felt proud of the No 1 RFC double-breasted tunic. Many of the trousers were far too long, with lumps cut off.

Our regimental number was stamped in large figures in the service cap, helping one to memorise it by removal.

Much of the time was spent polishing infantry tunic buttons and polishing the army boots, a great effort of rub, rub, rub to try to get a shine on what was a greasy surface. One could understand where the saying of "spit and polish" originated.

There was a camp barber, an old ex-army sergeant and his male assistant in a bell tent which served as their shop. I doubt whether he had any academic training as a hair stylist, but he could cut hair.

From a parade we were marched in small parties to his tent. He had a sense of humour, because he asked certain boys, "How would you like your hair cut, son?" He did not ask me, but whilst awaiting our turn we remarked, "He is quick on the job."

We soon found out why! It was because as soon as you sat on the rickety chair, the miserable-looking assistant flapped a sheet around your neck and the hand-clipping machine commenced at the back of the neck, quickly up and over the head from ear to ear and all was off, leaving one nearly bald, except for about one inch of tuft in front; the assistant was a very busy man with the sheet. Some boys did not like it, but who cared? My father always used to cut my hair, so I had not much to come off. Even then it was never this short. How we laughed at each other! Looking into our steel-plated pocket mirrors, we called ourselves "Convict 99" and other names I will not disclose here. Each boy's name was ticked off by an NCO.

As far as I was concerned, the food at Farnborough was good or, should I say, to my liking. I see in one of my letters home I stated: "I eat well. I have always eaten up everything they have given me, including onions and watercress. Bread puddings I love. The plum duff for dinner was grand and I could have eaten until I burst." That sounded a good report for the cookhouse staff.

One supper I detailed in a letter was: "It consisted of good gravy, peas, one thick slice of bread and various kinds of stuff mixed in. I have not left anything on my plate yet." A good, healthy sign for those at home for a growing youth.

The June weather was glorious, with plenty of sunshine and extremely hot. It was a regular occurrence for many boys to faint. Some were taken to hospital.

The strength had grown to a total of about 400 boys. No more were being enlisted for the time being and what an odd-looking lot we were; tall, big ones up to 6ft in height and small lads who looked little more than infants. I was in between, putting on weight and feeling well, as is quoted in a letter sent home: "I am as brown as a walnut and eating well. You would hardly recognise me." I continued: "The other chaps have got their tunics on, but I am in my shirt sleeves. One lad was looking very hot and he told me that, 'He could write home better letters when he had his tunic on than with it off'. It would have been interesting to see what he wrote."

The authorities had rushed this enlistment of the boys to Farnborough with no policy that the RFC had fully prepared and there seemed to be no plan. Much was done in a most haphazard fashion.

The few officers were practically all ex-Army in military uniform, displaying wound chevrons. The NCOs were all men transferred from the Army after being wounded in service abroad and they also displayed wound chevrons. They were responsible for handling the men sent to this depot for accommodation and dispersal to the various posting units at home and abroad. Along with additional ex-Army NCOs, mainly corporals, some of them came to our Boys unit under the command of Major Parkin.

This mixture of assorted NCOs caused ill-tempered confusion.

We were all inoculated and vaccinated, which meant 48 hours excused duty. We were done in such large parties that we all had a couple of days with little to do but nurse our sore arms and, in some cases, our feelings of sickness. My jabs were satisfactory, but some of the boys were very ill and remained under the treatment of the medical officer, with one or two even having to go to hospital. This was a brand new experience for most of us.

The tremendous heat prevailed. Many enjoyed it and derived immense pleasure from watching the different types of aircraft flying about, a fantastic air display for us.

With the initial formalities over and our civilian clothes posted home, parades began more in earnest in the infantryman's uniform. "Falling in", we proceeded from "numbering" and "forming fours" to "sizing". My word, how necessary this was! It sorted us out all right. The NCOs had a merry time in differentiating between the lot of us, the tall and the short, because there was as much as two feet in variation. Some boys thought they were young giants, taller than they were and had to be shifted so many places in the ranks by busy, uncomplimentary NCOs.

When formed in this pattern we looked good, but on the march the short ones had a devil of a time trying to keep pace. Wearing army boots nearly as big and heavy as themselves, they looked pitifully out of proportion and were put to a difficult strain of effort with tough NCOs bawling out a pace.

We were put through the "saluting drill" with gusto, a necessity for the unit, being so close to the important establishment of Aldershot. The different methods of salute got us rather mixed up, more so the highly efficient NCO who gave a terrific hand-wriggle when he saluted. Anyhow we managed to get along with the ultimate solution of the forefinger of the right hand one inch above the right eyebrow.

One feature was that in the Royal Flying Corps, men had so little drill that some hardly knew it existed. Some "overseas" men voiced their opinions about us being "put through it", as they said. They did not care, because they were going overseas and so objected to it without fear, but we could see that they had not experienced it and did not like the idea of Army drill methods being introduced and spreading.

The RFC did not have any special disciplinary NCOs. Nearly all the NCOs were technical tradesmen or professionals of some sort or other and the pilots and observers and, true to say, they had not much time for the military drill bashing NCO.

We reached the stage of doing drill and PT every day, gradually being brought to a point of knowing the drill orders and looking a bit like a uniformed unit.

The march to the bathing parade at Aldershot swimming baths was great fun and welcomed in the hot June weather. On the days we were marched, the whole lot of boys, to the Aldershot Queens Parade Ground, the officers and NCOs put us through (or themselves) a sort of battalion (then) or now wing parade. We knew nothing of what the officers and NCOs were performing about, except that a great deal of shouting and bawling took place. We hurriedly marched in the direction told and carried out the manoeuvres as pushed or jostled into place by excited and infuriated platoon commanders and the attendant fussy NCOs to the requirements of our separate unit and en masse.

I remember as we entered this parade ground at Aldershot, seeing something unknown to me and many others at that time, a fair-sized metronome. At its side stood a big, fat sergeant, with his stick under his left armpit, shouting through his bushy moustache and prominent teeth: "Left, right, left, right. Keep in step. Swing those arms." He did his mighty best to get, and keep us, in marching time and order to this contraption upon entering this Holy of Holies. As it was slightly uphill, the little boys found it most difficult, striving in vain to keep pace and time, with legs twice the length at the front and rear. It looked comical and quite ridiculous. It proved the reason of not splitting in to groups or platoons, the tall boys in one and the short ones in the other.

We carried out this performance many times, but it seemed to some of us even then as if those responsible had not the sense to notice the need to sort out this untidy and unsightly problem. As it was, it looked bad for those in charge of the parade, which was taking place in full view of the military onlookers.

We were allowed out to Aldershot in the evenings with a pass. It had to be in the walking out dress of the RFC, including the cane. Inspection was at the tent of the guard corporal. He made quite a "regimental" ceremony of it.

Four of us from our tent decided we would have an evening out together in Aldershot, George Fleming, two others and myself. We obtained our passes, dressed in our brand new Royal Flying Corps uniform, satisfied the guard corporal and, lovely, we were out, facing the public for the first time. Upon instructions it was not permitted to walk out more than two abreast, canes had to be carried at horizontal position, with the bottom of the cane to the front and you had to march, not stroll or loiter about.

We proceeded to Aldershot and then the fun began, with soldiers, airmen and "Red Caps" everywhere. Officers seemed to be by the hundreds and, knowing instructions to salute all officers, the game began. I saw little joy in this, because we were constantly saluting. In order to make no mistake, we saluted everyone who looked like a commissioned officer. We saluted one wearing a "Sam Brown" and an officer-looking hat and he roared at us: "You don't salute me, lads. I'm a sergeant-major. Get moving!" Well, we didn't know; we did our best. It was better to salute than not to do so and get into trouble.

Anyhow, we carried on this saluting, which was apparent to me worse than any ordinary daily parade in camp, but we had to be careful, otherwise our names would be taken and then it was up for "jankers", which meant extra drill and duties in the camp and no passes, which many boys "collected".

The final crunch came as we passed a cinema. We knew that certain officers of the Army wore a kind of ceremonial uniform. Outside this cinema, at the edge of the pavement, was a fine, upright looking officer, wearing some medals too, apparently waiting for a taxi. As we passed him, canes went under the left armpit and on the march, two abreast in fine style, a first-class salute was given. "What's your game?" came from him in no uncertain tones. "I'm no officer. Scram, or I'll set about all four of you. You little devils!"

Not fully trained, our performance could have looked ragged enough to indicate "taking the mickey". He definitely frightened us and we hurriedly marched away in quick time, ran up a side street and round on to the main road, as though nothing had happened. We got marching smartly again, and . . . it was not us anyway!

I am sure that whilst the boys were at Farnborough more sergeant-majors were saluted than at any time in Army history.

I had had enough of this and said to my companions: "I am going back to camp, I'm fed up. If this is going out for the evening, then I would rather stay in camp." They decided to stay out until pass time was up, but I left them and marched back on my own to camp. I saluted everyone who looked like an officer, muttering nasty curses to myself as I made my way back to camp. I was soon back at my tent, feeling free from that lot and swearing "Never again!"

Later, we found out that the "officer" we saluted outside the cinema was a commissionaire, a retired sergeant-major who had been through the Army School of Physical Training at Aldershot and who had been a boxer. I kept my word and never went out of camp again, only on forced marches and parades.

The Army Physical Training School stationed at Aldershot contained the cream of Army gymnasts. Some of them came to our Boys camp to put us through some PT exercises. They wore red and blue horizontal striped jerseys and dark blue slacks, along with white slippers.

At first they gave us a real fright, they were so quick, so agile. In our small parties under them it was "Move, move!", louder and sharper – and we were in the army boots, as heavy as lead. Making us jump about and double certainly did us good.

The toilet arrangements were extremely bad and ablutions not so good. Washing water was obtained by the sharing of the men's posting section out of a trough or from fire buckets in which we fetched water from the nearby stream; the latter was our tent boys' method of washing.

The lavatories were the worst contraption I had ever seen. I absolutely hated them but, for the sake of nature, had to use them. It consisted of a long, deep trench. At one side of this trench were stout, upright poles about a yard high and about six yards apart, in line. Long poles were nailed on top in a line with the posts and the trench. A canvas sheet measuring about eight feet high encircled the whole of this area, leaving one opening, the width of a door. This was the entrance to the "lavatories" and also the exit. For its use one had to sit on this horizontal pole. If you were tall enough, your feet touched the ground, but if you were of short stature, you had to balance as best you could, with your feet off the ground and hold on tight, knowing that a quantity of sewage and sludge was behind and below you in the stinking trench.

Some people must have had their fun in rather peculiar ways. The overseas posting men used this toilet too and some of them, in particular the big, heavy ones, would sit on the middle of these long poles and wait until some of the boys came and sat alongside them on the pole.

They looked like a long row of birds sitting on a perch. At a given moment these heavy men would bounce the pole up and down as they sat down on it, with the result that the small boys with their feet off the ground lost their balance and fell backwards into the trench behind and below and became immersed in rich, messy, stinking manure.

This nearly happened to me and I decided, "They are not going to have me." If the need arose when the place was busy, I squatted on to a position over and above a pillar and kept one leg at either side of this post, which kept me reasonably secure. Nevertheless, this "lavatory" was one thing at the camp which I really hated. I absolutely dreaded the place. Whether for good or bad, I tried to regulate a period for this purpose. Not going out of camp gave me this evening opportunity, because such fine and lovely weather meant that most of the men and boys went out on an evening pass.

One of the extra duties on "Jankers" was the shovelling of a layer of soil over the contents of this lavatory trench.

Some of the other extra duties on "jankers" included picking up paper on a nail attached to the end of a stick and then placing it in a sack, topping up fire buckets, moving tents and boards, cleaning NCOs' boots and buttons and all sorts of odd jobs, with plenty of defaulters. I must admit I behaved myself at Farnborough, because I did not get hauled up for any default.

I was enjoying the fact that I was in the Royal Flying Corps, proud of my uniform and included in the thousands serving my King and Country. It was a new adventure of camping out with boys from many other places and with different dialects, living an outdoor life in the RFC, a great event, for we had volunteered our service with a spirit and enthusiasm, which was an experience we young lads could not express without feeling pretentious at the prospect of being an important young man in a man's world of the powerful weapon of war, destructive without regard even to oneself. But the only way of life that at its own moments of hate shone with a false glitter of glory, which became embedded into the young, energetic mind, leading him on to the future fulfilment of the nation's requirements, a man's duty in the pursuit of this great war.

I would sit outside the tent watching the aircraft flying overhead and recognised the BE2C, BE2E, FE2B, RE8, Vickers "Gun Bus", Sopwiths and various others. Some were strange to me and were on an experimental test flight from the Royal Aircraft Factory. They gave displays of aerobatics I had never seen before – and I was thrilled.

The drill and PT were beginning to show themselves. We could perform the elementary movements in platoon drill. Our marching was improving, keeping much better in step; our backs were more erect, while our service caps held on to our head better and remained at the correct position, one inch above the right eye.

The organised training here was drill and PT, tent inspections, kit inspections, the folding of blankets, lectures on discipline, Officer and NCO ranks, cleanliness, orders and duties, and the many little, but important matters that must be instilled deeply into the young . raw recruit, who has suddenly changed out of his civilian life to the mode of life of a uniformed member of HM Forces and the many elementary items needed to be taught (even the importance of your number). Standing to attention when in front of an officer and address to the rank of the NCO, was not easy for a boy in those days, who had not seen much of the life or works of a soldier as provided today by the older generation's knowledge, the radio, television portrayal and the cinema. So the mass of 400 boys collected together for initial training with no set pattern, no previous experience for the officers and NCOs. It was no easy matter for them, when every problem and answer needed to be at their finger tips.

This was a first occasion and so the mass discipline was crude, a jumbled mess of orders, shouting, instructions, methods of principles of obedience from the corporals upwards.

Often we wondered what would become of us because no one appeared to have any idea how long we were to remain at Farnborough. Rumours spread. Various ideas circulated. One was that we might be sent to various aerodromes of the RFC at home and put to work helping the mechanics. This I hoped would be true. Some thought we were being trained to enter the Army, as it was, but no one in authority gave us any indication as to our future. We carried on with the camp routine.

I had a parcel sent from home containing biscuits, cake and fruit, but I wrote my thanks, telling them not to send me any more, as I was feeding all right here and they needed the rations for themselves.

My mother sent me some small cloth bags she had made. I asked for these to put my brushes and small belongings in. They were very useful, because we had only the kit-bag to contain everything. I asked for a wrist watch with a safety cage over the face. These large watches were then fashionable, so my parents sent me one. Being illuminated (a revolutionary idea then), it came in very useful. I kept it for a long time during my service.

I stated in one of my letters home, "On Saturday night June 16, 1917, we had a visitor. A German aeroplane flew over the camp. He was very high. One of our machines went up after him. It was a Sopwith with a gun mounted, a small, very fast machine. After it had returned, one of our NCOs told us that our machine did not catch him, as he had had a very good start."

A warning was sounded, but we had no alert. We just took things as they came, with no air raid safety precautions laid down and no shelters.

The weather was still hot. I went with some of the boys from our tent to bathe in a pond down on the aerodrome. I did not look long at the water to decide not to go in, but all the others did so. Aircraft seemed to take turns to fly low at us and we soon packed up and returned to camp, with aircraft still diving at us.

It was during this night that a terrific thunderstorm broke out. We were asleep in the tents when the storm broke and the deluge came in torrents with thunder. Within minutes we could here shouting and a commotion in camp. We looked out and saw that a number of tents were down. We dashed out and eased our ropes. The water was running along like a river. Immediately we piled up some of the tent boards on top of each other and placed our blankets and kit on top of each other, as water was running through our tent. It was inches deep, but not so bad. We tried to help other tent pals, but returned to our tent saturated in only our underwear. We dried off in our "safe", but also very wet, tent, which was still warm.

Early in the morning when we looked out, there was chaos. The storm was over. We found many boys' tents had blown down. Kit and blankets had been washed away and some were covered in mud. We retrieved as much as we could, but some boys had lost a great deal of kit and blankets. Tents of the overseas men and cadets had likewise suffered. Rumour spread that some of the overseas men helped themselves to a lot of the boys' kit and blankets. How true this was we never knew, but I would be inclined to believe that all the lost goods, especially floatable ones, did not go down the river.

The weather cleared nicely and it became hot again. Kit inspection took place as soon as possible. We, who had lost nothing, helped to erect old and new tents and a drying out procedure took place. It was like an open market.

Some boys had very little kit left: others lost some items. Blankets were missing galore. Some private belongings were also lost, but after a lot of inspection, scrutiny and enquiries along with officer consultation on the spot, boys eventually had blankets and kit replaced. Whether they had to pay for these items did not seem likely, because we heard so little about the matter afterwards.

No one appeared to have any stoppages in pay. We did hear some time later that it was a free issue. Fortunately it did not concern me so much, because our tent was not damaged and we lost no kit or blankets. We only had water running through the tent. It soon dried out and we were quickly back to ship-shape, helping others to clear up. It was good to see boys from England, Ireland, Scotland and Wales, new together, all united in one sudden emergency effort. Everything soon returned to normal – the NCOs saw to that. Drill and PT became the pattern again.

New intakes of boys (recruits) were arriving at the camp and getting in to uniform, as we "old sweats" imagined, they looked proper "rookies".

It was announced on parade that in a few days' time some of us would be moving to a camp near Tring – about 30 miles north of London. The boys who lived nearby said that there was no aerodrome or aircraft factory near the place, which was known as Halton, so we felt it might only be a temporary move and speculated upon the idea that we should be on that camp for only a month or so.

Practically all we originals at Farnborough were detailed on parade to prepare ourselves for moving. There was the usual kit inspection, medical inspection and the departure date and names on the rota placed on the routine orders.

CHAPTER THREE

THE ORIGINAL 400 "TRENCHARD BRATS" ROYAL FLYING CORPS BOYS
TAKE OVER HALTON CAMP WEST FROM THE ARMY. ARMY NCOs DRILL
TRAINING. ARMY SCHOOL. BOYS' PRANKS. TERRIBLE CONDITIONS. BOY
ACTING LANCE-CORPORALS. FIRST LEAVE FOR RFC BOYS. BOYS' SPORTS
DAY, THE FIRST, AT HALTON.

Practically all the original 400 boys had been detailed for posting. On
the morning of Wednesday June 20, 1917, our blankets were returned
to stores and we paraded in full Royal Flying Corps uniform. Kit-bags
were placed in Leyland lorries and off they went. After roll call and a
rigid parade inspection, we marched off to the railway station, giving
our fond farewell in typical Army fashion to those left behind.

We were put on a special troop train and steamed out for a place
known as Wendover, near to Aylesbury in Buckinghamshire, and not
far from Tring in Hertfordshire. Some of the boys said it would be all
right, because it was on the Great Central Railway line to Marylebone,
London, and also up north through Sheffield.

George Fleming, my Sheffield colleague, was not included in the
party; his parents had managed to get him a special leave to attend a
pianoforte examination, which had been set prior to enlistment.

We thought he was a lucky blighter to manage a leave so early. He
promised me he would visit my parents, which he did. They were very
pleased to see him and hear how I was getting along.

The train journey took about three hours, moving slowly most of the
time. Each boy had been issued with a travel ration of sandwiches to be
eaten on the train. These we enjoyed to varying purposes. I ate mine
and liked them. Some had more fat in them. Some boys used them, or
what they did not want, as ammunition to throw at any target they
chose, even at passengers standing on a railway platform, as we passed

by. This did not last long. Rations soon ran out.

These were the pranks of young lads, exuberant, pleased and excited at being on a train, as a body of young troops, away from the parade discipline of NCOs for the first time and a release from the orders and demands of military constant routine.

The coaches were the eight aside, non-corridor train, so NCOs were not in close contact with us.

Boys near the windows hung their heads out of them and made all kinds of cat-calls and flirtations. The flinging of kisses by hand to selected females as we moved along gave much to the enjoyment or embarrassment of those concerned, a passing phase that did no harm to anyone and pleased the boys immensely.

It was a nice, warm morning when we arrived at Wendover, a small, clean-looking railway station.

After preliminaries, we paraded outside the station and "fell in" as at Farnborough. The whole parade marched off with additional NCOs barking out the step. It seemed a long march along the uphill road.

We arrived at the camp known as Halton. At the entrance a large

Hut group No. 1. Halton Camp West. Boys section RFC July 1917.
From the left: Top row;—Boys. Gowers, G. Heys, T. Dawkes
Bottom Seated;—Boys: J. Ross, R. L. Baker., H. Myles, J Chatfield

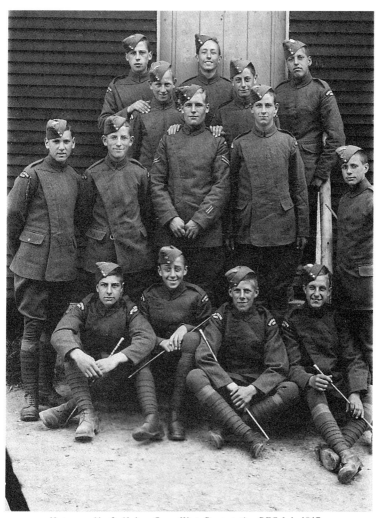

Hut group No. 2: Halton Camp West. Boys section RFC July 1917.
From the left: Top three;—G. Reid, Biggs, Wagstaff,
Next two;—H. Myles, J. Chatfield,
Middle row; —Mann, H. Eggleton, C.P.L. Morgan, Lambert, Wright
Bottom seated;—N. Holt, T. Dawkes, G. Ward, J. Ross

board indicated it to be West Camp.

I shall never forget the sight of the tall, athletic-looking Regimental Sergeant-Major in RFC uniform, who was in charge of this parade. His name was RSM Morse. He was the complete model of the true military product of RSM at that time. Straight back, head held high, marching like a ballet dancer, on his grim face he sported a black moustache waxed to long, thin points the width of his face.

His appearance frightened us to the tips of our army boots. He was the first RSM of the Boys Section at Halton and scared us all by his tremendous military bearing and disciplinary demands.

When marching he would swing his arms at the outstretched position, straight at the elbows. His hands went up to the level of his chin at the front and near to that height at the back of his knees. His legs were as straight as pencils. When he approached and saluted an officer, his right foot came to the position of attention from a high altitude, with a bang that stamped the ground below like a hammer, the magnificence of a complete soldier paying his full respects to officer rank.

Proudly he led us into the Halton Camp West from Farnborough to be the first entry of boys into the Boys Section of the Royal Flying Corps School of Technical Training, Halton, which started on this date of Wednesday June 20, 1917, the predecessor of the now famous Halton Apprentices School, Royal Air Force.

We entered Halton West Camp with no special ceremony; it was just a simple march in after a halt outside, having been taken over from the Army by an advance party of a few RFC administrators, cooks, fatigue parties, officers and NCOs who awaited our arrival.

Once inside, we were marched, complete with knife, fork, spoon and mug to the dining hall, a large, wooden hut, for our midday meal. Following this we paraded outside what was the Headquarters, a number of wooden huts situated in their own little compound facing a fair-sized parade ground.

Officers and NCOs inspected us. Fussing about seeming to be without purpose, but without any planned routine. It appeared to be a mixture of orders and instructions to themselves – "Yes, Sir." "No, Sir." "Very good, Sir." "Mr so and so." "This?" "That."

Eventually we found out what the whole matter was about. It was to make a decision and carry out the sorting of us out by singular selection into two "Companies".

The tall boys were in "A" Company, the short ones in "B" Company. The problem was those in between. I was just tall enough to be placed into "A" Company.

Both Companies contained about 200 boys. The two Companies were then allotted the officers and NCOs, previously selected. They took over and marched us to the lines of huts and again sorted us out to our respective huts and hut NCO. A nominal roll was made out for each hut and displayed inside.

Each hut party was called a "Platoon". The hut party I was in, which we occupied as our home, was identified as hut No "6" on "C" Lines.

We "fell in" as "A" and "B" Companies and were given a summary of details by our respective Officer Commanding and his staff. The Officer Commanding "A" Company was Lieut Dewhirst, a military officer, with as his seconds in command, 2nd Lieut Cairns, and a 2nd Lieut Lockwood.

"B" Company was commanded by Lieut White, MC, a military officer and two other officers.

It was soon noticed that 2nd Lieut Cairns was a real RFC officer, wearing the pilot's wings, and that 2nd Lieut Lockwood was also in RFC officer's uniform with no wings. Practically all the other officers in this original set were military officers, wearing the uniform of their regiment and badges. The Commanding Officer of this West Camp Boys "Battalion" was Major Nixon, who wore RFC uniform, with the Observers brevet on his tunic. We knew and remembered him as being an 'airman on horseback', because he always attended parades riding his horse and we also concluded that he went to bed with it!

The NCOs of "B" Company were Sgt Blundell and Cpl Vine; others no one remembers. The NCO in charge of our hut and "Platoon" was Cpl Morgan, who came from Barnsley, near Sheffield. He was a young collier and had been wounded in France whilst in the Army and transferred as a disciplinary NCO to the RFC. He had some fingers shot off his right hand.

The very first address of this original RFC Boys Section at Halton was sent home by me as follows: "Boy. J. Ross No 83445. 'A' Company. No 6 Hut. 'C' Lines. Royal Flying Corps School of Technical Training. Halton West Camp. Buckinghamshire."

The corporal of each hut has a corner to himself at the entrance. The huts were Army-type wooden huts built on stilts and had a combustion stove in the middle aisle. The beds down the hut sides were three long boards placed on two low trestles, each about eight inches high, one each end. On each bed were four blankets, one calico palliasse and pillow. Above each bed was a small shelf. Our kit-bags were collected, hut parties detailed. Each boy was marched to his bed, above which he had to put up on a card his name and number.

Some boys who had pals from their home town managed to swap bed places in order to be near to each other. Our corporal did not mind, since the companionship of these boys grouped together helped to establish a close comradeship. Helping to mould a good disciplin and an association of responsibility, which spread amongst a hut full of young boys fairly new to each other.We were all equally the raw recruit and there were no signs of any special favour for any one boy. We were all the same, it worked well.

I did not find any other boy who came from Sheffield in our hut. All asked each other, "Where do you come from?" I bedded down alongside a group of boys from Portsmouth and Plymouth. One was a real Cockney lad and we all became good pals.

My first two neighbours at my side were Tom Dawkes (from the South Coast) and Harry Eggleton. "Eggy", the Cockney, was a sturdy youth wearing spectacles and we got on well. Other boys in this hut I remember, since I wrote their names on the back of a photograph. They were: Joe Chatfield, Crockford, H. Myles, W. Pope, H. Holt, R. L. Baker, G. Heys, G. Reid, G. Ward, Gowers, Mann, Biggs, Wright, Lambert, Wagstaffe, Vaughan and McLeod and others I cannot trace.

In hut parties we marched to the old horse lines and from huge piles of straw filled our palliasse and pillow. The idea was to fill as much straw into these articles as possible and so we did as the corporal suggested. "Put plenty in lads," he said. "You will need it." Back at our beds we had never seen anything so funny for a bed. The paliasse looked like a large cylinder and the comic situation arose of sleeping on it, while to lay on it was an achievement within itself.

It was like laying on a roller. If you dared to move to one side, off you rolled and bang on to the floor with a wallop. We did not sleep too well at first, because at any time of the night some boy would roll off on to the floor with a thud, much to our boyish amusement. Others within seconds, because the disturbance and laughter could overbalance and roll over and out. Once you turned off balance, you had nothing to hold on to. Nothing could save you – and over and out you had to go.

A favourite way of NCOs to get you out of bed after reveille was to lift up the middle board at the foot and so, on to the floor you spilled. We also had many pranks amongst ourselves with tilting this middle board.

The straw was uncomfortable. Being new, the sharp ends dug like knife points into the flesh, an added discomfort until the straw thinned and bedded down when it became quite a reasonable Army mattress to lie upon. In order not to get my face next to the blanket, I placed a spare shirt between my face and the blanket, because many boys reported sick with impetigo, a skin eruption on the face, which we regarded as a contamination from the blankets.

We were not issued with sheets, as soldiers did not have the luxury of sheets in those days.

Instructions were given how to place our equipment and uniform not in use. The order was to place it on the shelf, neatly folded and the same width; greatcoat, tunic and breeches, spare pair of boots at left and right side, issued military water-bottle, mess tin, pack and haversack placed in proper fashion over the top of these pieces of equipment, blankets folded to small size and width and placed in correct position at the head of the bed, spare linen folded and laid neatly on top.

The hut issue of mops, brushes, shovel, "squeegees", a large zinc tub, table on trestles, two long forms made of wood (no chairs), were amongst items listed on the inventory, the responsibility of the hut. The zinc tub was for the purpose of hut details to collect the ration of coal and coke for the stove in each hut. Fire buckets at both ends of the hut were to be constantly filled with clean water and not to be used for any other purpose. Upon the fire alarm, the ringing of a huge bell, we had to fall out (and in), as detailed, with the fire piquet at the ready.

We were becoming use to Army hut living, feeling much better than the tents of Farnborough and a more secure way of "living in".

The ablutions were outside and between the hut lines. Washing facilities were provided by a long trough with water running down the middle from a tap at the top end, one trough to so many huts. You selected your position in line to wash and, if required, shaved in cold water.

The toilets were in line with the wash trough and each set of toilets allotted to certain huts. These toilets were in a set of six seats (a block of wood with a hole cut out), but with one on its own at the far end, reserved, NCOs "for the use of".

Built of corrugated iron, they each had a separate compartment, with a small door and each seat was over a bucket. This line of buckets was approached by the fatigue men (general duties), who emptied them by raising up the long door at the rear, on hinges, thus exposing the whole line of buckets and dragging them out one by one. This had certain dangers. Afterwards the application of strong disinfectant always smelt so refreshing.

The advantage was that being around mid-summer we had nice weather, a good start, getting us accustomed to the camp and routine, because when the winter came it brought a very different picture of the weather and conditions.

We were "fell in" and marched to practically everything except the canteen, ablutions and the use of the toilets. We marched to the dining hall carrying our knife, fork, spoon and mug, were ushered into our row of forms at the plain wood-topped tables, as there was no such thing as a tablecloth. The food was brought to each table down the middle aisle. It was the duty of the boy who sat at No 1 position nearest the aisle to serve out the food and pass the plates along to the end of the table, finishing with himself.

"Pass the plates along!" was the cry. Often the boys at the top end of the table had a short supply in order that there would be ample left for the boy serving.

As we were "fell in " for the march to the dining hall, it was possible for any boy to get a turn at being the "server". He then saw to it that he got plenty'of food when he had his chance to be the "server" at No 1.

There was plenty of trouble when the No 1 served it out so badly. The officers had no idea and those with so little food raised such a definite complaint that the Orderly Officer, Messing Officer and NCOs buzzing around rectified the complaint, sometimes "swapping" the plates.

The bang on the table with a stick by the senior NCO heralded the attention for the Orderly Officer and the cry, "Any complaints?" brought complaints galore.

If it was about the quality of the food, the Messing Officer would taste a sample and frequently was his reply, "This is better than in the Officers Mess," that boos and cat-calls gave vent to the boys' feelings, because, at times, some of the food "dished up" at Halton was poor. Huge quantities were pushed aside because the boys could not stomach it.

Breakfast started with porridge, bread and margarine, a slice of tinned meat or hard-boiled egg, sausages and kippers. Dinner was a variation of meat, stew, tinned meat, sausage, potatoes, vegetables, meat pie (we felt of doubtful origin), prunes, rice pudding, bread pudding, custard (unsweet), baked roll duff and other "dishes". Tea was bread and jam (plum and apple), margarine, a kind of rissole, slice of tinned meat, fish, one hard-boiled egg, a tinned fruit available at the time: like a jam, some suggested it was turnip. Then there was rhubarb, cheese, cake baked in the cook-house in long lengths and then sliced. There was no soft fruit, but available in the canteen at odd times, a jam tart would appear, which was not bad.

Peas and beans were so hard, they were like bullets, and some other food like kippers uncooked. There was no menu, and therefore no choice. You sat at a table, each table of about 20 boys, and waited to see what would come along. If the rare, unmentioned tit-bit appeared, a huge cheer would be raised

The tea was often tainted with the grease of a previous meal and tasted horrible. I suppose we drank it because we were so thirsty and used to it. And at any meal one was liable to find a dead earwig in it. It would have been better if the preparation and cooking had been more carefully handled, because there seemed to be plenty of some provisions, even if delicacies were rare.

One can imagine that the canteen did well with the provision of extras. The favourite dish amongst the boys was egg and chips, a canteen standby which, to their credit, the supply always met with the demand.

Their famous rock buns and pastries were popular too. It must be noted that the canteen, often given the title of "the Institute", in those days belonged to the "Navy and Army Canteen Board". It was not until around 1918, when it was taken over by the NAAFI and run on similar lines.

In the dining hall we had much fun in our own way. One was beating time with our utensils to a rhythm started by some boy. The din eventually became of tremendous volume as our metal "drum sticks" smacked down on the wooden table tops. The only way to stop it was to for the cooks hurry up and get some food on the tables.

There was the infectious game of one boy catapulting some soggy missile at a boy on another table, using his spoon as the catapult.

Catching a boy, unwares with it hitting him on the back of his neck started it. Those on his table would retaliate, catapulting bits back in the direction of where the first shot came from; some more fat into the face or neck for those in range, then the cannonade increased.

A miniature war begun, with as many boys taking part as remained in the hall, finishing up with boys gathering up handfuls of leavings and slinging them at the enemy until it became wise, and necessary, to run out of the dining hall. I took part in these "fat fights" and, with other boys, laughed until we were nearly helpless and, like others, suffered acutely from some accurate aiming and bull's-eyes from the enemy at another table.

Officers and NCOs were annoyed about it, but there were plenty of boys on "jankers" and they got the extra duty of clearing up the mess.

Another game was that when the last boy was eating, we would call out "Wow!" as each portion entered his mouth. Some comedian would make himself last, so that he could have fun with us and as he got food near his mouth, he would stop and, our "Wows" would he half completed. He would often hesitate with his feeding hand so that the "Wows" became a jumble of part "Wows", then quickly he would shovel it into his mouth, when a huge "Wow, wow!" would fill the hall, but he had just beaten us to it. And so it would be repeated with great laughter. Often there would be as many as 20 or 30 boys in a group around him, some standing on the tables and others leaning over his shoulders in order to get him out on his "timing". If the fun was crude, it was of our creation, and thoroughly enjoyed.

It was noticed that some boys did not know how to use a knife and fork. They were probably never taught at home. The manners of some were terrible, but the indications are often that at times like these, the worst comes out in all of us.

Some boys could not face certain meals and I saw them push the plate away and walk out of the dining hall, leaving only a small number of boys sitting at the tables. Such a lot of food must have been wasted. So many did not like porridge.

Kippers they would not face. Being very fond of kippers, and any sort of fish, I would help myself to the untouched extra fish not accepted by a colleague and, with extra bread and margarine, enjoyed many a splendid and plentiful meal

When a meal was provided which some liked, others would talk of snails crawling out of it and similar sickening things, so that the boy with a sensitive stomach would push away his plate and leave the table. His food would then be grabbed like vultures by the story-tellers who "worked" a double ration.

This did not turn me away from the food, since I was not so easily fooled by them.

Naturally some boys were hungry and extra greedy. There was a period when night raids took place into the bread and cake stores at the cookhouse. The store was broken into quite frequently and large quantities of bread, cakes and other foodstuffs taken and hidden in the huts, some eaten and some sold to the boys.

This created a night alert. A special guard was put on to the cookhouse. The same boys risked it again, were caught on the spot, placed in the guardroom and dealt with by the Commanding Officer in the appropriate manner.

Later on as the numbers grew, there was bound to be a certain few who were thieves and rogues and we had our share. Complaints came to the camp from outside about many incidents caused by the boys.

There was a "break-in" at a jeweller's shop in Tring, and another in Aylesbury, which were alleged to have been carried out by boys from Halton. Police visited the camp and made a search and investigation. Nothing developed, but rumour passed along by whispers amongst the boys claimed that in a certain hut one of the wall-boards had been made by a boy into a dummy panel and the jewellery was concealed in this secret hiding place.

Which hut it was I never knew. It was supposed to be amongst the huts of later arrivals, but it was said there was a small fortune in it and that it was never discovered. I believe this story to be true.

In this assembly there was a large number of well-behaved boys, good lads. I made pals with many who were of great integrity. We sorted ourselves out. When others were out of camp (some nearly every night), we would be sitting about in our small groups talking, doing our own washing, writing letters, discussing aeroplanes and flying, etc. I darned all my socks with an extra layer of wool in order to reinforce the heel, which with heavy wear made my feet terribly sore in the hard, heavy boots. The outside laundry facilities came our way at a later date.

We were still in the recruit stage, with limited basic training, kit knowledge, inspections and individual training. The drill and marching were sufficient to start us off for the beginning of a constant infantry drill extended course of training of which we were totally unaware at the time.

Upon our entry to Halton, there was the hut inspection on the first day. This was a very important event for the officers and NCOs.

They inspected and scrutinised everything; this must be placed here, that must be kept here, no, there, windows must be kept open at all times, no talking after "lights out", cleanliness and a tidy hut, no kit left about the beds or floor, no smoking (some boys smoked "fags" galore), stoves not to be lit during summer, boys to be responsible for barrack damages, obey hut corporal at all times, and so on. Whilst stood to attention at our beds, they were checked for many things, even to the equal distance between them; at the same time there was kit inspection.

They gave it a thorough going over and left us in no doubt as to hut behaviour and our responsibilities. Which seemed to be fair enough and understandable levelling us up or down, as the case may be, for each and everyone.

As we were young volunteers, I don't recall any of the officers or NCOs saying that they were pleased to see us. Or even give us a welcome and that they hoped we would settle down, be comfortable, be good lads and even enjoy ourselves.

They were grim, severe-looking and stern to the importance of the inspection, giving us the first achance to have a close look at them. We soon understood the military attitude of complete subordination and acute supervision: you don't ask, you are told; you do, or else. I am sure every boy soon realised that the officers are supreme and NCOs see that their instructions are carried out without question.

There were no aircraft here, no aerodrome, no workshops, just huts and sheds and camps. (Sheds for the horses by their appearance.) There was a canteen, the YMCA, a tin church and a corrugated tin theatre, commonly called the "Bug Hut". The civilians who ran it had some difficult moments if the audience did not approve of some artiste or performance, as the boys who attended often took ammunition in the form of hard peas, uneatable at a meal, and peppered the performers and the audience in front. I was guilty and enjoyed myself as a missile aimer many times. A more respectful name for this theatre was the title of the "Blood and Thunder".

There were tough tests for artistes. I remember one stout lady, a soprano, cat-called so much that she left the stage weeping, crying out,

"I shall never come here again!" I would say that any performer needed guts to appear a second time, but some did and stood up to it very well. The family of "residents" took some hard knocks from the boys, but they gave such plays as "Murder At The Red Barn", "Sweeney Todd", "Silas Marner" and many others. They never gave up, but battled on.

One thing that made life unpleasant at first was the number of earwigs. They were in the huts, kit, clothing, beds and in the food. As fast as we killed them, they still came on the attack. We all took part in annihilating them, but soon got used to them and killed them with little concern.

Huts had to be scrubbed out each week. Pails of water were used and all the boys took part in this job, some with brushes, others with "squeegees" and the floors became cleaner than the table tops in the dining hall. The table and forms (we had no chairs) were dealt with in the same manner. Competition was held for the declared cleanest hut in the lines. This created a spirit of determination to beat the others. So keen did it become that we would search for pieces of broken glass. With these we scraped the brush handles and other woodwork, which eventually became beautifully white and clean.

To see the boys all working together at these domestic jobs was worth seeing, pooling ideas with the corporal, scrubbing, cleaning windows, polishing the stove, cleaning everything in sight, even trying to get a polish on the red-painted fire buckets, a keen desire which helped mould a loyalty to the hut we all shared.

There were times when, as only natural amongst a lot of boys, there developed a jealous rivalry between the huts and hut fights took place, some in good humour and some with devilish intent, usually when the NCOs were not about.

There was the occasion when some boys from a hut opposite ours threw some wet, soggy papers at us in our hut. We approached their hut and emptied a bucket of water containing these papers back into their hut. They came back and threw water into our hut. Over we went and gave them a bucketful. And so it gathered momentum until it finished in a proper riot, with both sides throwing buckets of water into the enemy's hut, all of us filling fire buckets from other huts and the ablutions as fast as we could, chain-bucketing them to the respective doors and "Splash!" it all went in.

It is true when I say there was no real ill-feeling about it and we had spectators from nearly the whole line of huts cheering us on and enjoying the contest. Laugh, we were doubled up at the fun of it, but not for long. Down came a sergeant and a corporal – and the sergeant played hell with us. He shouted and raved, but when he saw us soaked to the skin, he shut up and we felt he had a slight grin on his face as he went away with his corporal and with our roars of laughter behind him.

No damage was done, except that the floors had an extra swilling. Some of us, including myself had a cold soaking, requiring a towelling and a change of clothing. The hot sun soon dried things out and the "squeegee" cleared the water from the huts.

The sergeant did not report us, but he saw to it that no boy from the two huts was able to get a late pass out of camp that week.

Many pranks were played on each other and other huts. In the cold weather when stoves were lit, someone would climb on to the roof of another hut and put a disused, wet cloth, or other article like an old plate over the top of the chimney and smoke out the occupants. The hut would become choked with smoke and fumes.

A smouldering rag underneath a hut would cause boys to think that the hut was on fire until they discovered the cause. After gathering handfuls of stones, a gang would creep up to another hut and, at a given signal, sling the stones into the air to drop on to the top of this hut and then scamper back. We would peep through the windows to watch them come out to see who had done it. All kinds of tricks were played in hut combat.

As we settled into West Camp, the duties and orders became a gradual routine, with the discipline getting tighter as we progressed in our daily training.

Reveille was very early when at the first whistle blown by the Orderly Sergeant, repeated by other NCOs and becoming a deadly shrill.

It was a case to get out of bed quickly, or NCOs dashing on their rounds of the huts, shouting "Rise and shine!" soon had you out of bed by the simple trick of lifting up the middle bed board at your feet. This quick upending soon had you rolling out on to the floor in quite an unceremonious manner one side or the other. There were many reposing bodies of young manhood toppled over the edge to land with a bump on the floor in all the undignified postures of nature's own work. The tilting of the middle board was likely to happen at any time you were relaxing or sleeping by some playful hut mate. The only way to square this was to await your opportunity and have him out with a bump; it happened so often, one rarely took exception to it from a pal. One effective method to avert this was to leave the foot of the middle board on the floor underneath the trestle. It was uncomfortable, but practical. Sometimes your trestle at one end would be placed by someone at a leaning angle inwards or outwards, so that as soon as you laid on the bed, flop, down it would go and collapse underneath you.

Upon reveille you had to be quick because there was very little time to gather your washing and shaving outfit get outside to the trough to complete your preparations in readiness for the PT parade, including a quick cleanliness inspection by NCOs before.

We had no PT kit. We paraded in hut parties (platoons) and doubled to the parade ground in our shirt sleeves, braces down, slacks held up by a belt and, in our Army boots, our own hut corporal, sometimes the instructor, dressed in a similar fashion.

Later, PT instructors were transferred to the RFC from the Army PT School and Regiment at Aldershot. They arrived at Halton complete with the same outfit of red and blue horizontally striped jerseys, dark blue slacks and white slippers. They soon set about us, putting us through the usual range of standard exercises, knees bend, hands outstretched, up, down, jumping, feet apart, out, in, and all the body, legs and arms exercises, all the movements "at the double", and with many PT games like "O'Grady says". There was another game with one boy chasing the next boy round the circle, hitting his backside on the journey. There was leap-frog and the famous "hands down" complete with groans, up and down. All movements were "at the double" and we were wearing Army boots too.

One of the instructors was called Staff Sergeant Oberhulzer. He had been a champion wrestler and interested us by showing us how to wrestle with his various holds. With selected boys, who were volunteers from the big lads, he would wrestle with two or three at a time. They would finish up losers after being all over him, pinned down by his arms and legs, much to our delight and utter amazement. He was very popular with the boys. Gentle, he never hurt anyone. A giant of a man, we admired his tremendous muscles and strength.

Following PT, within minutes we were marched to the dining hall dressed in our khaki tunics with buttons polished and wearing our service cap. Note that at that time boys and even men were not issued with the peaked cap. Slacks had about two inches turned over and down at the top of our puttees just below the knee.

After breakfast we made our way back to the huts. There was not much time left after breakfast and before dinner for "falling in" for the next parade.

The whistles would be blown and the call, "On parade. Move! Double up. Double!" sounded all around. The hut corporal would get us quickly out of the hut and we "fell in" as a hut party. Separately each hut party would then be marched to the edge of the parade ground where we would all stand "at ease".

The two Companies of "A" and "B" were made up of about five platoons, each consisting of about 30 boys (missing out the sick, hut orderlies, those on guard duties, in detention and others not on parade). The "markers" fell in and marched so many given paces to their respective positions, "A" Company first, "B" Company at the rear. On the command, "Parade fall in!" we doubled to our Company and "fell in" two deep. On some occasions we were marched in hut parties to the marker, but it got jumbled up at times and was hardly used. The three-deep was not used as a form of drill or marching at that time. Roll call and a sharp reply demanding Cpl, Sgt, Flt Sgt, or Sir, as the rank warranted, with a sharp jump to attention.

Any boy late on parade was for "jankers". We were "sized", the short ones positioned in the middle and then the monotonous and keen inspection took place.

Inspection took place at morning and afternoon parades. The keenest was the morning inspection, when the OC inspected dress, hair, cleanliness and the need to shave, even if the boy only had fluff on his face. A tap on the shoulder by the officer's stick from the rear invariably indicated that you needed a haircut, so the Sergeant would record your name. A visit to the barber, checked by the Sergeant, a short, back and sides being noted.

On the morning parade the fatigue parties would be detailed, various numbers of boys sliced off a Company and marched away. The remainder were then given drill, mainly in platoons, forming fours, forming two deep, marching in line advance, retreat, wheeling, slow march, changing step, about turn, saluting drill, and so on, often done "by number", calling out en masse. The boy placed in the "blank file" was often one who had soured the NCO for some reason, which meant more work in many of the drill movements.

Afternoon drill, with a full complement on parade, became a

"Battalion" later Wing Parade when the two Companies performed the mass movements making the officers subordinate to the senior officer commanding the parade.

"Jankers" was the slang given to punishment, anything from extra drills, confined to barracks (CB), loss of pay, or detention. For any disciplinary fault, marched before the Officer Commanding, or for a serious charge, before the Commanding Officer, and to be marched off to the guard-room "fell in between two men" was so common that the guard-room became nearly as busy as the canteen by the implementation of such a lot of trivial "charges".

Some of the new NCOs put one on a charge for the slightest thing . . . and I am certain no boy evaded a "charge". I remember one very young corporal, not long transferred from the Army (his RFC uniform was brand new), came in with some new intakes. He pulled me up for some trivial thing and demanded my name and number. I said, "83445 Ross, J." He said, "83 . . . " then paused. I said, "Double four, five." He snapped at me, "Four, four, five. Remember that – you don't double me or I'll double you!" He glared fiercely at me and marched quickly away, leaving me standing to attention, forgetting to remind me of my default.

I laughed at it, uttered some unkind remarks to myself about him and his future career, in jargon not quite complimentary and he lost a good opportunity to put me on a charge.

The Royal Flying Corps numbers of the first Farnborough original boys were from around 81,000 to 84,000 with gaps in between.

The later boy arrivals at Halton were given numbers around and above 155,000. Those who arrived later were given numbers around the 330,000 level. We originals were in the 80,000 level, the Farnborough intakes. We lost some of the older boys who were posted upon reaching 18 years of age. We met some of them later in squadrons, being posted all over the place and the Fleet Air Arm.

I got a surprise when stationed at Ambala in India when told one day that a new arrival from England knew me very well; he had seen my name on orders. I found him – and behold, it was my joining up pal, George Fleming. Later he was posted to Home Service and again visited my parents, giving them news about me.

At Halton "stick drill" was taught, a very important part of training, because the carrying of the cane was an integral part of the Royal Flying Corps dress and we had to know how to use it correctly with a horizontal swing for drill, ceremony, guard duty and walking out.

When walking out or on certain drills the cane was carried in the right hand, held loosely in the fingers at the middle, with the bottom end of the cane to the front, top to the rear and kept horizontal. It was a strict regulation cane, length just over two feet. It had a ferrule at the bottom and a cylindrical knob with the RFC crest on it at the top which we polished.

When standing "at ease", right hand placed in left hand, the cane was held with the fingers and thumb of the right hand, with the bottom of the stick up and out at the front of the right armpit. The salute was given with the stick (cane) placed horizontally under the left armpit, knob to the front. When on the march it had to be done for saluting in a correct movement. Stick drill was executed as follows: on two left paces, stick placed under left armpit, right hand smartly down to side, salute four paces then, on the following two left paces the stick back to horizontal in the right hand. In drill we often had to call out the movements. It is remarkable in all drill movements how calling sharpens the efficiency of each one to the ultimate and as a unit.

Avo 504 crash. Leuchars, 1919.

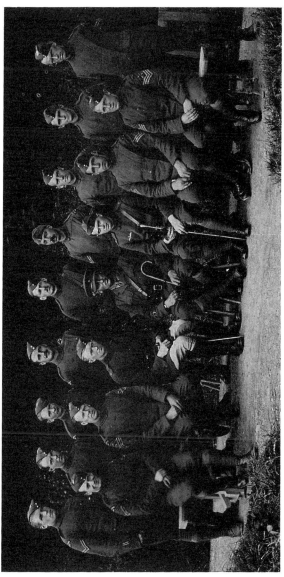

The ORIGINAL Officers and NCOs of the ROYAL FLYING CORPS Boy Service
June 1917 at West Camp Halton. "A" Company. 1st Battalion. (Also "B" Company)
200 Boys each of the original 400 enlisted Trenchards "Brats".

Top row left to right:
Cpl Morgan. Cpl Dunthorne. Air Mech Widdop. Cpl Perkins. Sgt-Mjr Morse. Cpl Philpot. Cpl Oldfield. Cpl Wilson. Cpl Spavin.
Bottom seated:
Cpl Smith. Flt Sgt Parkinson. 2nd Lt Lockwood. 1st Lt Dewhirst. CO. 2nd Lt Cairns. Sgt Mansfield. Flt Sgt Freeman.

Headquarters guard and guard duty at the entrance to the camp on the Wendover-Tring road was known as "stick guard". We all took this in turn by Company and mainly detailed down to hut level. It was a 24-hour guard on the gate and a 12-hour guard at HQ. The sentry did his patrol in a kind of "slope order" with the top end of the stick placed in the palm of the left hand, the bottom end of the stick above the left shoulder. Upon the salute, the stick was grasped by the right hand, placed under the left armpit and the salute given. This was done to the rhythm of marching time. Upon a sudden appearance, the officer got a late salute, but he knew the drill – and if it was smartly and correctly executed, all was well.

We Farnborough RFC boys had no rifle drill during our Boy Service.

Our progressions in drill and the movements of military practice became so good that when we formed up as "A" and "B" Company, we led the later intakes in the "Battalion drill".

Every day it was drill from squad drill to the big parade with an occasional route march on the Wendover-Tring road. We did not carry the cane on all the drills, as stick drill was at squad and platoon level.

Certain drill instructors were very fierce and often seemed merciless, I suppose, that all recruits must be graded to the lowest common element, then revived and brought up to military requirements.

The first Officer Commanding the two combined Companies "A" and "B" was Captain Routledge, later on he became the Camp Adjutant.

Our "A" Company officers are previously mentioned. The first Sergeant in charge of "A" Company was Sgt Parkinson, soon to be promoted to Flight Sergeant. The Flight Sergeant rank was distinguished by a four blade propeller mounted above the three stripes on the arm.

The complete list of the First Officers and NCOs of our "A" Company, 1st Battalion, the No 1 of the Royal Flying Corps Boy Service in June, 1917 at Halton was: Officer Commanding 1st Lieut Dewhirst, 2nd Lieut Cairns and 2nd Lieut Lockwood, Flt Sgt Parkinson, Sgt Freeman, Sgt Mansfield, Corporals Morgan, Spavin, Wilson, Oldfield, Philpot, Perkins and Dunthorne. Corporal Smith was in the pay office at camp HQ and Air Mechanic Widdop, the lorry driver.

All these mentioned officers and NCOs were fairly good fellows.

The more vulgar ones came along when recruitment of boys increased entered Halton and when the new ex-Army NCOs arrived. The original NCOs were promoted as the Boy Service increased in numbers, some of the corporals reached the rank of disciplinary Sergeant-Major. As they were promoted, we lost them, except for one or two. As they moved to the other sections of the new intakes of boy entrants, many of these new NCOs came into "A" and "B" Companies.

These disciplinary NCOs, having come from the Army, some from horse regiments, knew nothing about flying and aircraft, but those who re-engaged after the war got promotion to Squadron disciplinary Regimental Sergeant Major in the new peace-time Royal Air Force Squadron.

The drill formula of the Royal Air Force is the product of the different ideas from various regiments pooled into one pattern and adopted as the standard drill. This originated in the first Boys section in the Royal Flying Corps when drill ideas, methods and practice were introduced with modifications as the years passed by up to the present high standard of continuation drill that we see performed in today's ceremonies.

Flight Sergeant, later Regimental Sergeant-Major, Parkinson and Corporal, later Sergeant-Major, Perkins both wore a medal ribbon of the Boer War.

Lieut Dewhirst left us to become Officer Commanding one of the other Boy Sections of new entries and 2nd Lieut Cairns took over command of our "A" Company, being promoted to Captain.

We liked Captain Cairns, because he was a real Royal Flying Corps officer. He was a pilot, wearing the Pilot's Wings and had been shot down in France, invalided and transferred to our Boys Section. He had a very bad stutter, but learned to produce his words in a gradual way as our drill training proceeded. We in "A" Company felt proud of him, because he was the only pilot amongst all the officers and NCOs in those early days. Moreover, Capt Cairns had been flying and fought against enemy airmen. The inward pride and great respect we had for him was manifest, a feature we felt he knew. Our extra loyalty to him helped him with his parade commands. Knowing so often what his orders would be, we braced ourselves for them and put an extra good effort into the movement.

Cameras were not allowed on to the camp. The only photographs we had taken on the camp were shot by a photographer from London, who had a branch office in Wendover. He was only allowed into the camp on occasion, so there are not many photographs of us, only of small groups, and these very rare. No photographs were taken of the "Battalions" or "Companies". Had there been any, I would most certainly possess some. Consequently, no complete pictorial record of the original Royal Flying Corps, Farnborough, Halton Boys exists.

We had two inoculation parades, one on June 23, the other on June 26, 1917. This was our second experience of anything like this – and there was no escaping it. It was surprising to notice how the boys who seemed to fear nothing and were cocky in attitude, rolled over on to the floor in a faint as their turn came for the jab. Many of us took these jabs without concern, feeling that it was also our duty to carry these 'stalwarts' outside, a job we relished, removing some of these clever "don't care for nobody" bodies. We laid them out and they needed the aid of us who were not regarded by them to be in their class of swagger and bravado. So as they revived, we let them fully know our regard and contempt for them in no uncertain tone.

We were also paraded for vaccination on July 17, 1917. I was returned to duty after this in quick time, the "bully boys" were once again weak. There was always boisterous play amongst us. One boy, Pat Mills, a good athlete, had a very bad arm after joining in a rough game of hut football, charging about with the rest of us. His arm got knocked too much and he had to have hospital treatment, but his constitution was strong and after some anxiety he got better.

Some footballs were provided and matches played between huts and "Companies". No other kit was issued except some jerseys obtained for the matches fought out on the parade ground by "A" and "B" Companies . I got no further than the hut team, as we found we had some very good players. One, in particular, was a Sheffield boy who enlisted after me and was in "A" Company, a tall lad named Wilkinson, a centre half reputed to be a nephew of the old Sheffield United player of that name. Although he played in early "Wing" teams, he did not go into any big club. A. G. Carnill, a big lad, was the only boy to play regularly in the Cranwell Station rugby team.

Football is always a game to be played by those in the Forces at any time of the year and a kick-about amongst a few is a good pastime, easing a lot of tension. The only organised game was football. No facilities for any other game existed as are provided today.

We had no cricket gear, so the cricket we played was amongst ourselves, with a home-made bat, an old tennis ball and any suitable object for the stumps. Lively contests took place between the huts, urged on by frantic supporters to "run it out" when the ball, with a mighty clout was hit over other huts . . . or even through a hut window, for which we gladly paid barrack damages.

It seemed we boys had been assembled into West Camp, Halton, as a large enough camp to accommodate.The authorities were not prepared with any ideas as to what to do with us other than military drill.

It was a rush enlistment of hundreds of boys marshalled into one big camp. Officers and NCOs were left to improvise some sort of disciplinary routine to keep us occupied, whilst the "planners" thought up some method of technical training. Thus, the order was drill morning and afternoon continuously. It had been given the "posh" title of "The School of Technical Training", the SOTT for short, but during our stay at Halton we had no technical training. There was not an aircraft within miles, no aircraft parts, not a spanner or even a file except those used by the men who repaired barrack damages or the lorry driver's tool-kit. Yet the recruiting advertisement in the newspapers suggested, "Boys to be trained in the workshops". Our stay at Halton was never arranged for any organised lectures or training on aeronautics, or the work of, or even the traditions of, the Royal Flying Corps. It appeared to us that we might just as well have been a Boys Section in the Army.

At a later date there appeared in a field near Aylesbury and Wendover an old Maurice Farman biplane. Housed in a canvas hangar, it was used to fly out at dusk on odd days of the week. Sometimes it would fly with lights showing, navigation lights, and we felt this wonderful for Halton. This field was some distance from the camp and immediately placed "out of bounds" to all boys.

With others I approached the edge of this field, but we found it not worth it, as the aircraft could not be seen. It was in the hangar, so I never bothered any more about it, except when it was in the air – and even then it would be flying for only a few minutes.

It was some months after our arrival at West Camp that we had a delivery of one Rotary Aero engine and an old fuselage that appeared to be from a BE2C. These were placed in one of the corrugated iron sheds previously belonging to the horse section. Only certain boys were allowed to go and play about with these two pieces of aircraft, and I was not one of the lucky chosen ones. There was room for many unserviceable aircraft.

About this time we all had been before the CO for an interview so we could be classified into various trade groups. It could not have involved much serious selection, because there were only two main groups. One was the "Fitter Aero", while the other was "Rigger". With my previous apprenticeship giving me a certain amount of knowledge of locomotive and motor car engineering, I was assigned to the "Fitter Aero" learner classification. Boys without any previous type of engineering work were classified as "Rigger" learner, and one could see that the two groups worked out on an even numerical basis. George Fleming, who had returned from special leave and in "B" Company, having been a clerk in a Sheffield office, was placed in the "Rigger" group of classification. He told me that he had visited my parents whilst on leave. Naturally, they were pleased to see him and to hear that I was keeping well and had settled down in the Royal Flying Corps. This was true. I felt fit and well.

The coolness of the shower bath was a welcome relief in the warm evenings. These baths were in a row of corrugated sheds, each with a little door about four feet high. Each bath was the size of shower space. The bath was about one yard square and one foot deep, made of concrete, with a rough surface of pebbles on the sides and bottom, which could be rather uncomfortable and sore. The only means of water supply to the shower was above, like a watering can nozzle with two chains, one opposite the other at the side of the nozzle, one for cold, the other warm – provided that the boilers had been lit. I used the cold shower with relish in the evening during the hot summer months.

There was the weekly bath parade when we were marched to and from these baths by NCOs. The water was warm in summer, heated by a boiler at the end of each set of blocks, but in the winter period it was something of an ordeal; the supposed hot water was always warm, but it would be turned off to conserve it. If not sharp enough only the cold, icy water came through. Furthermore, stripping in the small, uncovered alleyway in winter was a perishing job with bad weather and bitterly cold winds howling around your body like a miniature whirlwind.

In winter with snow on the ground the NCOs saw that all in turn paraded and stripped, checking names under the shower. It was awful, a teeth-chattering experience stripping in the open air alleyway. This we hated because snow covered the small plank that our change of clothing was placed on. With snow still falling it got soaking wet before we finished the bath. We often stripped off again in the hut and, with only a towel around us, dried our clothes around a very hot combustion stove.

We managed. That was fixed on orders, snow, rain or sunshine; could not be altered. It was a common saying amongst us from NCO downwards: "Orders is orders, and must be obeyed."

Of course, there was plenty of mischief. When having a warm, stand-up bath, a "kind" neighbour would reach over from his cubicle and splash, down would come a torrent and blast of icy cold water. I got my share of this sudden freeze, but got even by returning the compliment on to some other boy. One method to try to prevent it was to soak a piece of old rag in cold water, by the side, keep a sharp look-out upwards and administer a good, solid wet clout to the hand reaching over the top of your cubicle to get to the cold water chain. We tried to take the chains off the cold showers, but they were too well fixed on.

We were all treated the same. Our grumbles and curses about it were a godsend to NCOs who had many of us on defaulters' parade next morning for insubordination, answering back, refusing to obey an order from a NCO, or for the use of bad language on the bathing parade. This did not strengthen the thin veil of good relations between NCOs and the boys.

A trick which was practised was with the toilets already mentioned. The rear long, wooden flap could be raised on hinges. We also had a game with wet, cold mops. We would creep out of the hut and stealthily approach the rear of this line of buckets. Upon a given signal, this long flap would be raised open, exposing the seat of a boy or boys sat on the toilet. Then, all of a sudden "Wham!" – and the cold, wet mop would be pushed on to the exposed backsides, with a resultant roar that would startle the devil himself.

We all experienced this. Some of us avoided it by crouching on the wooden seat with the hole in it, with our feet on either side of the hole and our backsides above the seat of operations. Often I would hear the noise of the flap being opened and the mop tickled underneath, when I would be above it and out of range.

After the attack and so much commotion, the culprits would quickly retreat and be laid on their beds quietly reading or busy to the effect of "I don't know anything about it". There would be the occasion when a sergeant would be seen entering the separate one at the end, "NCOs, for the use of". There would be a whispered consultation amongst us. We would plan our attack and select our team. Out we would creep, three or four of us, two to to operate the small flap and one or two armed with a wet, cold mop, not dripping with water as this would give the information as from which hut had mounted the attack. A hush and a quiet signal, a nod in acceptance, then "Wham!" quick, sharp, the flap closed, and a smart tip-toe away, all in a few seconds and an unpopular sergeant had his egg-shaped backside given a rare old wet, cold mopping!

The retreat to the hut had the accompaniment of a loud, bellowing voice: "What the . . . I'll get you for this, you young so and so's!"

The sergeant would then enter different huts to try to find the wet mops, but they were never found, because all the mops were damp from daily use, and we all looked so innocent, it really could not be us.

Sometimes a sergeant would remain in his toilet long after an attack and when all was quiet, quickly depart, feeling wise to retire later than to admit that he had been "mopped". Laugh, at times we laughed so much that some boys jumped on to beds and covered themselves under the blankets to smother the laughter. I remember one boy crying with laughter about it when the sergeant bellowed, "You! What are you laughing at, lad?" The boy replied, "I'm not laughing, I'm crying, Sergeant. My dad's left home."

The sergeant left the hut. We asked the boy, "Has your dad left home?" "Aye," he replied, "every day to go to work."

Our fun and games might appear to have been crude, but it had to be made by ourselves and was created as the occasion arose.

Another game often repeated was that if a boy was sweeping up or sawing logs for the Officers Mess, Sergeants Mess, or any similar action calling for elbow movement of one arm, we would gather behind him, each one holding the elbow of the boy in front. Linked together, we all went through the same motion as one. It looked and sounded good, much to the amusement of officers, NCOs and onlookers, as each forward motion was done with strong grunting.

Our only entertainment on camp other than the canteen was the YMCA and the "Blood and Thunder". We had no service theatre. Radio was only in its military infancy. There were no such things as radio sets. Television was unheard of, while there were no tape recorders and cassettes. We relied upon newspapers and magazines. For music we had some old wind-up gramophone, or the old piano in the YMCA and the canteen, the Institute.

The gramophone, with its large horn, scratched out music from "Chu-Chin-Chow", the "Maid of the Mountains", a march or two and ragtime music. Some boys had mouth organs which were very popular. We would get together in the hut and have a sing-song of the popular war-time and sentimental old songs. Some of them were: "Tipperary", "Pack up your troubles", "Show me the way to go home", "Just a song at twilight", "When the sun shines bright on Charley", "There's a long, long trail", "I want to be right down in Dixie", "Daisey, Daisey, all for the love", "Yip e haddy Ihey Ihey", "I love the sunshine and the roses", "Somewhere a voice is calling", "Who were you with last night?", "Smile awhile", "Carolina moon", "Alexander's ragtime band", "Back home in Tennesse", "Bless them all", "Good bye-ee, don't cry-ee", "By the light of the silvery moon", "In my little grey home in the west", "Come, come, I want you only", "There's a silver lining", "Kitty, Kitty, isn't it a pity", "When you come home, dear", "Love's old sweet song", "Nellie Dean", "Everybody's doing it", "You were my baby doll", "Oh! Oh! Antonio", "Give me a cosy little corner", "Every little while I feel so", "She'll be coming round the mountain", "We were sailing along", "In the twi twi twilight", "Good-bye Dolly, I must leave you", "Ragtime Cowboy Joe", "Give me your smile, the sunshine of your", "Sister Susie's sewing shirts for soldiers", "Fall in and follow", "After the war is over" and "Kiss me goodnight, Sergeant Major".

When on route marches on the Wendover-Tring road, we would sing when marching "at ease" a varied assortment of songs, some containing our own words and lyrics which startled passers-by. When passing a female pushing a pram, there would be a loud chorus from the marching mass. A wailing cry of "Oh! Oh!" growing louder and louder. If a male was carrying a baby or was with a lady with a pram, the mass cry would be "Ah! Ah!" Some of the cries made to people as we marched past created amusement by the wit and fun of it; to some it caused extreme shock.

We sang our own song of the RFC boys. It had many different words to it. One verse, subject to change of words, went as follows, sung to the tune of "The Church's one foundation":

"We are Fred Karno's Army. We are the RFC. We cannot fly; we cannot fight; what earthly good are we? We love our Sergeant-Major. We're as happy as can be. Mein Gott, Mein Gott, what a bloody fine lot are the boys of the RFC!"

Another marching song was this:

"Whiter than the whitewash on the wall (repeat). Wash me in the water that you wash your dirty daughter and I shall be whiter than the whitewash on the wall."

The first RFC Boys Band was formed. It started with one side drum, nobody seemed to know where it came from. More drums and bugles came along, then trumpets were obtained. Instrumentalists practised far away from our huts. This trumpet band grew so that an NCO who had been in a band took charge and was made the Bandmaster. His name was Threlwell (some think it Thelfell), a short, stocky fellow who marched very proudly leading his boys, erect, with chin up, chest out and four reversed stripes with a brass drum badge above, placed at the bottom of his sleeves. He trained this band on his own to a very good standard and proficient enough to lead us on route marches on the Wendover-Tring road.

At first only the side drum we had would beat out the time for marching. On one occasion an Army band was on the Wendover road. We halted the band formed up in front of us; they played us on the road and into the camp gates. It was wonderful how this bucked us up and gave us a splendid march. It was the first military band to lead us. We thought it was great. It was the band of the Northamptonshire Regiment.

Our boys' band provided the bugle for reveille and lights out, doing away with the whistles of the NCOs. Quite a lot of drill was done to the tapping of a single side drum beating the tap-tap of the movements and the roll of the drum and "Tap" for the "Dressing". The band eventually got some musical instruments. In time, with practice, they performed well enough to play the boys' camp march, which was to the tune of "Colonel Bogey".

Fatigues were often done by platoons. The sergeant would call Number One and then on up to a certain number, or he put his arm at the side of a boy and order the remainder to "Right turn" and be marched off by a corporal or a selected boy to take charge. Generally we had some idea what kind of fatigue it would be, a "cushy" one or a rotten one.

The fatigue at the Officers Mess or at the Sergeants Mess was popular. Here we helped in washing plates, etc, getting the good chance of a tit-bit of food left over from the mess steward which was quite a treat.

Tent Pals. RFC Boys Halton West Camp 1917.
Top Row: Left to Right: Hawkins, Biggs, Potter, Ross.
Seated: Stewart.

Two RFC Boys Halton West Camp 1917.
Standing: Herbert Myles.
Seated: Joe Chatfield.

Our cookhouse fatigue could be a good or bad one, depending on the job itself. Under the eagle eye of the NCOs, one was a Corporal Cowstick, washing the plates and dishes was unwelcomed. There were hundreds of the greasy things to wash – and if one was found unwashed, the whole lot was put back into the water and you started all over again.

The hot water was provided from an outside field kitchen boiler, which we stoked up well.

The cookhouse sergeant was a dark-haired man, with a very dark moustache, twisted to a point, and with very flat feet. He plodded about the cookhouse with never a pleasant look on his face, which made us feel he didn't like us. Other fatigues were fetching coal for the Officers and Sergeants Messes and our own cookhouse, HQ fatigues, cleaning up the camp, picking up paper with a nail on the end of a stick, carrying bed boards and blankets, tables, forms, etc to huts awaiting new arrivals and other hut preparations, helping to unload the Leyland lorries, which came in with goods from the stores. These were checked. Sweeping up and helping in domestic duties in the Institute and the YMCA also had to be done, being rewarded with a cup of tea and a rock bun or even a slice of cake. Helping the General Service men working at the incinerator and swilling and disinfecting the toilets was not a pleasant job, but polishing and cleaning a comical sort of home-made fire engine fixed on to a two-wheeled carriage was a nice little duty. Whether the thing worked we never knew. Some fatigues were a good "scrounge", others damned hard work and dirty. We got used to the trap which was a good ruse to get volunteers for a certain fatigue. It came about that boys would not "fall out" for what sounded like a nice "cushy" fatigue. Being used to the bait, it often resulted in, "You! You!" and being marched off to an unknown destination for some easy or rotten fatigue. "Fall out those who can play the piano" was an early one; out fell the eager pianists and upon the chosen number required, the order was, "If you can play the piano, you can move one." They would be sent to the Officers or Sergeants Mess or YMCA.

I fell for the cry of, "Fall out any boy who can play cricket." Not many fell out and I joined the selected party. "If you can play cricket, you will know how to roll a cricket pitch." We were ordered on to a lorry. Off we went to a place we did not know, where we had to push a huge roller up and down the pitch and its near surrounds. But worse was to follow, as we had to clear up into buckets the droppings from cows of which there were plenty. We took a beautiful aroma back to our huts – hardly to the delight of our room mates.

It got that boys would not volunteer for any request. The officers, knowing this, got NCOs to detail parties. A "cushy" fatigue could compensate for a rotten one.

Intakes of new boy recruits were coming into the camp and it was about full. Some were entering the now vacant North Camp. Most of these recruits were signed on for a longer period of service, some for eight years and four Reserve. Some of these boys were, in later years, promoted to high rank. One of them, who must have re-engaged for a longer term of service, finished his career with progression in the RAF to a high rank, upon his retirement from the service, of Air Vice Marshal, W. Opie, CB, CBE, RAF (Retd).

In West Camp doing plenty of drill, we had quite a military style and a pleasant diversion came along. One or two huts were emptied and made into classrooms and an Army school started. I commenced my Army schooling on Tuesday July 24, 1917. Our teacher was a lieutenant belonging to the Army Education Corps.

He wore the uniform of his Corps and the Corps badge on his military cap. We sat on wooden forms at tables on trestles. He used a blackboard and chalk. The four walls were bare, with no charts, just a bare classroom with the teacher sat facing us, pencils and paper at the ready, these articles being provided. One or two of the brainy soldier NCOs helped in our classes in these huts and, in a certain way, did quite good for dictation, composition and spelling. Spelling consisted mainly of words from Army orders and technical terms used by the Army, with composition to punctuate correctly by example.

We were being prepared for the sitting of the examination for the Military 2nd Class Certificate of Education. Upon the advice of the lieutenant, I bought a book, *A handy help to obtaining the Military 2nd Class Certificate of Education.* I found this very useful, the arithmetic interesting, with good examples.

When one considers the military words, there were some difficult ones to spell, such as "piquet", "accoutrements", "furlough", "manoeuvre", "campaign", "ricochet", "plateau", "reconnaissance" and many others not generally in use, but of particular value for matters that concerned military values.

The arithmetic "syllabus" for 2nd Class studies had problems and examples set in the form of military scope, the cash account being in the form of a messing account for a Regimental Institute. The subject invariably concerned the soldier and his way of life.

One simple example was this: "A garrison of men, total 525, have provisions to last 17½ days. How many men should be withdrawn to make the provisions last seven days longer?" The answer was 150. This was our way of living.

I also bought "Handy Help" books upon the 1st Class Certificate of Education and map reading.

We were paraded for school on certain days of the week and were encouraged to make time for the "homework" in the huts in our spare time. Wanting to pass this examination and go for the 1st Class, I stayed in camp as often as I could. I did test examples and old examination papers from the book, set in test ABCD, etc, on any piece of scrap paper; checking the answers given at the end of the book. This proved most valuable with complete assurance when checked and correct, or sometimes otherwise. found to be.

Our washing was now being collected by an outside laundry. Those who sent it paid for it out of their small pay, but some boys still sent washing home in parcels.

This gave some of us more available time for our studies. I was passing my own tests, even helping some of my hut pals and others at arithmetic.

Boys who lived in or around London got away on a weekend pass frequently. We who lived a longer distance away rather envied them. I wrote to my parents telling them I would not be coming home on leave until I had saved up enough money, but I was hoping with others that we might soon get leave with free warrant.

We had been having heavy rain with thunderstorms. I wrote home on YMCA headed writing paper telling of the awful conditions of the mud, with the camp one deep "pudding". Anyone having been at Halton in those days will remember what that awful chalky mud is like. It clings around your boots, building up a huge mass. Your feet ache in pulling your heavily laden "ammo" boots out of it, making a terrible mess of everything. Duckboards disappeared underneath it. The scraper took some off before you entered the hut, or any other building, but plenty was deposited on the floor, which needed constant scraping and swilling. Cleaning your boots was a real problem, having to get them ready for wear on the afternoon parade, with them properly cleaned and polished only to mud up as soon as you stepped outside and on to the parade and the inspection. The best way was to scrape the boots with a knife, then a wipe with newspaper, following with a tremendous brushing with boot polish to try to get a shine as always demanded.

Our puttees were "mudded" up to our knees, needing a scrape and vigorous brushing with the stiff issued brush to put on clean again. All this had to done during the dinner break, ready for the afternoon parade inspection.

During a clear weather period we had to set about an extra cleaning up of the camp of everything stationary or moveable. A high ranking officer was expected to visit us.

The great day arrived. We were thoroughly inspected and awaited his arrival. He flew into a clearance near to the big house of the Rothschilds in his own aircraft, made a very bad landing and crashed. I do not know what service type it was. Our visitor was General Bonham-Carter, who had a false leg.

He inspected us and said that we were a fine body of youths who would be a credit to the Royal Flying Corps. We all got special leave, on Monday July 30, 1917. I got home for the first time, proudly wearing my full dress Royal Flying Corps uniform. With the inspection for leaving we were passed out at the guard-room as properly dressed and made our way to Wendover railway station and some of us on to Aylesbury to catch the express train north on the Great Central Railway.

We were very excited and took over a compartment of eight for ourselves. We had some good laughs. We were amused when one boy decided to promote himself and on the journey pulled out of his pocket a pair of corporal's stripes and started to put into effect his own promotion. Busy with needle and cotton, he got one sleeve all right. He got so engrossed in his workmanship that he did not notice he was sewing the two stripes upside down on the other sleeve. We kept him talking and did not tell him. As the train was entering his station, he put his tunic on and discovered his mistake. He was amazed, but it was too late. We had him on the platform looking bewildered, with us all calling out, "Cheerio. So long, Corporal." The train steamed away, leaving a very embarrassed and red-faced boy to face the Military Police at the station. Back at camp after leave he got put on a "charge" for his self-attempted, and badly constructed promotion.

Some boys on leave put a white band on to their GS cap in order to appear like cadets of officer rank. They must have carried the deception well, for they even had a small group photograph taken.

At that time, members of HM Forces were compelled to wear uniform when on leave. Military Police on railway stations and patrolling the streets would pull you up in order to inspect your pass and that you were properly dressed, even to the wearing of "ammo" boots.

We were proud of our uniform. Our parents and families were proud of us too. Photographs of us were always on view in the house with a Union Jack nearby. My photograph joined in alongside those of my brothers and relations in a group with miniature flags of the Allies surrounding us.

One of the first things to do on leave was to visit the photographic studios, because your photograph was in great demand for those at home, relations, the places you worked, and your old school. All these places, like factories, shops, schools, meeting places and places of worship, had a large display of photographs exhibited in a frame proudly stating their "Roll of Honour", for King and Country, with details of the unit, ship, wounded and those killed in action.

These portrait studios did a good trade, because it was the only means of getting your photograph taken. My father was pleased with me, while my mother was delighted to see what a healthy lad I looked. and I felt well. My head and shoulders were more erect from the drill and PT.

My father took me all over the place, introducing me as another of his sons serving his King and Country and in the Royal Flying Corps too. I admit I walked out in my uniform with the spirit and swagger of a keen airman on leave. It had been instilled into us at Halton that we had to impress the folk at home, be proud of the service and the uniform. Most of us did just that.

They were the days of our youth. We used more toleration and accepted our status without being so demonstrative of what we thought was not to our liking and expecting everybody older to provide for our pleasure and spare time activities. We had our ideas and our dissensions, and when we had anything to complain about, we did so in no mistaken manner and the officers and NCOs knew it. We did not wilfully destroy or create damage for the sake of it, or behave like bully hooligans to the general public. For one thing, the older generation would not have put up with it. They had the power to punish us by a good punch or two where it hurt most. This did us no harm and maintained general good behaviour. We accepted the fact that in our time, we had got to help to get the war over. We should, within months, be in the fighting zone ourselves and felt it was our duty to "do our bit" to prepare to get at the enemy in a short time and in service to our King and Country and our people was essential. In 1917 the war appeared to be shaping up to a long, drawn-out conflict, but we were happy; there were happy faces about, even when losses were great and very heavy in France and elsewhere.

There was, amongst all the sorrow and grief, a sense of responsibility, pride and sociability passed down from the older generation to we young ones. We adopted a real purpose and inspiration, a positive outlook and got no further than a moaning and groaning, which was the serviceman's privilege and a good outlet when kept well within the limit.

People would stop me in the street. Some I did not know, but they showed their pleasure and interest. Neighbours were very friendly, and my leave was a happy event. My pals left at home were eager to know what it was like in the RFC.

My mother was delighted to have me home again and I am sure she would have liked me to stay at home for ever, but she knew I could not. Mother gave me a noble welcome, as did my father; they said not a boy, but a young man was home for a few days. My sisters fussed me like I had never known before and I really enjoyed myself.

I cannot help but recall the look on my mother's face when she saw me with my cap off for the first time. She looked hard at me and said, "John, whyever did you let them cut all your hair off like that?" I told her, "Mother, you have no choice. You are marched to the camp barber. Your name is ticked off the list as your hair is cut. It only takes about half a minute and you are done." She accepted it, but admitted that it was not the best example of military hairstyling.

The four days leave passed quickly and I was ready to return to camp before I had hardly settled down to do the things I had hoped for.

On Thursday August 2, 1917, I set off from home. My sister, Clara accompanied me to the railway station, my other sisters being at work. I had a parcel containing a large portion of my mother's home-made parkin, a favourite cake of mine.

At the old "Victoria" station in the Wicker, Sheffield, I boarded a

London express train for Marylebone, stopping at Aylesbury on the Great Central line, said good-bye to my sister and away. A number of boys of the RFC joined the train on its journey, and from Aylesbury we got the local Metropolitan train to Wendover.

Being summer it was light as we tramped from Wendover to West Camp. In those days boys were not privileged. We were forbidden to ride on any RFC vehicle. No transport was provided and it was a long walk back to camp for us. We arrived very tired at the guard-room, handing over our passes and "Get to your huts. Git movin'. Move." rang in our ears as we trudged our way back to our huts.

Upon arrival there was always a cheer. You could hear the cheers all over the camp, as boys arrived off leave and what a nice greeting it was. Some had arrived only minutes before, others hours before, some to come. If you were a lucky one, your bed was in good order and you found it as you had left it, but wary if some pal had kindly made the bed for you and fixed it so that it collapsed when you got into it, or even sat on it, or your bed was full of brushes and a mop, or to discover that a false bed had been made with blankets folded in at the top. A good inspection for a family of earwigs was necessary with a boot at the ready.

One was wise to inspect the whole outfit, that is if you managed to get in off leave or any other pass before "lights out". Everything was soon back to the normal routine as before and after a wash, a tidy up and an exchange of leave gossip, one usually opened the parcel from home for a share out with your pals, except for the odd boy who would lay in bed with his parcel hidden under the blankets as he tucked into its contents all by himself. Some boys had a quiet weep by themselves, so we tried to buck them up a bit.

The following day, after medical inspection, our hut was isolated for 10 days, one boy being taken away to hospital with diphtheria. We came out of isolation on Sunday August 12, 1917. Following the excitement of our first leave, this became a dreary episode. We, and the hut, were fumigated and did our drill away from the others.

Our hut corporal (ex-Army), Cpl Morgan was in charge. We were not allowed to send out any letters. Being confined to the hut, I managed to get in some "swatting" – we called it studying – so the time was not wasted.

Medical inspections were plenty, held in the hut and not disturbed by outside influences. After a day or so, we moved into bell tents rigged up nearby until the hut was given clearance after sealing it up and giving it a thorough fumigation. We fit boys enjoyed the tents for a change.but we were soon back in the hut, it being passed for habitation by the medical officers.

On Saturday August 18, 1917, we had a school test. I was satisfactory and could proceed towards sitting for the "Military 2nd Class Certificate of Education". Many boys were not successful and were put back to the huts provided for starting lessons again.

We fortunate ones were able to advance on to Sections C and D with averages, percentages and proportional parts, pay and mess books and accounts. Handwriting and spelling with composition and dictation were studies arranged by the Army Schools syllabus, so we were preparing for the preliminary test prior to the examination proper.

There came another great joy when I was granted another long week-end leave. This was from Friday August 24, to Sunday, midnight August 26th, 1917. It was very acceptable and I enjoyed myself once again. It quickly passed by and I left home with my sister as before on the Sunday afternoon to catch one of the few Sunday expresses to Marylebone stopping at Aylesbury.

On Wednesday September 12, 1917, we had our very first Boys Section Royal Flying Corps, Annual Sports Day. The parade ground was marked out by boys on fatigue duty with the whole arrangements of the events built up with what equipment was available, much of it amateurish, but it worked.

The early stages of elimination were carried out by NCOs at hut level and by platoon competition, we had great fun in the process. This competition was performed in the "ammo" boots. The boys desperately tried to get a place in the events pitting their skills at athletics, whilst wearing slacks and army boots. To see boys puffing and blowing in a long distance race, high-jump, long-jump, hurdles, and other events heavily handicapped, with sleeves rolled up, would make our present day athletes shudder at the sight. Those who did well enough to beat the others were the local hut heroes of that particular event.

Practically all who attained the competitive level necessary for the finals on the sports day received plimsolls from the PT staff, who managed to scrounge them from some unknown source. The great day came. Officers and NCOs joined in and played their respective parts, even to our joy of seeing NCOs racing and puffing along in "ammo" boots in events of their own. The "ammo" boots came in useful in the "tug of war" between the different Companies who were permitted one huge sergeant for anchor man. The majority of the boys had never seen or experienced such a large gathering of various sports like this and it was a great event for all us.

The organisation was good, but the method would be ridiculed today. However, we all thoroughly enjoyed ourselves and I would say that the fun and games, excitement and endeavour has not been surpassed at any RFC or RAF sports day. A tribute to the PT staff, officers and NCOs of this first Royal Flying Corps Boys Section, arranged and contested under such primitive conditions. There was no officially printed programme, only the typed foolscap sheets of details on paper used for the notices and Routine Orders and these not available to everybody, but who cared? It was good enough for the occasion, helping to make the organisation of events a qualified success, carried out with good timing and Olympic endeavour.

The winners were acclaimed with terrific cheering, without the award of a cup or medal, the only prize being the knowledge of having won. He – or they – became the hut hero of the day, often to the great surprise of the successful contestant who astounded himself at having such latent talent. I wrote home, "A jolly happy day was had by all."

In each hut there was the occasional dispute and a fight. It was only natural among a lot of boys. The bully would try to show his superior talents of power and push others around. Sometimes a gang of boys would enter and try to upset the orderliness of a hut. One day we had unwelcomed visitors from another hut who started to interfere with some of our beds and equipment. They picked on one boy, rather pale-faced, holding his head slightly to one side, and pushed him, and others around. He pleaded, "Leave me alone." The big bully pushed him and sent him rolling on to his bed. This quiet boy defended himself from further torment and immediately tore into the lead bully. Swiftly and solidly he laid the bully out with short, sharp, crisp punches, shouting as he finished, "Get out, all of you, or you'll get the same!" Some of us, now "top dogs", joined in and the rest of them, mesmerised by the swift flattening, gave little resistance and we won the day. The invaders collected their leader and carried him to their hut.

Our protector was called Vaughan who, it turned out, was an amateur boy boxer in the district he lived in the North East. The news spread about the camp and our hut received little interference again. It proved the old story to be careful when trying to upset others in the

Forces you do not know. This boy, a rather quiet lad, gave no previous indication of his boxing skills, but later won the championship of his weight in the improvised boxing matches held by the PT staff. The gloves and other furnishings for boxing were provided by the magic wand of the PT staff.

On Thursday September 15, 1917, I was made the senior boy of our hut. I was to be in charge of the hut, answerable to the hut corporal. These appointments were by order of the Camp Commander. Each hut had a boy selected for this promotion. The authorities decided that the selected boy would be made an acting lance-corporal and wear one stripe of that rank. This actually came about and I became an acting unpaid boy lance-corporal. As far as I know, this was the only time and place in the Royal Flying Corps – and later the Royal Air Force – when this rank was made and acknowledged.

I was not keen about it and did not want the job, but carried it out. I'm pleased to say that the boys in the hut played their part with me and gave me no trouble, nor did I seek it, but helped them to keep the hut clean and tidy. My kit and bed "lay out" had been estimated as a good example to the satisfaction of the hut inspectors to be copied. I helped many a boy to fold his blankets and kit to suit the instructions.

We raw young NCOs were put in front of small squads of boys and instructed how to give orders and to command them. I had fears about it, because some were so good at it that they became near to be drill experts and took over many senior NCO duties, it looked to me as though they would become permanent drill and disciplinary NCOs. I did not want anything to interfere with my becoming a skilled mechanic, and a flyer. I admit I put little effort in my performances as a drill instructor. I could see the point of having a knowledge of leadership, which would help in the future, but I was not interested in copying some of the objectionable manners and vulgarities called out to us at drill by certain offensive, uncouth and detested NCOs whom we hated.

The officers told us we were specially chosen, that it was an honour and credit to us, but whilst I could see the point, I was not impressed. I had not joined the RFC to do this. I remember on one occasion I gave a right wheel instead of a left wheel and my squad turned and marched slap bang into the side of the ranks of another squad, causing a real mix-up, much to the frenzy of senior NCOs. We had to fetch them out after the halt one by one and, with a "marker", reform my jumbled mess. I got a rare "ticking off", much to the delight of my grinning comrades. Inwardly, I thought it very funny and laughed to myself.

We were not given a course of NCO training, but picked it up by trial and error in front of a squad who enjoyed the mistakes we made to the fury of some dedicated senior NCOs, who had to reorganise many a tangled mob back in to his beloved squad.

The boys, our own pals, had great fun in our attempts as NCOs. In fun they ragged me when taking them to a fatigue, like purposely getting out of step, marching away at a drifting angle, some having a crafty smoke, or marching at so quick a pace that some had to run to keep up with them. Laughingly I promised to thump the culprits, which was not exactly in accordance with the King's Rules and Regulations, but it never happened,we were good pals.

I remember marching a fatigue party of my hut pals to the cookhouse. After handing them over to the cookhouse sergeant, I went outside and found a rusty, old, disused field kitchen hot water boiler. Intending to do a little studying, I sat on top of this old boiler and got out my bits of paper to "swot".

I must have dozed off. Suddenly I woke up and leapt off this boiler, with my seat at a very high temperature. Some of my pals had quietly crept up and lit a wood fire underneath. When the fatigue was completed, the sergeant said to me, "These have been good lads." He gave us a mug of tea and some cake, saying to me, "Sit down, corporal." I refused to do so and he nodded in approval, unaware of what the boys were grinning at.

I had another long week-end at home on leave from September 21 to Sunday midnight September 23, 1917. It was another short but glorious stay with my parents and family.

There was a shortage of food, with people queuing up at shops for certain articles and the few luxuries available. Often a queue would disperse, as one shop closed people rushed off to another shop that had opened.

Very often a member of the Forces would be permitted by the queue to enter directly into the shop that had opened to make a purchase. When on leave, you spent some of your time purchasing foodstuff and items that were scarce. At times you were too late: the last items had been sold or placed under the counter.

The "Black Market" flourished, with high prices for goods which were difficult to obtain.

I took off my stripes on the journey home and tacked them on again whilst sat in the train toilet when approaching my camp station. I did not want my stay at home to be as a lance-corporal in the Royal Flying Corps and my family did not know of my promotion. There were no men lance-corporals in the Royal Flying Corps.

With other boys we were back in camp on this Sunday evening, rather tired after the long, weary trek from Wendover railway station, settling in and telling stories of our leave. Some boys proudly showed photographs of the girls they had met and been out with, even to "posh" postcard photographs of girls they boasted about as females they'd spent the night with. As other boys would inform us: "Don't believe him. He is trying to impress us. He's just showing off." You can buy the postcards they showed us, some exactly the same; the imaginative swains. We reckoned it made them feel manly, more so when we pretended to be interested in the stories they told us of their amorous nights of achievements as we encouraged them whilst sitting around a bed saying, "Go on . . . tell us more."

One boy who lived in London said to us that he would prove them to be making up the stories about these females and he brought about half a dozen of the very same photographs after a week-end leave in London. He purchased them from a bookstall and they were the same picture postcards as shown to us by the story-tellers.

We helped the boys who had difficulty in writing letters. If it was to a girl, we included words of utter rubbish and wonderful affection for them to copy.

CHAPTER FOUR

FROM WEST CAMP TO NORTH CAMP. MILITARY EXAMINATIONS. WINTER AND FREEZING CONDITIONS. SICKNESS. FIRST BOY RFC MILITARY FUNERAL. AIR FORCE FIRST MEMORANDUM ISSUED TO ALL RANKS. SOME WORDS OF WISDOM FROM NCOs.

On Friday September 28, 1917, we were all uprooted and left West Camp for North Camp.

North Camp was more on a slope and seemed to be a larger camp. I wrote home telling them that as a camp I did not like it as much as the West Camp. At any rate, I was settling down. One good thing about it was that North Camp had got a very good, large YMCA, with four billiard tables in it. In my spare time I learned to play billiards and snooker. I had never previously been in a billiards saloon. I quickly learned the game and became fairly good at it, finding it very relaxing and beating most opponents.

We settled in the huts in the same hut parties as before, and in the same platoons and the two Companies but to our surprise and satisfaction we now had to be "fell in" and paraded as "Flights" and "Sections". My address in September 1917 became: No 83445. Boy, J. Ross. "M" Lines. Hut number 31. Number 1 Flight. "G" Section. SOTT Halton Camp. North. Royal Flying Corps. Buckinghamshire. A change from the Army terms.

We cleaned our huts and the new utensils, scraping the wood handles, etc, with broken glass as we did previously and performed the same practice of filling our palliasse and pillow with plenty of straw.

The daily routine was as usual. By now we were becoming very proficient at drill and felt superior to the new intakes entering Halton.

Then came the dental parade, I had to have one tooth out, one to be filled. The dentist had his "surgery" in a bell tent. With the assistance of two male dental orderlies at the ready with the tools prepared, the reluctant customers were paraded for the ordeal.

The "chair" looked a second-hand contraption. Our names were checked, and we were told to "Sit down". A sheet was placed around your neck as in the barber's chair by a swift curl and shake by an eager orderly. A jab in the gum by the dentist with cocaine – and the tooth was out before you could say "Oh!" and out in to the sunshine you went. The next boy's name was called as you left the chair. The filling was worse, the drill was worked by one orderly pedalling the machinery like an old treadle sewing machine. With a grunt and a groan, and a squeak that was in definite contest with the "Hoos" and "Haas" of the suffering patient, and, I imagined, music in the ears of the machinist working the treadle. When the filling was completed your name was ticked by the orderly, meaning (from his parrot-looking features) "Operation completed". Needless to say, my filling came out at a later date when chewing gum one night on guard duty. It remained like that for a long time.

On Thursday October 18, 1917, we Boy Lance-Corporals were moved from our own huts and marched to the section of the camp where new intakes had arrived. Each one of us, with a shining stripe on our sleeves was placed in charge of a hut full of recruits who had just been kitted up. My bedding and kit was brought to the hut.

I was furious when I entered my hut at the sight of these young civilians milling about with no idea of orderliness or discipline. The fact of leaving my old hut pals did not help matters. I admit that I suddenly became what would be called today a teenage rebel. Whilst inwardly fuming I got down to my duties and studies when I could. I took charge of the new boys in no uncertain fashion. I soon had them sorted out, letting them understand I was in charge and standing no nonsense, obey all instructions as laid down, or, like a real NCO, "You'll be for it! Listen to me and I will help you."

I taught them how to fold blankets and kit, get properly dressed including the correct way to roll on the puttees. The orderliness and the cleanliness of the hut was insisted upon. Most of these boys saw the need of it and gave me some assistance in seeing that it was done. I spent a lot of time in helping them with their puttees. The news rapidly spread that a fee was payable for this service and these boys insisted upon giving me a few coppers in return for my good deed. This I accepted with great thanks as it helped me to save a bit and also pay for my billiard and snooker games with my old hut companions.

Being solely in charge as a boy yourself of a hutful of boy recruits was no easy matter, but I stuck to it and even got a recommendation and praise from Officers inspecting the huts. Actually I hated the job. For one thing, I was performing a duty which should be done by a trained disciplinarian, an NCO, with some measure of seniority and age, and I felt strongly that we Boy NCOs were being exploited.

What was worse, it was cramping my studies for the 2nd Class Army Certificate of Education. I knew that the examination would be taking place on November 5, 1917 by the Routine Orders. I had passed the preliminary examination on October 22, 1917, with nine out of ten in Arithmetic and eight out of ten in Composition, Dictation and Technical Terms and so I was a candidate for the examination.

On the morning of November 5, I paraded before the O/C this section with a request as a Boy Acting Lance-Corporal. I told this Officer that I wished to relinquish the rank of Lance-Corporal and to return to my hut on "M" lines. He tried to smooth me over, but I was rather stubborn and determined. I said the rank was only acting and I wished to relinquish it as it was my desire to take the 2nd Class examination and concentrate on of my studies for Air Mechanic in what spare time I had as I wanted to be a good airman, Sir. I waited stiffly at attention. The Officer whispered to the junior Officer at his side. His action seemed painful but favourable. He looked straight at me and said, "Quite all right. Granted. It will appear on the DROs as from today."

I saluted him smartly and marched off with a feeling of great relief. In the Orderly Room I told a rather bewildered Sergeant what had happened. I cut off the single stripe, gave it to him and sped away sharply to my old hut. When they came off the morning parade I told them the news and they gave a great cheer. Actually, we cheered everything we were pleased about for the other boy, even if he got a letter from a girl. My hut pals helped me to carry all my kit and bed back again from the recruits' hut. One of my pals who had been made the Senior Boy and hut lance-corporal greeted me. I told him, "You keep it. I don't want it." I know it pleased him when I told him I would offer him no opposition to his new promotion. I handed the stripes off my uniform to the hut Corporal. The Boy lance-corporals in charge of recruits' huts kept the address of the old hut and section and where we continued to we collected our mail. For me, it only lasted a fortnight and I was glad to give it up.

On that particular day, November 5, 1917, with other boys I sat the first official written examination given to the Royal Flying Corps Boys Section. It consisted of the syllabus as laid down by the Army Schools and on the rules in the book I had bought and studied: *For use of men in the Army studying for the 2nd Class Certificate.* The tests were on Army forms C 315 and C 2107. The subjects were Arithmetic, Composition, Writing from Dictation, a DR and CR account and Daily Messing Account. Time allowed for the examination was four and a quarter hours.

To me it was a fascinating day. I had worked hard and solved the arithmetical examples. Every scrap of paper was utilised by me to work out one problem or another and I felt confident, a feeling of assurance one needs for any examination.

I enjoyed the exam and afterwards spent the evening going over with other candidates the points and questions we could remember. We wanted to jump on to the more important examination later, which was the Military First Class Certificate of Education. We were informed that the results would not be declared for some weeks so I kept up my studies of the problems in the First Class "Handy Help" book I had bought. Classes were only held for the boys who had not attained the preliminary exam level for the 2nd Class Examination. It was only later that certain special classes were held for the First Class candidates.

I received a letter from home containing the usual postage stamps for my use. My father said there had been a Zeppelin over Sheffield district. It remained overhead for some time, moving away without dropping any bombs. I wrote back telling him that on Monday October 1, 1917 the camp lights were extinguished and we were in darkness for some time. We went out of our huts and watched the sky, as we could hear dull, heavy thuds in the distance. Just before 9 pm the sound of a heavy aeroplane or a Zeppelin over the camp moved in the direction of London. Then we saw shrapnel bursting in the sky. At the same time, the explosion of bombs could be heard amidst the sound of gunfire. On previous nights we had heard the sound of gunfire and the explosions of bombs, but this was the first time we had seen shrapnel burst in the air. We were captivated by this spectacular firework display.

Next morning we were told that a German "Gotha" (a twin engine bomber) had attacked London from the North. To me, I thought it sounded like the Zeppelin I heard when it attacked Sheffield.

No organised Air Raid Precautions operated at the camp. There were no shelters and no instructions on the taking of cover. I don't think anyone bothered; as long as the lights were out, that would have to be sufficient. With the boys, it was a laugh, another episode bringing us nearer to the thought of action against the enemy. Beforehand when we heard the thud of bombs in or around London we saw nothing and would say, "The so-and-sos are at it again."

I believe the directions were to the effect that as "soldiers" we were not expected to rush for cover and hide away from the enemy, but to train to stand and face the enemy. Often in the dark nights the camp lights would go out and nothing would happen.

These were the only precautions. Had the camp been attacked we should have had to remain in or by our huts with not even a rifle at our disposal. In fact, we never had any rifle drill or shooting knowledge. Often we slept until reveille, not aware that all the camp lights had been extinguished and the enemy were not so far away in the air. Sometimes, if not sleeping to well, one would hear the sound of aero engines above and dull thuds in the distance.

Quite a lot of American troops had arrived at one of the camps and we found them so different to our own soldiers. They wore the old Boy Scout type of hat, knee breeches and leggings and a few had puttees. We boys laughed at how peculiarly they spoke. We did not mix with them, as their camp was put "out of bounds" to us; a good thing too because they had such a lot of money to spend and our pay was so small. The comparison could have trouble. Their attitude was different to the British serviceman who had a degree of discipline which we understood. We were kept well apart, except when out on a pass for the evening when there were clashes and the MPs and SPs had to sort things out. Passes became harder to get and we were virtually confined to camp.

The results of the examination were posted up and I saw that I was one of the successful ones who had qualified, gaining the Military 2nd Class Certificate of Education. What a pleasant relief it was and we celebrated it in the camp YMCA amongst our pals.

The unfortunate ones had to go back to the class to prepare for it again, but I got down to studies for the Military First Class Examination, Part One. This examination is taken in two parts, Group 1 and Group 2. You had to pass Group 1 before you could take Group 2.

The schoolmaster was very pleased with us. We told him we were determined to prepare to take on further studies. The arithmetic was much more advanced. I bought two more of the "Handy Help" books. They were confined to the work required by the Army School Regulations for obtaining the First Class Certificate. One was for Arithmetic, the other *For Regimental Classes of Instruction and to candidates for the Military First Class Certificate of Education. Map reading.* I also bought a protractor as requested by the schoolmaster.

This book fascinated me. At school and at home I was good at geography, but this was better. It taught me how to "read" a map, the use of a compass, the scales of a map, hill features with contour lines, and the meaning of conventional signs. The questions mainly comprised of military purposes or for such as an aeroplane or aviator travelling or descending, etc. It was one thing that brought us much nearer the aspect of flying because our training was more for the Army than for an Air Service unit. We had no classes for any technical or flying instructions so far at Halton. On rare occasions, we had a talk on flying by some Officer Pilot or Observer for about half an hour, mainly on his experiences. One Officer Captain McGregor, an Observer's wing on his military tunic, who wore the kilt of his Scottish Regiment gave us an interesting talk.

I was enjoying the "plottings" and fixing the bearings on the scale drawings of the charts in the book, which stimulated my endeavours towards the observations from the air when the chance arose.

Quite a lot of new Officers (a few RFC) and disciplinary NCOs arrived at the camp as boy recruits came in. Some boys were on a longer regular service enlistment, others near to 18 years of age, for the DW period (duration of war) only. After a session of drill and PT, they were posted to man service and drafted.

We in "A" and "B" (Company) Flights were the pride of the camp. Our drill had become so sharp and efficient that we were being classed as good as the Guards Regiments. The link between the NCOs and our drill performance came to the automatic perfection of a clockwork precision. We took part in many "Wing" parades in which there seemed to be thousands of boys on parade. The boys' trumpet and part brass band played on all of these parades, large and small. "A" and "B" were always the leaders and set a good example to the others. They went on a big march in London with other units on a special ceremony. It was a camp and Boy Service honour I missed, since they selected a party of boys who all measured about the same height – and I was one of the few not quite tall enough.

Church parades were held in camp after a keen inspection when the boys' band led the way to the old tin church. Those not C of E who had no Chapel to attend – I was listed as "Congregationalist" – were often put on cookhouse fatigue, having huge buckets full of potatoes to peel, or other duties as required. We would watch the parade move off to the church. How well they marched with the band and looked splendid in the uniform of the Royal Flying Corps. We felt a tinge of pride in them, a much improved spectacle than the parades at Farnborough and Aldershot. The boys sang the popular hymns with lusty voices which sounded heavenly in the quiet distance.

Another great day arrived when we were granted our first Service leave of seven days. I went on my leave on Wednesday 5 to Tuesday December 11, 1917. The weather was cold and greatcoats were ordered to be worn.

I enjoyed this long leave as week-end leaves seemed so short and I was able to get about and visit relatives and friends. The train arrived in Sheffield after midnight and as there was no transport. The old electric tramcars did not run after a certain time of night. As taxis were not to be found I walked all the way from the station to home at Woodseats. After the drill, marching and PT at the camp I found no difficulty in the five-mile uphill walk.

All were in bed when I arrived in the early morning so I sat in the rear garden until I heard my father come downstairs. Our dog, a beauty of a Chow called Vic (for Victory), knew I was about, but he made no noise as I whispered to him. When my father heard me and opened the door I got a good reception from him, intermingled with a most excitable greeting from good old Vic, a fine dog who went with me on many country walks.

I settled in at home, my mother was delighted and saw to it that I had a good breakfast to start the day, and a good homely welcome. There were visits to the portrait studios in the city as people did not possess cameras. There were no such things as cine-cameras, tape recorders and anyone caught taking a photograph would have been suspected as a spy and given a painful reception by the public in the first place! There was the journey with parents, the family, the lot in some cases, to the city portrait studios. On your own, then in groups, you were positioned, with the fussy photographer delicately

*On overseas draft ex RFC Boys
Blandford 1919.
Top: Left to Right: Ross J., —, —.
Seated: Smith, Baylis, —.*

RFC boy J. Ross, on leave 1917.

positioning each person with such grace: this foot here, turn your body slightly this way, in a little, back there, stand still. You stood proudly with your parents, mother sitting, maybe a sister sitting, and so on beginning to feel cramped and slightly jaded. All would be staring at some object on the facing wall, drapery or item as directed by the cameraman. Now ready he would hide himself from all of us, tucked underneath yards of black cloth, feet mixed up with the tripod, a flash with, "Smile, please" and then the ultimate snap, a picture of glory. Then it was all over the finished result to be called for at a later date. They were scrutinised with severe criticism. The photographer, ever out for extra business, would suggest with polite emphasis the need of possessing enlargements and for only a little extra cost, coloured by hand painting. A surround could be bought mounted with flags of the Allies, "For King and Country", words of greeting, or poetic verse. Finally it was placed on show, placed in the family album or distributed to relatives, friends or other places.

One good feature was that our hair had been cut by the camp barber much better with a little more left on top.

The shortage of food at home made one wonder how the folk kept so fit. They had to manage with so little. The Ministry of Food introduced food control with ration books with coupons representing one week's ration of butcher's meat, cheese, lard, jam, margarine or butter, and tea. One coupon for each item and one or half a coupon to buy a meal outside. One egg when luckily obtained would be shared in a family for a taste. The Ministry issued recipes for various dishes to prepare by the manipulation of potatoes, tinned meat and concoctions made from turnips. A luxury or something "under the counter" was a windfall. I would not let my family send me food parcels, I knew we were better fed and they had difficulties getting food themselves. The local shop was your registered shop and when it opened the housework was abandoned to join in the rush.

On the domestic scene, in every house it was hard work. The kitchen had a range coal fire and large oven. With the iron kettle and iron pans in great use, it was used mostly for home baking. There were no electric work-saving appliances of every description as we use today. It was the washing tub and the "Dolly". Every bit of it was laborious, performed by manual hard work.

I enjoyed washing up and helping in the home, sleeping between sheets, dainty cups and saucers on a nice table-cloth, the real comforts of home. Also the pleasurable outings with family and friends and good conversation with the older generation. Leave came to the end and I was sorry to have to break up a glorious week, but I was in the forces and must not show my inner feelings. Our training gave us the discipline of being proud and loyal to the service, respecting your individual standards, not letting the family spoil you, be cheerful. I was ready to go back on duty. Preparing to leave I joked with my mother, laughing to keep her in good cheer, she gave no indication of what every mother felt when her son (and I was the third and youngest) was going "off to war" again. My father was at work so again my sister Clara accompanied me to the Sheffield "Victoria" Railway Station to see me off.

The train was late leaving Sheffield owing to fog delays were late on arrival at Aylesbury and had to wait nearly one hour for the train to Wendover, making us much later than expected.

It was very cold and we had a freezing tramp to the camp with a biting wind in our faces. It was turned "lights out" so we had to make our way to the huts in the darkness owing to an air raid alert, but according to my letter home I notice it says, "I was soon asleep, in camp, dreaming of the happy time I spent with you all." Evidently my bed had been prepared for me by my hut colleagues.

Some boys were absent from leave, a few brought in by police whilst one or two were never seen again whilst we were at Halton.

I learned that whilst on this leave volunteers were chosen to enter for remustering as Wireless Operators. A lot of the boys in our Flight, with others, had volunteered and were posted to Farnborough on the morning of Wednesday December 12, 1917. Some were from our hut and after cheerios, good-bye and "thumbs up" they went off to start the course. They had to be 17 years and 10 months or over. As I was only just 17 years of age I could not have joined them even if I wanted to.

Many made the grade and, I heard, were flying in some instances within a few months. Strange to relate I do not remember ever meeting any of them at later RAF stations. Some of the boys at that age who did not volunteer, and those who were turned 18 years of age, were eligible for man service. They were drafted away to service depots in order to be trained alongside the skilled Air Mechanic in whatever duties that they were classified as or capable of doing. They were transferred first to West Camp and placed on drafts to units as previously mentioned.

Some were remustered to trades they knew something about. One boy from out of our hut wrote to me after he had been posted overseas that he was a clerk in HQ Middle East, Cairo. Others entered the Transport Section, Carpenters, Gunnery, Instrument Repairing, Clerks, etc, while a few ultimately became Pilots and Observers, starting at NCO rank.

This served the RFC purpose because they had completed their recruit drill, PT and Military training, and proficient to a degree. It was sufficient to go directly to work training with competent men (all ranked as Air Mechanics) and learn the essential RFC requirements as and where they were needed. All were trained to the RFC method, even motor drivers from civilian driving were tested and made to start learning the RFC requirements.

This depleted our hut and Flight complements so a reshuffle of boys took place to complete the hut strength and Flights. This meant certain huts became empty and available for new entries. In hut parties we were moved from one hut to another. Our address changed to different huts on different lines became so mixed up that our mail was called out by a NCO from the mail bag. Each boy eagerly listened for his name and a letter passed over to him. A look of disappointment came when the bag was empty and there was nothing for you this time.

We were still in North camp. Some of us, the originals decided that if we did not get Christmas leave we would have a celebration on our own and we each put 2 shillings (10p) in a "club" to draw out at Christmas. With complete confidence upon my integrity they elected me the treasurer and custodian of the money which I held up to the day.

On Sunday December 23, 1917, a special parade was held after Church Parade. In Royal Flying Corps uniform and full muster, it was a sort of "Graduation Day" in its own miniature way, a forerunner of the large impressive ceremonial of the present-day graduation parades at Halton. We fortunate ones who had passed the examination and qualified for the 2nd Class Military Certificate of Education were called out of the ranks individually. Each boy, when called, marched out to the table on trestles where various Officers of the camp stood, saluted, and the camp Adjutant, Captain Routledge, handed to the boy his certificate of success. Those who had been posted had the certificate sent to their unit. The certificate is quite an official-looking document on Army form C 309 and awarded on the Authority of the Army Council on the recommendation of the Inspector of Army Schools, dated October 31, 1917.

This indicated once again the RFC had no method of its own laid down for Boy training and was relying upon the Army to provide it. In a way one could understand it because there had never been such a large concentration of boys in a camp before and no one had ever had the experience of handling such a large number of young lads. The Navy and Army boys were only in small number and units, but this was something new, something big. The Royal Flying Corps started this on a greater scale than they themselves could cope with. The late Lord Trenchard's idea (he was then Major-Gen Trenchard), was good and progressive, but no thought was given to any immediate technical training. This matter could have been organised by some of the many technical experts in the service and put into operation by lectures and classes in a simple way using the spare unserviceable aircraft, of which many were lying about at various aerodromes. We could have stripped these, rebuilt them over and over again in the old horse lines of sheds never used. Therefore, much of our time was wasted and our interest diminished by too much monotonous drill and military training.

I was proud of my attainment at that time and placed the certificate between my uniform on the shelf for safe keeping until I could get it home.

It was only two days to Christmas Day and as we could not have Christmas leave we were getting ready for our first Christmas in the forces, in camp and in the Boy Service.

It was strange that leave in those days, as in all three forces, was regarded by Officers and NCOs as a forbidden luxury. They always appeared reluctant to grant it and we were told: "What do you want leave for? You're in the Army now." To get a pass was an achievement. More often than not you would get abuse from certain NCOs if you dared ask for a pass. You were their property and you should not think of going home on leave. The very word was enough to send some NCOs into a state of frenzy.

It was a rumour that it was plotted to keep us all in camp for Christmas so as to harden us whilst away from our mothers at Christmas so that we should not be spoiled and return to camp with an acute longing for home. I had a feeling this could be true, but I did not make a fuss about it because I knew my brothers would not be on leave and I wanted to be a true "soldier" like them, at least in the spirit.

Christmas Day, Tuesday December 25, 1917, there were no parades, and we looked forward to it. Reveille came at the same time, but there was no NCO doing his rounds and tipping us out of bed. We got up and we tipped those sleeping out of bed, shouting, "Merry Christmas, you lazy so-and-so's!"

We paraded for breakfast at the usual time, a good idea to get it over and cleared up ready for the feast. We knew that preparations had been made to provide us with a good Christmas dinner and looked forward to it with no more parading.

As we "fell in" for the march to the Christmas dinner it did not seem to be a parade. Everyone was jolly and the NCOs marching us to the dining hall were relaxed enough to shake off the shackles of doom and resembled khaki-clad beardless Father Christmas's directing his flock to a feast of goodwill.

We sat down to a plain set of tables as usual and gossiped amongst ourselves in more excited terms than before. There were no great indulgences, no beer, wine or spirits or smoking. These were forbidden to boys although many were fully experienced in the art of drink and booze and, smoking.

Nevertheless, this being our first Christmas in the forces, and in camp, it was obvious to us we were going to enjoy it because it was different to the daily routine and there was a nice appetising smell about the place.

We had a good dinner of Xmas fare, with plenty for all. Each boy got a good equal share. What pleased us immensely was that the meals were served by the NCOs to each individual boy in true tradition of the Service, a real treat for us boys and something extraordinary to be waited upon by NCOs who rarely appeared any regard for us, but it all went off very well. Upon the call from the Orderly Officer "Any complaints?" he got the rare compliment of a huge cheer from all the boys. Some of the attending Officers looking on gave indications of being happy about the whole affair.

It was a nice day's holiday for us, with a good meal for all. Under the circumstances of wartime shortages a treat that we appreciated. In my letter home about it I wrote, "A jolly good time in the RFC Boys."

The few of us who had pooled 2 shillings (10p) for a bust-up had a share out from me, the treasurer. We had our celebration on the Christmas Eve in the evening in the YMCA. Tea, eggs and chips, a snooker game and billiards, which we enjoyed to the tunes of the day and Christmas carols played on the piano by one of the YMCA staff. A lot of boys had gone out on an evening pass, so we were not overcrowded, making it a very pleasant evening for us.

The YMCA were very good to us. I joined them and still have the small linen-backed New Testament Bible they gave me, presented by the Trinitarian Bible Society. The cover states "Army Testament".

The dark nights and winter had set in. At times the snow and bitterly cold winds approached from the Chiltern Hills. Sometimes the snow came thick and heavy with deep drifts. If possible we had to have the morning parade and inspection before it got too bad. This meant we had to march off and be organised into snow-clearing squads making pathways to Headquarters, ablutions and all other buildings of importance. Enjoying this better than the drill, we shovelled away, but upon orders "Get a move on!" we purposely made it as long a fatigue as we possibly could. We were practically snowed in on some occasions and had to trudge through it to the dining hall and other compelling places.

The hot combustion stoves were our greatest comfort and we saw that our coal and coke ration was up to strength. On fatigues near the

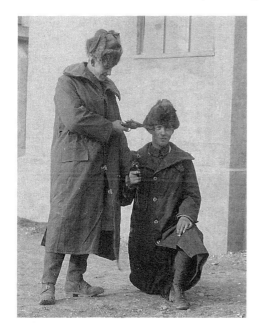

*Two ex RFC boys
(RAF) in Russian kit.
Blandford (Overseas)
RAF 1919.*

woods we collected cones fallen from the pine trees. These made excellent extra fuel and burned furiously, but we had to hide the additional collection so we buried them in holes dug under the hut. The woods were out of bounds, but we made it an organised "scrounge" even to taking a haversack and gathering them after dark. Opportunity came when a fatigue party got close enough to fill a few pockets and to stuff them down our trousers to the turn over at our knees above the top of the puttees. We fetched our fuel ration from the store, checked, and recorded it in a zinc tub, oval with a handle at both ends. When filled it took all the strength of the two boys to each tub to carry the load to the hut. Colleagues would meet them part way on the return journey to help because only two boys per hut, per tub were allowed to enter the fuel shed. But the most valuable contents demanded certain economical use to make sure that the contents lasted until the next issue.

The ablutions were a real problem. Being outside the huts in the lines, the tap was often frozen up and we had to break the ice to get at what little water was laying at the bottom of the long guttering which led away from the tap and the communal wash trough.

There was a rush from the huts after reveille in order to get a place. It was quite an ordeal out in the wintry cold with soap, towel and shaving kit to get washed and shaved ready for morning PT parade.

Although it was not permitted we used to put a fire bucket on top of the combustion stove and use what warm water we could get. We took our turn and. the boy who was in last had what was left of the murky water. We did not always manage this comfort because NCOs were vigilant, looking out for this sort of thing. We would get ours on the stove early, take it off and hide it under blankets well before reveille and with a face full of shaving soap had a shave, then a quick dab on the remaining portion, we would be partly ready before dashing out to finish off in the icy cold.

On many occasions the NCOs would find the warm water in the fire bucket and he would immediately pour the contents outside the hut and sling the bucket back inside the hut. If, as always was the case, no one admitted it, the hut complement would be reported and all would be punished with CB and extra drills, no passes, and extra vigilance by NCOs.

We were inspected every morning for shaving and general

Major-General Hugh Trenchard 1914-1918.
Later Lord Trenchard, CBE, OM, GCVO, DSO, DCL, LlD.
Kind permission "The Aeroplane" 3rd June, 1936.

cleanliness. I seemed to need a shave every day and got quite good with the issued cut-throat razor which had a fairly good edge on it. Some boys did not need to shave, but others had to shave by order of the inspecting Officer even if it was only like a bit of fluff on the chin.

There was only one type of safety razor I remember on sale at that time. This was a very expensive thing which was known as the "Durham Duplex" safety razor. You ran it up and down a special strop to sharpen it, turning over the edge at the bottom and top of each stroke.

Only one boy could afford it we called him a "softy" because a real fellow prided himself with his prowess with the use of a good cut-throat razor. Sheffield was renowned for its manufacture.

The use of a safety razor was frowned upon by Officers and NCOs. I imagined it was because it was not included in the issued kit and equipment and any civilian article was "taboo" or prohibited.

It was gruesome to see some of the boys cutting and chopping their faces at attempts to shave themselves, but they had to endure it. Some shaved their incompetent pals until such time as he mastered the art himself, no easy matter for some boys.

When the fire bucket luxury was not available, rows and rows of boys, many stripped to the waist with only a towel over the shoulder, broke the ice in the trough. To wash and shave was a shivering sight and a punishment itself, an ordeal we all had to endure. Yet what is worth repeating is that the spirit amongst the boys was to set a good example of "Let's get on with it" and "We can take it". If any boy did not keep himself clean he would be pounced upon and be forcibly washed and scrubbed by others which made him keep himself clean in the future. It was remarkable how one got used to adverse conditions and treated them as part of the ordinary routine.

Snowball fights between the huts were commonplace and it was great fun. You never knew where some of the enemy were, probably on top of the hut dropping snow down the chimney to put out the hut stove fire, but we'd have him down and his hut fire would suffer the same fate. A biff at the back of the neck indicated you were surrounded and these "battles" went on until both sides were exhausted. But they were enjoyed, and even on PT the instructors would organise a snowball fight between two parties. Starting at a point facing each other, we would see who could drive the opponents back and off the parade ground. This, before breakfast, gave us a good appetite for whatever was provided, and for most of us another cold wash.

At night we often got out of our beds after "lights out" and quietly put our blankets around the stove to warm on the forms and then we would "kip in" with our feet to the stove in a circle, all snuggled together. With a good fire burning, it was warm, cosy and comfortable, and we slept well.

Sometimes we would arrange this before "lights out" and sit in circles around the stove like Red Indians. Within the glow of the fire we told stories, tales and jokes, good, bad and indifferent. At times we laughed so heartily it brought along some patrolling NCO who broke up the party with "Get to your beds!" with a reprimand and "jankers" next morning.

Instructions were issued that the windows in these wooden huts be kept open all night, but because of the cold draughts practically all were closed by the boys. This was discovered and to make sure this order was carried out the top section of the window was removed on two windows, the second window from the door on one side and the second window from the other end of the hut diagonally across. The boys who unfortunately had their beds underneath each of these windows had a shocking time when it rained, hailed or snowed and the wind blew. Their bed got soaked, sometimes covered in snow . . . with them in it.

We tried covering the holes with a blanket or newspaper, but if the draught did not blow it in some NCO did. Finally we moved their beds after "lights out" forward in to the aisle. It was all we could do because NCO patrols were constantly on duty outside the huts to see everything was in order. Each morning we helped them to place their beds back to the original place. NCOs, upon morning rounds of "Wakey, wakey, rise and shine!" either did not notice or turned a blind eye to it.

With a few others I was one who, after sleeping well, regularly got up before reveille, but some were "out of this world" well after being tipped out of bed, and, even asleep on the floor with little more cover than nature's own endowments, and we had to force them awake.

The awful wintry weather and bad conditions began to tell upon some of the boys. The "sick parades" grew, with longer and longer queues with more "M" and "D" (medicine and duty) and No 9s. On Tuesday January 7, 1918, the whole camp was placed under isolation. It lasted one week.

The preliminary examination for the Military First Class Certificate of Education took place and I passed it on January 17, 1918. I also passed the other tests which were held on January 25 and 28, 1918 and with a few others was getting ready for the Military First Class Certificate of Education Examination.

Amongst the later arrivals of boys one died of meningitis. He was buried in a little cemetery near Aylesbury. It was our first Military funeral.

A large parade was formed. Lining up in our RFC best uniform, we all marched in funeral procession behind a Military band on loan from the Army. I believe it was the Northants Regiment. Having been drilled at slow marching we did the march for this boy with perfection. The band giving us perfect timing made many an onlooker gasp in their moment of respect as we passed along. This we noticed from the corner of our eyes as we marched. The "Last Post" was sounded by boys selected from the boys' trumpet band while a firing squad made up from men from the RFC trained in rifle drill (no doubt ex-Army men), fired a volley in salute at his graveside. I remember seeing his parents and family so upset at the graveside that I felt, as did many other boys, that if they knew some of the conditions we were experiencing here they would blame the camp for losing him.

In our young minds we were rather upset as it was the first time this had happened. We had never paraded on a Military funeral before, and with no rehearsal, no previous details, it seemed so strange, so formal and yet so authentic.

On the return to camp the band played breezy marches and we marched away from the cemetery along the road to the tune of "He's only one of many, he's dancing his heart away". This infuriated some of us – and what we mumbled to each other about it was not to the credit of the Services. Upon our dismissal we approached our hut Corporal about this shocking lack of taste in music and an insult to the tribute to a dead boy. He told us that it is customary on all parades marching away from a Military funeral to play the troops back to Headquarters with a gay and light-hearted step of music. He was sharp with us and said: "Remember this. For you it is over. Forget it and carry on with your duties." He told us "that is what the music intended" and that is the way the Army do it.

We were not very impressed by this, but after thought and discussion realised that amongst fighting men in the forces there could be some logic in it and to die in the service of your country was an honourable thing. If your name was "on it", or to be the unlucky one, it therefore was inevitable.

A small, dedicated class was formed to be schooled for the Part 1, Group 1 of the First Class Military Certificate of Education after having passed the preliminary tests. We sat the real examination on Friday 25, Monday 28 and Tuesday 29 January, 1918.

I was one of the lucky ones who passed this examination. We waited for further instructions about continuing for Part 2, the final phase of the First Class.

A lot of sickness persisted. On February 15, 1918, our hut was isolated with one boy going down with Scarlet Fever. During this period I reported sick for the first time since I enlisted eight months ago. Those who tried to pretend being sick by various devices hardly tricked the MO. It rarely "worked out" because sick parade was held before morning parade and so M and D did not excuse any parades.

I was visiting the toilet far too frequently, others in the hut were upset in the same manner and swore that they knew we all had been well "jolloped" and could taste it in the tea. Anyhow, being in isolation made our M and D from the Medical Officer rather stupid because with the hut being isolated we were all excused from duties. We soon got well again and the hut came out of isolation on Sunday March 3, 1918, but a boy went down with measles and the hut was isolated again, this time for 21 days. During this period Scarlet Fever broke out again and the hut was closed. We were moved on Thursday March 14, 1918 to a hut in "H" Section in North Camp.

The same need for isolation occurred in many other huts so many times we should have been thoroughly steamed and germ-free. Nevertheless, much sickness prevailed throughout the camp. Severe wintry conditions did not improve the state of things. Whilst rigorous training and a severely rough outdoor life may be necessary for military training, as a means of toughening up the individual, it could be undertaken and withstood by most adults, but not for boys still in the process of growing up when food was in short supply. This sort of spartan life was too severe for boys who, not being mature enough, had not the reserve of strength and bodily stamina to cope with such dreadful and out-of-date conditions.

The open life of outdoors and roughing may be a good thing and enjoyed by those accustomed to it or as a break in a regular routine, but there were too many of us, week in week out, confined to those old huts in bad conditions. These were aggravated by the continuous drill which had a lot of "bull" and boredom. There were hardly any social activities and no signs of any technical instruction or Flying Corps knowledge. To make us feel an integral part of the Flying Services, we felt that we were wasting our time and not learning a trade in the Service. This was not good for our mental approach and not any good for our bodily fitness.

Any picture of life we had was from our parents, relations and friends, who were all weary of this great war. The early silent films or the sparsely printed newspapers contained the latest war news. Young lads ran around the streets selling them, crying out "special!", "late war news!" for one old penny. Papers were gobbled up by eager and anxious readers. Sports news filled a little gap, or the boys' books or our father's old books, like *John Brown's School-days, Uncle Tom's Cabin, Treasure Island*, and so on; old magazines, comic papers, like *Comic Cuts, Magnet, Chips*, with Sexton Blake and Sherlock Holmes. *Dickens* and *Chatterbox* were mainly for the elite. The teachings of survival, current matters and worldly affairs was largely left to the valiant guidance of those stalwarts of the YMCA.

Youth organisation was practically non-existent: mass education was not understood and practised as it is today. Individual opportunities were very limited. We were restricted to Routine Orders, with a social life as we found it or made it, with no station activities, no dances, no society or club for sectional interests, only the canteen, out on a pass and the comradeship of hut colleagues this was the limit of service provisions.

The Royal Flying Corps being so young (only five years of age) and built up from scratch in the ruthlessness of war, was overwhelmed by so many boys being enlisted and suddenly crowded on to them that they found it not easy to cope with. No one seemed to produce any plan or indicate our future. When the sarcastic NCO predicted our career with a sneer as prospective Generals we did not realise that it was possible, yet it turned out to be. Some of the later recruits, on a longer engagement than ours, did attain high rank and some even senior rank.

When in isolation we had plenty of drill and, away from the other boys it was a continual bore; kit inspections galore all laid out to the official pattern, including knife, fork, spoon, razor, comb, toothbrush, mother's friend, latherbrush, bootbrush, button brush, button stick, holdall and so on with the remainder of the kit; medical inspection also very frequent.

Certain NCOs were getting intolerable. The outbursts about our parentage and relationships in such filthy language belonged to the gutter or compost heap rather than young boys, many of us from good, decent homes, with a strict respectful and unabusive upbringing.

We were always a "sloppy lot", always being reminded "If you broke your mother's heart, you won't break mine." "You there, you little worm, I've seen better things crawl out of cheese." These were a few of the ordinary cries, but some of the "cracks" at us were so obscene and personal, particularly about "heads up" or "stand at ease", or to "stand still". "You're like a . . . " could not be repeated in print.

It is remarkable what one can get accustomed to. Although we did not like it, we got to the state of detesting the very sight of some of the NCOs. The slightest hint of objecting to a command, or at the slightest cause, you would be "put on a charge". The offence on defaulters parade would be the indefensible charge of "inattention on parade" or "insubordination". We knew our elders were facing terrible conditions in France and elsewhere. Our families on the "Home Front" were also having a hard time so we felt it our duty to accept these circumstances.

The public and press were alarmed at the air raids getting worse, although the RFC was doing its best. We in the Boy Service were restless, a rumour started that we might be transferred to the Army at Salisbury Plain or Spittlegate. Arguments in Parliament clearly indicated that extra drive was needed. The man approached was outside Parliament a General who in the Boer War fought against us, but had recently beaten the Germans in East Africa. General J. C. Smuts was a genius of strategy who feared nobody, giving sound logic to his arguments. He took on the job of sorting out our air defence and RFC limitations. There had been growing talk of the need to combine the RFC and RNAS.

General Smuts did not waste time. Under his demanding influence the link came into operation. It came about with new regulations called the Air Forces (Constitution) Act 1917. Procedure was laid down for the conditions of transfer or attachment to the Air Force of all ranks from the Royal Naval Air Service and Royal Flying Corps on a day to be fixed by the Order in Council.

During March 1918 a pamphlet was issued to all ranks which gave the complete conditions of the transfer. This was the Air Force Memorandum Number One with procedure for the "Constitution of the Air Force". Any Officer or man may be transferred or attached to the new Air Force without his consent, with a provision that any person may, within three months of transfer or attachment give notice to his Commanding Officer that he does not desire to be so transferred or attached. The transfer applies to Boys.

The Boys' rate of pay was to be increased to five shillings per week. The rates for Officers, NCOs and Men were listed in many, and new, classifications.

The classifications cut out many Naval Officer ranks, absorbing them into Military from Generals to 2nd Lieutenant, Probationer. The ranks from the Warrant Officer down, with trades, were listed separately, with a mixture, mainly the RFC, with appropriate RNAS included.

The day fixed was April 1, 1918. The link-up became a jumbled affair when working together started.

Transfer was drawn up with the pay being adjusted for certain activities, conditions and allowances. For Officers the top General's pay was £2,000 per year. The pay of the 2nd Lieutenant 10s per day, 8s per day (Flying) extra, Probationer (Flying) 4s per day.

The NCOs and other ranks pay structure is drawn up in three classified branches, briefly detailed as follows:

Daily Rates of Pay:

Technical	*Non Technical*	*Clerks & Storekeepers*
Top Chief	Sgt-Major	Master Clerk 6/9
Master Mechanic 12s	1st Class 7s	Flight Clerk 5/6
Master Mechanic 11s	2nd Class 6/6	Sergeant Clerk 4/9
Sergeant Mechanic	Flight Sergeant	Clerk 1st 3s
6s to 7s	3s to 4/4	2nd 2s
Air Mechanics	Military to	3rd 1/6
1st 4s to 5s	Private	
2nd 3s to 3/6	rank up	
3rd 2s	1st to 2s	
	2nd 1/6	

All Boys – Commencing rate of pay, 1s.

With the war still in progress not much change took place, the pursuit of the war being dominant. The first to be seen were the young Officers, mainly pilots from the flying training establishments in the new Khaki Royal Air Force outfit, just commissioned.

The other ranks carried on as usual. The classification of trades was so immense with pages of them, that this book does not intend to list them. When the war was over a slow, gradual acceptance of the transformation took place.

On a parade we were told that some of us would be moved to an RNAS Boys' camp at Cranwell in Lincolnshire and an advance party would proceed on Monday April 1, 1918. This draft would be the first unit of the Royal Flying Corps to join up with the Royal Naval Air Service upon the foundation of the new Royal Air Force. I was one of the selected party. We were thrilled at the opportunity to get some technical training as we felt we had been "let down" by the RFC. For a year was taken out of our young life by drill and more drill, yet calling hope" for us, we were feeling great. One good feature about it was that the rigours of Halton had built us into a strong and sturdy bunch of youths. We were ready to go.

Some "words of wisdom" from NCOs remembered by ex-Boys are:

Sgt – "Sweep this 'ere floor out of the doorway."

Sgt – "Get these windows open; it stinks when I come in."

Sgt – "You'll be on a charge if a full fire bucket is empty."

Sgt – "Any lights on after 'lights out' – and you'll be 'Done in a flash'."

Sgt – "When going on a pass hand it to the NCO at the guard-room. He will look at it – then stamp on it."

Cpl – " 'As you were' means 'Just as you was before you were'."

Cpl – "All boys as is short of deficiencies and hasn't got them, 'Fall in' outside and go and get them."

Cpl at lecture – "A food complained about may be taken by the Orderly Officer and stirred up at the cookhouse."

Cpl – "Boys not issued with puttees don't put them on."

Cpl – "The command 'About turn' means you come back from where you was going to."

Cpl at Aldershot baths. Small party – "When dressed, 'Fall in' at the deep end."

Cpl ticking off Boy – "When I'm talking to you, look me straight in the face, and you won't like it."

PART TWO

CHAPTER FIVE

TO CRANWELL, A SHIP, HMS *DAEDALUS*. FOUNDATION OF THE AIR FORCE BY RFC AND RNAS BOYS. TECHNICAL TRAINING BEGINS. CRANWELL RAILWAY. INSPECTION BY HM KING GEORGE V. CAPTAIN PRINCE ALBERT OC BOYS WING. "LIGHTER-THAN-AIR". BOYS DEMONSTRATE FOR LEAVE. MIXTURE OF UNIFORMS AND RANKS. NEW RANKS.

We anxiously awaited instructions about our move and it appeared on orders with a new date fixed. On the morning of Saturday April 6, 1918, we left Halton camp and were put on a train at Wendover to proceed to Sleaford.

It was a rather subdued journey. Following the boring drill and bad conditions we were leaving behind us, it presented a great opportunity for us.

We were not a large party. We knew that this advance party was to perform and celebrate the official merger of the RNAS and RFC in some form or other and on a Naval Air Station, but we had no instructions as to *how* it was to take place.

Upon arrival at the entrance to the Cranwell Air Station we were lined up (after disembarking from lorries) two deep. RNAS Boys were in the front rank, and we RFC Boys the rear rank. A strict inspection, and we "formed fours" and marched off side by side, RNAS Boys in Naval Blue and RFC Boys in the RFC Khaki walking out uniform. The two contrasted in a most conspicuous way, but looked impressive, the very picture that was it intended, a real "link up" indeed. The Officers and NCOs leading us were paired together in RNAS and RFC uniforms.

With the Cranwell Station Band leading, we marched as one unit into the station. A flag was hoisted up inside the entrance and we were informed later that it was the new Air Force Ensign.

Marching inside to the station Headquarters we heard quite a number of sneers and very uncomplimentary remarks about the RFC from the RNAS men. They did not seem to relish the thought of the RFC coming to their station, but we marched in with our usual extra smartness, arms swinging and heads high, which we felt was showing the RNAS boys and men watching us that we were a much better trained lot and could show them a thing or two at drill, if nothing else. This was true because we knew later that the RNAS admitted it.

After inspection outside the Cranwell station Headquarters by Senior Officers, who scrutinised us with eagle eyes, they gave us a pep talk about the traditions of the station and the prospects for the new Air Force. We were made to understand that this parade was the first official parade joining the two Services together and would go down in history as the foundation of the new Air Force.

We were then marched off to our part of the station to the accompaniment of cat-calls and boos from distant RNAS men. This was the first encounter of many incidents that followed, proving there was a deep feeling of jealousy and animosity between the two rival Services. This took some time to iron out and heal. Ultimately we became closely knit as one Service in the supreme Air Force of the world.

A section of the station, newly built and known as East Camp, was placed at our disposal and for accommodating the arrivals who followed us from Halton. Known as the "Boys Wing East Camp", Cranwell, it was mainly composed of Royal Flying Corps Boys.

We few boys strolled around the dormitories and were impressed. Much to our delight we saw that instead of old army huts our billets were in two-storey buildings of brick called "dormitories". These were a real home from home. They were nicely heated, warm and comfortable rooms with plenty of space. The beds were on three boards with trestles much higher than at Halton (about two feet), strong, and not a straw-filled palliasse but three "biscuits", a locker each, flush lavatories, perfect ablutions with hot and cold water.

Actually I felt that it was good to be spoiled although we may have become too soft for the future rigours of overseas service. Anyhow, this was lovely and we settled in to the comfort and joy of first-class quarters – at a real air station with aircraft and a lot of flying taking place.

The dormitory I was placed in gave me the address of ZI Dormitory, RAF Training Establishment, Boys Section, East Barracks, Cranwell, Lincs.

These dormitories were newly built, much better than those the men occupied on the station. They were in army pattern wooden huts, but they were far better equipped than our old wooden huts at Halton.

Already we were part of the Army, even in the RFC, with our military training. Now we were mixed up with the Navy with Officers, NCOs and men with their own traditional ideas, routine and uniforms. The Naval method of salute being different; a right confusing mixture for the RFC Boys. We were puzzled by the RNAS terms, ranks, methods of routine and orders.

There were Chief Petty Officers, Petty Officers, Barrack Masters, Gun Layers, Master-at-Arms, Leading Ratings and so on, but we gradually got to know the respective equivalent ranks and meanings and we settled down on this "posh" RNAS now RAF Station.

There were a large number of young women in the WRNS "Wrens", units of the Naval Sections belonging to the RNAS. Later they were known as the WRAF, "Women's Royal Air Force", linking up with the few women in the RFC who were known as "Lady workers of the RFC". They mainly drove the motor cars of the high ranking RFC Officers.

Some RFC stations employed local females for work, such as sailmakers, repairing wing fabrics or other work. They were not recruited and did no service duties.

In addition to the large flying training section and the workshops, at the end of the aerodrome, and on its own, was the "Lighter-than-Air" section with the airships, containing its own gas manufacturing plant. It was known as the Airship Wing

Cranwell was a large station with good amenities we had never previously experienced. It had a gymnasium which was used every Friday night for music or a dance hall with the station dance band playing. It was also used as a theatre when the station concert party and drama group gave some excellent shows while the station band gave musical performances which I thoroughly enjoyed.

Chaplain of the station, a Naval Officer, the Rev F. W. R. Metcalf, MA, RN, was very popular and did good work amongst the boys. He used to tell us good stories of the sea, having had a vast experience on Naval ships and action all over the world, being in the Battle of Jutland in May 1916. In addition, he was a fully qualified Naval instructor.

The station had its own service postmen, three of them; Tom, Ernie and Bill. The hospital was known as the "Sick Bay", Cookhouse "The Galley", the floors were "Decks" and so on, as in the Navy.

There was a good station monthly magazine, *The Piloteer*, edited by 2nd Clerk Seymour, W. K., RNAS. Extracts from this magazine have helped me recall events and confirm the accuracy about the RFC, and the few RNAS boys and about Cranwell itself during our training.

One unusual addition to the station was its own light steam narrow gauge railway which ran between the station and Sleaford. Its real name was the "Cranwell Railway", RN. It had other names such as the "Cranwell Express" and the "Camp Crawler". The track was not levelled by any excavation or banking. It covered the ground and route across country in its natural way down in the hollows and over the bumps, it could be very uncomfortable.

Boys were not permitted to use this train, but we did when we could manage it. We were nearly always refused a ticket, and repeatedly being "chucked off" by adults who discovered us whilst on the journey.

I still have in my possession ticket Number 23679 printed "Cranwell Railway, RN MEN", with a red line down the middle.

The steam locomotive was made by Ephraim Bletcher. The small carriages were so delapidated by age and use that the upholstery and netting in the coaches were beyond repair. It was "rolling stock" all right and the springs so useless that it was said that all the shock was absorbed by the passengers. The old engine, badly overworked, puffed and puffed along its jangling journey often having to rest, in order to raise more steam, often carrying much more than its proper load.

The food was far better than at Halton and the "bull" a very queer mixture, mostly a lot of Navy and a certain amount of Army. We could see the strain on NCOs trying to cope and worked to the limit with this sudden amalgamation of the three services the Navy, Army and RFC.

As was only natural the station was run on the routine and discipline of the Navy. It was strange and laughable to us when we knew that it was called a ship, and was known, from the start in 1915, as HMS *Daedalus*, by some, incorrectly, as HMS *Cranwell*.

We had to get used to a lot of Naval terms and methods. One thing we did not like and take kindly to was to "scrub decks". On this duty we had to roll our slacks up over the knees and scrub the floor of any room as detailed.

Going off the station on a pass, was known as "went ashore" and many a naval man said he was "going ashore" when much to our amusement he was on a bicycle.

The station soon got down to a more organised method for to our training. Here was the scope for dealing with it in a practical way.

Some workshops were put at our disposal and under the instruction of Naval mechanics we started on Tuesday April 9, 1918, in the class for "filing" pieces of steel so as to fit together each piece in to a certain shaped design. It was interesting and I found it came easy to me. The instructor was pleased with my work and I got good marks.

About this time the station was experiencing a lot of extra spit and polish and acute scrutinisation by senior Officers which gave indication of some big event pending. We heard that there was to be a very important visitor and inspection, and, on Thursday April 11, 1918, the station was visited by HM King George V. We boys were formed up on the parade ground and inspected by His Majesty. He seemed very pleased with our turn-out and bearing and especially we boys in the uniform of the Royal Flying Corps.

The inspection over, he came in to the workshops and inspected us doing our work training with the file, scriber, rulers and emery cloth, etc. In our fresh, clean, new overalls we must have given His Majesty a good impression because he said so and how pleased he was to see such a fine body of young apprentices. We felt it to be true, especially after the Officers told us so on the following parade.

A son of HM King George V was posted to Cranwell, Captain Prince Albert. He became the Officer in Charge of our Boys Wing known as the "Boys Wing, Number 4 Squadron. West Camp, Cranwell". After the abdication of King Edward VIII, Prince Albert was crowned King George VI.

Prince Albert brought to Cranwell his ADC, Major Greig, MVO. Both were keen tennis players.

Prince Albert was wearing Naval uniform, having been in the Battle of Jutland as a Midshipman, then invalided by severe illness and transferred to RNAS, RAF.

Whilst at Cranwell he went through a course of flying training, usually on an Avro 504 K.

At a later date after the signing of the Armistice Prince Albert visited the RAF in the Army of Occupation touring the Royal Air Force establishments.

When we were marched before him in the Boys Wing orderly room, Cranwell, the defaulter found him sitting at his table surrounded by senior Officers. He would listen to the "charge" read out to him. The defaulter would be given the punishment as prompted by these Officers. With a stammer he had difficulty with the sentence given. We defaulters did not realise at the time that we had the honour to be punished by our future King.

Most boys did not care because you were a very lucky boy to escape being put "on a charge" for some silly little "offence". With others I was put on a "charge" for a trifling "offence" such as inattention on a parade, talking in the ranks, failing to salute an Officer, answering back a NCO when asked a question.

As it was with many of the boys, we were getting restless. We wanted to work on aeroplanes and to fly, the purpose for which we had volunteered and enlisted and yet this objective seemed far, far away.

The "Lighter-than-Air" section had many "Blimps", a small Naval Airship with a certain kind of small fuselage hanging underneath it and powered by a single engine with a crew of two or three. Then there was the huge Zeppelin, the R25. We always got a huge thrill watching it climbing up and hearing the roar of its engine.

The boys were marched as a "wing" to this "Lighter-than-Air" Section and taken in to the sheds after a clearance for matches and instruction on safety precautions, and managing to fall over the large hoses stretching all over the floor, carrying gas to the "envelopes" (gas bags). Outside on the aerodrome we were instructed how to work in teams under the direction of a Naval CPO and the POs in the handling of the Zeppelin' marching it in or out of the long shed and releasing it; also how to grasp it for anchorage by the handling guys when it approached to land. This was done first by working with an imitation airship later we performed with the real thing.

When one realises that a handling party required about 200 people to grapple with a Zeppelin (there were no mooring masts in those days, one can imagine how they rubbed their hands in glee at the opportunity of using the Boys Wing for this purpose.

Whilst it was interesting and I rather enjoyed myself at being one of the party there came a time when we were used by the "Airships" to an unfair degree, and you will read why later.

We were split up into groups of 20 to 30 boys, each group to its own Naval "Airships" NCOs with its own particular job to do. As much as was possible you stuck to the same NCO and duty. The main groups handled the nose guys, the rear guys and the gondolas and were mainly men of the Airships section.

The group I was in was a side group on the port side. We held a rope as in a tug-o-war team. Upon the orders of the NCO, we had to pull on to it or just hold it, as the case may be, upon release or anchorage, or marching the airship from or to a shed.

The NCO, being No 1 on the rope, would hook (or unhook) our rope as we listened to the orders given by the Officer Commanding for that particular manoeuvre.

When marching the airship out of the shed the huge team worked under the orders and instructions of the Officer Commanding the Airships, Lt Col Fletcher, AFC, who gave us our instructions by shouting through a megaphone.

Upon arrival on the aerodrome position for the ascend the orders would be taken over by the Officer in command of the airship from the front gondola, again by megaphone. Upon take off we all released the airship; it would rise, put its nose to the sky, the engine would throttle up and we underneath, more so those under the rear end, received an unwelcomed shower of stinking water mixed with sand as it threw out ballast. The same performance could happen when ballast ejection took place during the landing and the rear group then received the baptism.

The operation of getting the airship out of its hangar was not so difficult as getting it back into the hangar. If the weather was too bad it cancelled out the flying, but once it was out and the weather deteriorated upon its return we had a hectic time.

At any time we were liable to be assembled on parade at the double, leave whatever we were doing and following a roll call be marched away and across the aerodrome to the Airships Section. We knew it was to get the Zeppelin out and in the air or it was on its homeward journey.

Coming in could be tricky. Difficult situations often arose. We would be assembled in our respective positions, the whole party covering a large area of the airfield in the shape of an arrow head, and wait. In due course we would see it approaching and it would steer to the bottom end of the V-shaped mass of ground handlers with nose to the wind and lower itself in order to be grabbed by all on the ground by the guy ropes hanging from it. If all went well it was held fast by everybody on his respective position and marched off to the hangar, but not always did it work out right. Sometimes it would suddenly lift before all of us had grasped it and those holding on to the gondolas had quickly to decide whether to hold or jump away.

If the odd ones held on too long they could be quickly lifted, hanging on to the gondola rails at a considerable height and with serious injury they fell to the ground. This happened more than once with fatal results.

If the airship overshot the landing party it would rise and fly away in a huge semi-circle for miles in order to make another approach. This could take as much as one hour before it reached us again. We would grapple with it and haul it off, marching it back to its hangar and depositing it with a none to fond farewell if a late afternoon had been spoiled, and being hungry and thirsty after the long delay.

We always had to be careful with it because of the inflammable gas. Inside the hangar it had to be safely positioned and moored, but after our implicit team training and instructions we did the handling very well.

One can understand the Germans in 1914-1918 calling the landing troops the "Ground acrobats".

Another annoyance occurred when the Zeppelin returned to Cranwell on Saturday afternoon and one can imagine what the boys said when Saturday afternoon was spent as handling party rather than relaxing or going out on a pass and we cursed it on many Saturdays.

Another aggravating event was that when hoping to pass through the guard at the gate for a afternoon out at Sleaford or any other place, the guard, for the slightest reason, trump up some fault in front of the mirror and would order you aside "Over there, you!" They soon had enough men and boys to form a fatigue party.

We would be ordered on to a waiting lorry, and as the lorries filled we knew our fate.Our name and number taken so there was no escape and we were trundled up to the "Lighter-than-Air" section. Railway wagons loaded with coal were to be emptied and delivered to the airship's own gas plant. Names and numbers checked, overalls issued, and we had to unload the coal from the wagons into the lorries and then unload the coal at the storage point.

As one of the selected, I vividly remember being bare to the waist, sweating in the sunshine, shovelling coal from these wagons, black as a collier, swearing and cursing as only a disgruntled serviceman knows how. Sometimes four or five of us to a wagon and lorry, a rotten job; we were all tired out after this hard work which even a shower-bath provided made us feel no better. After all, it had ruined – our afternoon and evening out.

There was no wonder we disappeared out of the way on Saturday afternoon, waiting until it was all clear, and I only went out on the rare occasion.

I used to go to the flight sheds which would be closed for the afternoon and sit on the base of one of the stanchions and read a book and watch what flying might be taking place. I enjoyed a nice quiet afternoon.

There was always a rush to get off the station after lunch on Saturdays, so the guard had no difficulty in selecting enough boys and a few men for the coal fatigue.

This and the extra Naval "bull" did not please us and it was felt, that after the visit and inspection by HM The King, it was time we had some leave. Whilst we made requests about it and applied for it in the proper manner, it was always refused and appeared not even to be considered.

NCOs and men seemed to get plenty of "shore leave", but the boys could only muster a pass out ticket. These were refused after so many had been issued. We began to suspect a sort of 'bumbledom' oppression towards us.

Throughout the dormitories there was a grumbling and grousing and the boys were beginning to gather in groups and discuss the matter.

Often a meeting would be called around one boy's bed and news would quickly travel, trouble was brewing. We were getting in to one solid opinion and the anger grew to such an extent that, apart from the bit of a "filing" course, we were being used for all sort of fatigue duties like "Maids of all work" and the men had week-end galore, the trouble reached explosive point.

On the evening of Thursday May 2, 1918, we boys had a huge meeting. We quickly gathered in one large assembly. We decided to show them that we were getting "fed up" with not getting any leave and we should let them know it.

We tried to choose a spokesman but this was shouted down by many of the boys who called out, "Let us all go," "They will victimise a few," "They can't do much if we all go," "What about it, lads?" "Let's have a riot." In one huge surge we set off, calling out, "No damage, lads," "Make a noise, all shout for leave," "Go for the Headquarters and then the Officers quarters."

We knew the Prince was on the station and this would impress him, certainly get to his notice and let him see how we felt about things.

In our hundreds we stormed on to the Headquarters shouting: "We want leave! We want leave!" Then in one huge flock, we quickly stormed on to the Officers quarters. We had taken the station by a surprise attack, and before the guards and the few NCOs, could do anything. Frightened too by our numbers and show of determination, we shouted with all our might and with tremendous voice at the Officers quarters the same words, "WE WANT LEAVE! WE WANT LEAVE!"

This drowned and swamped all the attempts by the NCOs to stop us. Too late. There were too many of us, closely packed together.

Naval Petty Officers and NCOs were running about like scalded cats. We had got them hopping on one leg – and they knew it.

The determination of the boys gave every indication of a rowdy riot as we called it, today I suppose a "demonstration", but we meant it and the whole situation looked ugly. Even at this display of a mass demonstration there was a certain amount of discipline shown by the boys within the infringement of behaviour. The speed and efficient number in which it was carried out without any bad language or violence gave a good indication of massed training with unity of purpose.

In the turmoil I and many others did not see who came out of the Officers quarters and Mess, but a number of them came out and they yelled at us: "You will get leave. We promise you that." "Go back to your dormitories quietly." "Settle down." "Behave yourselves, and you will get leave."

We had launched this operation at the appropriate time and with such vocal emphasis upon the station that the Officers quickly decided the best action to take was to make clearly the promise of leave in order to get us peacefully back to our dormitories and it worked.

We shouted "Agreed, Agreed!" and passed the word along, "Get back, lads, get back! Keep in order!" We proceeded as we had come, in one huge mass back to our dormitories, happy but making no further disturbance. We awaited the next move, keeping in small groups and moving shrewdly amongst ourselves, talking in undertones, laughing at it, joking about the guardroom and its size. Some even predicted violence if any attempt was made to march any of us off to the guard-room.

There certainly was a quietness undertones determination in all the dormitories where we gathered that I think it all measured up to a point where the POs and NCOs could see we really meant it and trouble was still fermenting. This was no doubt passed on to the Officers because POs and NCOs came in and cautiously moved amongst us and to our utter amazement appeared to want to be nice and respectful to us.

We were a bit doubtful about this attitude, but listened to them at first with a dumb insolence. They took no action, but were sure to let us know that the Officers were going to see about arranging leave for us because "The Prince says so" and we will be told so tomorrow and must wait until the morning parade, and so, "Settle down, lads," "Settle down," "No trouble now," "Settle down." Instead of "'Ere you," this sounded different, more respectful, more polite, even requesting. We could feel and sense a margin of achievement for us.

The air seemed to be getting pure, away from the pollution from certain Naval and Military NCOs who, in combination, always breathed fire and brimstone at us. This time the turbulent waters of the ship HMS *Daedalus* were calmed by words of a comforting nature soothed to soften the tormented hearts of the RFC Boys Section.

Whether this episode went down in history or not, it was probably the first and nearest attempt at a small-scale mutiny in the Royal Flying Corps, Royal Air Force, Cranwell, a Royal Naval Air Station, by RFC Boys.

The night was peaceful and quiet and we "fell in" on morning parade, but it was not so noisy with orders and commands. It had a sharpness, but a quieter tone of respectability about it. It was obvious to us that the Officers and NCOs had arranged not to provoke us, if possible, to prevent trouble with us.

We were immediately informed that HRH Prince Albert had granted leave to all the Boys Wing. It would be for seven days. Orders would be issued to this effect.

The boys were all models of correct behaviour on parade. Everyone from the OC parade downwards could be proved to have indicated in some way a deep sense of relief and mild satisfaction that the trouble was over. No names were taken. Whilst we were reminded that what occurred last night was prejudicial to good order and could be a punishable offence, we expected some sort of "ticking off". I am sure that the slight grin on our faces gave some indication to the Officers that we did not bear any malice after all and the rollicking we got was expected. We gave full acknowledgement in response upon the parade dismissal of laudable cheers from all the boys.

I must add – and it is true – that this demonstration was not against the service, its discipline or any person. It was only for some leave, a break, or as one may say, a holiday away from the tensions on the station and fairness of leave availability between the men and us. Our patriotism and our loyalty to the RFC and new RAF was never in question.

It made those in charge and other responsible persons realise that in dealing with boys on a large scale like this requires a deeper sense of justice on simple human relationships. That was proved and many lessons were learned, gained the hard way by trial and error, analysed and resolved into practice and improved. Many recreational activities were devoloped over the years at Halton Apprentices School, solely concerned in training and guiding a Boy Service for future RAF requirements under the training of specially selected Officers, NCOs, Technicians and Instructors, a splendid achievement which has provided the Royal Air Force with airmen of all ranks which are second to none in the world.

There are other establishments of training I have not mentioned, but nevertheless worthy of the highest praise.

The boys all took leave on free passes arranged in parties. I went home on leave for seven days from Tuesday May 7 to Tuesday May 14, 1918.

It was a wonderful leave with nice weather and I enjoyed it. I went out and about very proud in my Royal Flying Corps uniform. We had helped to handle the huge airships, plenty of flying training to see and be near to, also having some technical training in the workshops. All of this made us feel we were part of, and really belonged to, the Royal Flying Corps.

One of my sisters, Edith, was one of my favourite visits, living in Darnall, Sheffield. Her husband was working his own business. She had good neighbours. One was always interested to hear news about me in the Royal Flying Corps. They were nice people called Hoyland. I always popped in to see them. They had a family of four. One son was serving in the Machine Gun Corps, the other two, with their father, were working on special war work of which the various heavy and light industries which Sheffield produced was exceptionally important to the war demands. The youngest was a girl called Lucy, three years younger than I. Being a member of the local chapel and its institute, she was busy with the other young people in its many activities. My sister gave this family a very great compliment often reading my letters to them.

This had been a good leave. My ration book issued at Cranwell helped my mother with my share of food every bit was welcomed. I put in plenty of work on my father's large allotment, getting the soil ready to produce the much needed vegetables, he also had eggs from his fowls.

Cranwell was not a long way from Sheffield. We grouped in small parties as we picked up boys on the journey, a local train of the Great Central Railway, changing trains, I believe, at Retford. We soon settled down and technical training became our great objective.

At this time, in May, in addition to the Prince, we had a new Commanding Officer appointed to the Cranwell Boys Wing, a Lt-Col A. C. Barnby. He had served in the Royal Marine Light Infantry. He joined the Naval Wing of the Royal Flying Corps in June 1913. Later he served in the Royal Naval Air Service, a pilot who had seen much service on land, sea and air. He was very keen and a capable sportsman, taking part in the sporting activities on the station. He was a good CO and although we somewhat feared him, we had a great respect for him. What was more, he was a pilot. Prince Albert remained on his staff in charge of his senior administrators.

We were split into Squadrons. I was in "A" (sometimes called Number 1). Our officer commanding was Captain White, MC, who had been "B" Company OC at Halton, Captain Macmillan and another Officer. Flt Sgt Parkinson was promoted and became our "A" Squadron Regimental Sergeant-Major. Flt Sgt Freeman and Sgt Spavin also from Halton were in our Squadron. Also from Halton, Flt Sgt Regan and Flt Sgt Fallon, now promoted to Sgt-Major. Other junior NCOs were from Halton and one, now promoted to Flight Sergeant, Flt Sgt Mullarkey, was a prominent figure on the parade ground as a drill NCO with his fearsome voice, stick under his left armpit, his long thin legs, in breeches and puttees, standing erect in the largest pair of boots ever manufactured, much to our amusement and his dismay, yet ever popular, to the men of the RNAS. We remembered him at Halton.

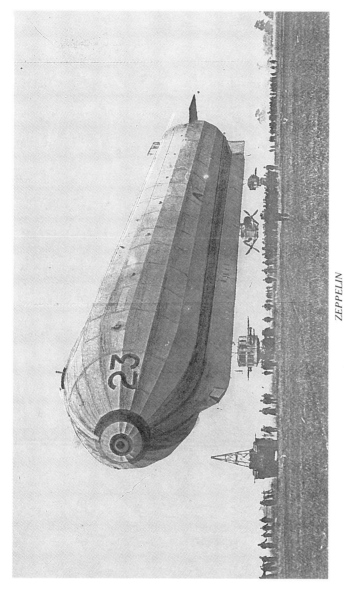

ZEPPELIN
British built rigid airship R23
Sister airship to the R25 stationed at Cranwell RNAS. 1917-1918. RAF
By kind courtesy of Chaz Bowyer collection

Further intakes from the RFC Boys from Halton arrived in great numbers. As the RNAS Boys were only few in numbers, East Camp, Cranwell, looked like an RFC Boys camp.

The station Commander at this time at Cranwell was Colonel R. A. Talbot, CBE, a Naval Officer, RNAS who was very popular with the Naval ranks. The GOC No 12 Group was Brigadier-General F. R. Scarlett, CB. He visited Cranwell at various times.

At the change over to the RAF in April 1918 the Commander in Command of the Cranwell Station was (newly promoted) Brigadier-General H. D. Briggs. Changes at top level seemed commonplace in the formation of the new Royal Air Force.

Now that the RAF had been formed, we were notified that there would be no further issues of the Royal Flying Corps uniforms, but we had permission to wear it as long as it remained passable; the same partly applied to the RNAS personnel. As replacements were required, the re-issue was mainly naval because the stores had stocks of Naval equipment. When we RFC replaced certain articles we looked a mixed and motley lot. Many of us were dressed in working and walking out outfits, looking half-soldier and half-sailor. Some, including myself, were fitted out with a khaki Naval cap with shiny blue peak, blue hatband with a cloth cap badge with a crown above a bird (albatross) in gold colour on a red background, khaki military tunic with brass buttons. Some of us changed these buttons for a set of the Naval buttons which were of a dark blue sort of fibre with an anchor on the facing. This was crafty because they did not require any polishing, and were a permitted issue.

The RNAS men were issued with khaki replacements as blue quickly ran out and they, in their turn, looked a similar comic outfit, with military items of uniform mixed with Naval uniform. Inwardly, they were furious because they were proud of the Navy, as we were proud of the RFC. Outwardly, nobody accepted the blame from the other for this partnership.

The Officers, too, were a mixture of uniforms, but they gradually adopted the new regulations of RAF Officers uniform. After April 1918 the first Officers new outfits were khaki tunic of military pattern, slacks and Bedford cord breeches, puttees, khaki military cap with black peak and black band with embroidered badge not unlike the badge today. Rank was indicated by bars on the bottom of the sleeve, with a sleeve badge above those bars consisting of a small gilt eagle and crown. Khaki collar and tie, and the approved buttons were RNAS type of gilt buttons.

I must mention that the Officers wearing the first RAF khaki also wore a popular "Trench" greatcoat. Some sported knee-length brown riding boots; some had knee length boots laced up the front.

The new Air Force blue was approved in July 1918. It was recommended that the new uniform would not be made compulsory until sufficient time had elapsed for the existing uniforms to be worn out.

The new blue was permitted to be worn by the Officers as Mess kit. The lower ranks did not get the new blue until well after the Armistice. In service in India we were in khaki from the middle of 1919.

The pilots wings and observer wings were the only flying emblem worn for a number of years after 1918.

The new RAF was given authority to have special awards for recommended Officers, NCOs and men, namely the DFC AFC/DFM AFM. There was no special award to celebrate the official forming of the RAF in 1918. The boys did not receive a medal, even those on the Official 1st Parade, and afterwards not even the General Service or Victory medal.

Boys wing RFC. RNAS. RAF Cranwell 1918.
Mixed uniform as issued for replacement.
Note: Military khaki tunic, RAF buttons, naval khaki cap with dark blue hatband, dark blue peak, naval capbadge with red anchor.
A working and walking out issue.
Boy J. Ross 1918

CHAPTER SIX

RECLASSIFICATION OF RANKS TO THE NEW RAF. INTEREST IN FLYING. UNAUTHORISED FLIGHT. FIRST RAF ANNUAL SPORTS DAY AT CRANWELL. STATION ACTIVITIES. FIRST RAF BOY TO BE KILLED BY ENEMY ACTION. A RUGBY SCRUM.

The Royal Naval Air Service, being an intrinsical part of the Navy, was steeped in Naval traditions, which were held in much regard. Therefore it was without doubt that Cranwell was going to retain its Naval methods and ideas up to the very last.

The Royal Flying Corps being a young service and composed of many Military men from practically every type of unit of the Army had not so much to lose.

This new Royal Air Force seemed to adopt a more Military principle and classification. It was not surprising that the RNAS were not so keen about the amalgamation.

We RFC Boys found the mixture of Naval and Military interpretations of orders, regulations and performances such that often we were bewildered. Our tenancy at this station became a complexity of ingredients trying to formulate by trial and error the new instructions and methods to be put into practice. The RFC Boys were the practice ground for the theories and the application of the new lower administration, sometimes a puzzle to the Officers and NCOs. Often it became quite farcical to our boyish minds.

It had not been a sudden decision that a new Air Force should be formed. After 1914 it was beginning to show that the enemy had much better aircraft than we had. The public began to realise it and voiced some doubtful opinions about our conduct in the air. As already stated, the expressions and concern about our heavy losses in the air brought about many discussions in Parliament. The Navy had its own estimates and bought their own aircraft from the selected manufacturers.

Opinions were that they had slightly better aircraft, whilst the War Office did not have so much money placed aside for RFC purposes and the standard performances were hardly equal to the enemy. The Royal Aircraft Factory did well under difficulties, improving the experimental types of aircraft and pooling expert knowledge instead of competing, Parliament saw the need. The new Independent Air force was proving itself. The decision had been made in good time to join the two Air Forces together under the establishment of one control.

The stubbornness of those who desired the Navy and the Army separate kept the RFC weakened, but rivalry existed amongst many ranks and was well understood. It was a good omen that RNAS and RFC Boys got on well together. We had not many links with the past and the future seemed more important. We were good pals, although proud of our old traditional uniforms. The pride of the RNAS Officers who were included in the previous pay structure was bound to be quite a sad occasion for many because their traditional ranks were abolished and like the ratings became Military:–

Wing Commander became Lieutenant Colonel.

Flight Commander became Captain.

Petty Officer became Sergeant.

Leading Rating became Corporal. Etc.

The Pilot wings and Observer brevet were the only two insignias to be worn on the tunic breast. The Sergeant Pilot, unless retained for some other duty, was regarded surplace in the peacetime requirements. The new young pilots, just passing out from the Training schools with qualification, were retained on a temporary basis to take over the duties of pilots not being re-engaged. Some were taken on afterwards on a regular engagement. The build up from this initial stage created new classifications. The need for a Royal Air Force Regiment was realised and formed. Then came the foundation of the Women's Royal Air Force. Halton was built up with permanent buildings around the early 1920s when not one entry of the Royal Air Force Boy Service was recruited, the whole having complete recognition.

The changes of badges of rank and the years of "Aye, aye, Sir", new method of saluting and many other service routines took some changing for the RNAS It was much easier in this respect for the RFC.

The main change for the RFC was the uniform. The Officers, the "Pips" of rank, the double-breasted tunic, badge and other matters concerning men and boys, but we had to swallow a lot of pride and traditions. The link was forged; a complete re-organisation a fresh page in history; the new peacetime Royal Air Force.

The wartime temporary serving personnel of all ranks who were not re-engaged, many after yeoman service, were being rapidly demobilised which left a new and much smaller RAF. Those accepted were signed on for a period engagement. We boys were coming into man service by 1918 and 1919. In our hundreds we played a big and important part, having completed our technical training, becoming the young nucleus of the new peacetime Royal Air Force as technical men mainly Fitters, Aero and Riggers. Some were Wireless Operators and various other trades, playing a big part.

In the new RAF the Officer ranks varied, many ex-RFC sticking to their old ranks and military uniform of their old Regiment, but NCOs and other ranks kept to the 3rd AM, later to LAC (Leading Aircraftman). The NCO ranks Corporal upwards, such as the many Sergeant Pilots after 1938-9, did not change to the complete Royal Air Force ranks fully until its constitution after the Second World War in 1945.

It was apparent that Cranwell, a well-established RNAS base with its vast airfield area and separate Airship section, would eventually become an important base. It was planned in the 1920s as an RAF College. It grew and was opened by Edward the Prince of Wales on October 11, 1934.

Flying training was still taking place. On any spare time I would sit on the grass and watch the flying "display". Being drilled on part of the airfield near the hangars some pilots in their aeroplane scattered us, leaving a furious NCO.

Unfortunately, some pupil pilots lost control, or wings came off. It was terrible to see the dust rising afterwards with the rescue parties alerted and rushing across to the scene in the Crossley tender. Sometimes fire broke out and there followed a mad rush with fire extinguishers.

I would hang around the flight hangars and listen to the conversation of pilots and cadet pilots and learned a lot. This was after our parades and classes as flying went on full tilt in the evenings.

I remember seeing a DH9 approach the hangars on "take off" and his propeller stopped. He turned back with his engine cut out and flew back down wind. The airmen on the ground called to themselves "Bank over, bank over," and "Come in," but he continued fast down wind and crashed at the far end of the aerodrome in a cloud of dust.

I learned the lesson that, in those days, a pilot must always keep his nose in to the wind towards the sock pole on take off and landing.

There was another DH9 who on "take off" lost his power. With propeller stopped I saw the pilot keep the aircraft nose in to the wind and over the hangers. At low altitude he gradually settled down and "pancaked" his aircraft on to the top of two huts right in the centre of the station. He landed with the fuselage between two huts, port wings on one hut, starboard wings on the other hut. Both pilot and pupil were stood up in their cockpits as the aircraft glided gently on to these huts. Upon the crash they climbed out and walked away. There was no fire but panic from inside the two huts concerned, but no one was hurt. I recall a young pilot standing near to me saying, "That was damned good flying. They kept ahead in to the wind and chose the right and only spot to land. If they had turned back to the aerodrome down wind they would have lost flying speed and crashed on to the hangars without a chance." It was surprising what little damage was done to the two huts, and all credit to the most efficient RNAS since the wreckage was cleared away in quick time and the two huts repaired.

At this time there were many various types of aircraft at Cranwell. The DH6, a box-like square wing tip biplane, upon which pupils did their first solos, a very slow aircraft which appeared, at times, stationary in the air.

The Avro 504, DH9, DH9a, Sopwith "Pup" and "Camel", BE2C, RE8, Armstrong Whitworth "Ack-Ack". The big twin engined Handley-Page 0/400, a new bomber, and often aircraft I did not recognise. I recall seeing a brand new triplane crash on the aerodrome.

The "Lighter-than-Air" section had the Zeppelin and many "Blimps" which sometimes came in, the envelope deflated and the small fuselage bumping on the ground and roof tops with the crew struggling to get it home. I always admired these men.

Some American Curtis aircraft brought by the Americans were stationed at Cranwell, but they did not often fly. The American pilots did most of their flying on our British aircraft.

The second week in July 1918 was a bad one for flying at Cranwell and ten pilots, instructors and pupils were killed in the seven days.

One, a Camel, was stunting when the wings collapsed. One wing came off while the remainder spun to the ground in a wide circle killing the pilot. Another Camel went into a spin at a good height and

never came out of it. Another one was an RE8. It came in with the top
wing on fire and crashed in front of the hangars, very little being left of
the aircraft, the instructor and pupil. It all happened so quickly. It was a
week with the breakdown team practically exhausted, and the station
losing some fine young men.

On July 23, 1918, the boys course of "filing" finished and we
commenced the course of bearing scraping. This came easily to me
because I had done this during my motor mechanic apprenticeship and
I proved satisfactory to the instructor. At this period we had lectures on
the internal combustion engine. I bought a book in Sleaford equipped
for making notes and drawings.

It was very interesting. My drawings became popular with the
instructors and boy colleagues and some took tracings of them for
themselves. The book is still in my possession.

The engine lectures were of the Renault 190 hp, the BHP 230 hp
Beardmore, Halford and Pullinger, often thought wrongly "Brake
Horse Power". This engine, the "Puma", was fitted in the DHp and had
a distinct tone to it, the engine not being cowled in.

We only got minor lectures on the Rotary and Radial engine. I
believe it was thought the stationary engine was replacing these
engines so we concentrated on the stationary engine, although the Avro
504 K with Rotary engine stayed in RAF service for many years after
1918. Radial engines became prominent too.

The lectures, notes on dismantling and erecting, were very good
indeed, with additional notes and alterations keeping us up to date.
Engine troubles and faults were included and the ignition systems very
informative. Naval Petty Officers (technical) proved to be excellent
instructors. We enjoyed taking our re-assembled engines to the "test
bed" when we would run them up to full throttle with the flat-faced
propellers; the noise was terrific. We stripped and assembled a radial
engine, a forerunner of many famous radial engines used later on in the
RAF, but the classes had a more comprehensive course with notes on
the Rolls-Royce 275, 300, 360, HP aero engines. This became most
valuable as I experienced when servicing the Rolls-Royce "Falcon" on
the Bristol Fighters in India.

Unlike today there was no experience of flying for the boys during
our service. Most of the aircraft were single seaters or two seaters.
There was not the large transport aircrafts used in the service today.

Handley-Page Aircraft Company had designed and built huge twin-engined biplanes known as the 0/400 with the intention of them with a later bigger version, the V/1500, being flown by the Independent Air Force, within the RAF, who were trained for long distance flying, to carry a heavy bomb load.

The 0/400 bomber which had a crew of 5 or 6, were stationed at Cranwell and were housed in special hangars situated near to the "Lighter-than-Air" section well away from the central layout.

One of my pals in the dormitory, Boy Walton (he was the proud possessor of a Douglas motor bike), told me whilst we were sitting on the grass watching the flying, that he had been up in one of the big bombers. I did not believe him and said: "Chance would be a fine thing. Besides, how could any boy get anywhere near them for a start?" I laughed and said to him: "You're pulling my leg. It's a fairy story all right."

He insisted it was true, saying: "Nobody else knows, only you. If you like I can get you up with me, too." He said, "Seriously, Jack, this is in strict confidence. My uncle is a Flight Commander flying the Handley-Pages. He told me I could bring a pal I could trust one morning and we could fly with him together instead of them using sandbags to make up the weight." He told me his uncle was on early morning flying duty this week and we could go early tomorrow morning and he would take us up with him.

Knowing Walton had come from a very good family and was not boastful, a big, tall lad I liked and got on with well, I believed him. It excited my interest. Being eager to fly I jumped at the opportunity and said: "All right. I would love to go with you."

We arranged to get up well before reveille, dress as usual for breakfast and training parade and creep out of the dormitory, and dodge PT. I awoke early and saw him sitting up in bed. We nodded to each other, got up, quietly dressed and tip toed outside.

All was quiet as we marched together like two men on duty across to the Handley-Page hangars where a couple of Handley-Page 0/400 were outside, with one of the engines "ticking over". Walton approached one of the Officers in flying kit. They recognised each other and had a few words. This Officer gave me a piercing look and nodded a sign of OK.

The mechanics knew and made no fuss, but helped us up the steps into the fuselage. Inside the fuselage was a wooden platform which we climbed on to so that we were head and shoulders above the top of the huge fuselage, I suppose it was for the mid-upper gunner.

Walton told me the pilot was his uncle and the second pilot a Flight Officer in training on big aeroplanes.

After the usual "run up" of the engines, we rumbled across the ground and with a roar and a shudder gathered speed and took off. Walton was used to it and told me to sit on the platform until we were off the ground. As we left the ground the rumble and rattle stopped and I encountered a smooth, floating sensation and the roar of the engines gave me the indication that they were pulling us through the air. The whistle and strength of the wind was terrific. I was absolutely thrilled. We were gradually leaving the aerodrome behind and below us . . . and I was having a dream fulfilled.

By now we both had climbed up on to the platform and stood looking out over the top of the fuselage.

It was a wonderful sight and experience for me, and, as the aircraft climbed higher, we could see the darkness of the night out to the west and the rays of the sunrise coming in the east. Indeed I was impressed. It was a most wonderful sight. Where we went I do not know, but we reached a fair height and had been over the coast for a short distance because I had noticed the dark sea below me.

Over Lincolnshire we banked and turned on numerous occasions, for the first time in my life I was interested in seeing the earth going away on one side and coming up on the other side.

As it was so windy and chilly we both got off the platform and sat inside, only to keep repeating this fascinating procedure for a look out and get another chilly blow. How we laughed and enjoyed ourselves each time we stood on this platform. We had such fun in pointing out to each other the various objects on the ground, the churches, farmhouses and villages, large towns, different patterns and colours of fields with trees like sponges and winding country roads. Before we landed it became rather misty out to the east and we could not see far in that direction, but it was clear looking out to the west. The early morning sun gave us these "fixes".

We were flying for over one hour, landing after 7 am. After "thanks" and saying how much we had enjoyed it, with a "thumbs up", Walton and I set off and marched as fast as we could to the dormitories. We had been in the air for a longer period than Walton's previous flights and got back puffing and panting just in time to join the work parade. We had missed our breakfast; were absent from PT and paraded with empty stomachs. Anyhow I had some chocolate in my pocket which I

Group at Leuchars RNAS. RAF
Assembly shop 1919. Some are ex RFC Boys
AC2 Ross, J. is the smaller of the two standing in the middle wearing white overalls.

Avro 504 K. Bristol Fighter in rear
5 ex boys. 114 Sqdn RFC. Later 28 Sqdn RAF. India. 1919
Moffatt. RNAS   Heys. G.. RFC   Potter, RFC   Ross. RFC
(Seated) Harrison. RFC

shared with Walton. It helped and we went to our mid-day meal like two hungry wolves.

In a letter home, which I posted in Sleaford, I told my parents my impressions which were: "We seemed to be floating in the air. Roads looked like winding tape, fields like a draughtboard with ragged shapes and sizes, trees like pimples on the earth and woods like sponges spread about. In fact it all looked like a small model on a brown and green surface. It seemed I could have put the whole station in my pocket."

This impression, of my flying experience, was truly narrated without any exaggeration to my parents, family and friends who had no knowledge of flying at all. All we knew about it was from a few still pictures in the press, on cigarette cards or the small films shown on the "Pathe Animated Gazette" at the cinema. This first flight at Cranwell still sticks in my memory.

I am certain that Walton and myself were amongst the youngest ever in the services to fly during the 1914-1918 war, and the first two Royal Flying Corps BOYS to fly. A point of RFC and RAF history we made which passed along unrecorded and unheralded because it was unauthorised. I have often thought about it because the risk was great. Had the aircraft crashed or was lost at sea we could have been missing and presumed lost, with no trace – and a lot of trouble for someone. It was a risk and adventure we were quite prepared to take. My parents never knew other than that it was a permitted thing to do. It may not be believed by some, but we actually did it.

George Fleming, my Sheffield pal, had been posted, having reached the age of 18 years, and so knew nothing about our flight.

Boys in the dormitory guessed Walton and I had been up to something as we were missing at reveille, PT and breakfast. One boy said he had seen us both creep out, dressed before reveille. They tried by various means to find out exactly what we had been doing and we told them we got up early to see some flying, and forgot the time.

This sounded like a feasible story, because they knew we both watched the flyers in our spare time. Some said we were bloody fools and it served us right to lose our breakfast just to watch a bit of flying.

Rather strange nothing happened about us being absent from PT. A day or so afterwards when watching the flying Walton said to me, "We must not go again to the Handley-Pages." His uncle had told him, "No more. That's enough for you. If you come again you will not be taken up. We dare not risk it any more. Other boys will get to know and they will come along. We shall get into serious trouble."

There would be during the day or evening, 20 or more aircraft at different heights going through training around or over the station. It was most fascinating and thrilling. I confess I gave to all the pilots my admiration and a sense of hero worship. I thought them wonderful, and I had a deeper inward feeling of regard for them than the "fans" outward screams appear to indicate to certain performers today.

There was a pilot on the station who was the CO of No 59 Wing (Flying) who had joined Cranwell in April 1918, an RFC pilot coming from the Royal Field Artillery in early 1915, Lt-Col S. Smith, DSO. A brilliant aviator and clever stunt pilot, we all knew when he was in the air in his Sopwith Camel. He demonstrated all his skills of aerobatics imaginable and, except for speed and power, no better than today. Often he was the culprit who would purposely come out of a spin, or roll and suddenly dive, at speed at such a low level he broke and scattered our ranks, much to our delight but to the fury of those drilling us. I am sure he had a huge laugh himself whilst we enjoyed the fearsome thrill he gave us.

As the older boys reached the age of 18 they were posted in batches to various parts of the country, learning the work from the men on the job. Fresh intakes of boys came in to take their place.

Young men selected from civilian life were being enlisted on a larger scale as Flight Cadets, training to be pilots at the age of 17½ years. As I was at this age I got permission from my father to put in an application for transfer to this Officer Cadet Unit.

My father agreed and promised me all expenses. He received from an RFC man at Coal Aston Aerodrome Sheffield a sample of a correct type of application. I wrote out my application and placed it in the Orderly Room.

I was detailed to appear at the Orderly Office. Full of high hopes I was marched before a Senior Officer. Reading my application he said it was quite proper. I thought, "Good, I am going to get my transfer," but then came the bombshell. He told me that no boy from this training establishment at Cranwell was to be recommended for transfer to the Flight Cadets Unit. We had enlisted for special training for the future RAF to service and maintain of aircraft, aircraft mechanics require intensive training, and we would be a very important part of the future RAF. These were his orders: no application from any boy will be accepted.

He told me: "The RAF can get its requirements for future pilots and observers from the civilian population who can be selected and trained as probationers."

That was it. I replied, "Thank you, Sir," saluted and out I marched, rather gloomy and feeling rejected. I told the other interested boys with the same view in mind, and they thought it rotten luck for us. But we knew "Orders is orders, and must be obeyed."

I wrote to my father the result. He quite understood the position. On a morning parade this information was read out and we realised that there was no chance for us. It was put on orders and I contented myself by carrying on with my technical training and studies. There was a stepping up in our technical training. I was extremely interested in the classes and that took away my ambition to be a pilot to some degree. I was satisfied of having at least tried. We had learned the lessons of being able to "take it". There was no option but to shelve the idea of becoming a pilot. .

Preparations were being made to hold the first RAF annual sports day at Cranwell. When it was decided, we helped to prepare the field for the events. We were regular "donkeys" for the station. I suppose we had our uses for all occasions, because our strength was always kept up by replacements.

The first RAF annual sports day at Cranwell was held on Tuesday July 30, 1918. It was to be a "red letter day" in the history of Cranwell, a day eagerly awaited by the majority and earnestly prepared for by the few. The weather was good. From early morning until long after the presentation of prizes a record crowd of spectators and competitors enjoyed a perfect day's sport in glorious sunshine. There were eight hours of sport . . . and not a dull moment.

2nd Lieut W. R. Castings was the chief organiser of the meeting, held by kind permission of Brigadier-General H. D. Briggs. Amongst the judges, which consisted of the highest and lowest ranks, but no boys, was Capt HRH Prince Albert. There was every type of event, special boys' and ladies' events. Prizes were given by the canteen committee and cups to be competed for annually.

Cranwell RAF Brass Band played selections of music, under the conductor G. S. Grunden, IAM.

This was the biggest sports day most of the boys had experienced or witnessed. The impressions were out of the ordinary when so many of all ranks got together, joining in a feast of competitive fun and games, rubbing shoulders with the aloof, and cheering on the efforts of an Officer or NCO. It was brought to a close by a concert on the parade ground given by the station concert party, CPO "Taff" Gibbon and the "Egbert Bros", who travelled from London to entertain us.

This was a different sort of sports meeting than the one we remembered at Halton. The Halton sports day was good for its achievements even though we were short of equipment. We could see the difference what organisation coupled with the possession of the right equipment can do, and the "ammo" boots were only worn when the event needed them.

To improve things, the boys were given another leave called "Summer leave". We felt that our boys' demonstration for leave had had a greater effect after all.

I had leave from Friday August 8 to Wednesday August 14, 1918. I enjoyed every minute of it.

I felt extra pride in myself. Whilst still wearing my Royal Flying Corps uniform because I had actually been flying and was now a real airman. My father was very interested in my account of my flight in the big bomber. I was pleased with myself because part of my ambition had been accomplished, having achieved the distinction of flying, something that so many who wore the uniform of the RFC had not, and never would. I felt mighty proud and important, but true to the traditions of silence in the service, although I told my father about this big aircraft, I gave no details to any other person.

My parents told me that they had seen the British Zeppelin, the R25, pass over Sheffield and were pleased to know that their son was one of the many who helped to handle this airship when on the ground.

Back at Cranwell, the training routine extended. On September 10, 1918, with others, I went on to aero engine overhauling. This was extremely interesting. I quickly got the chance to use the special tools and equipment, taking to pieces and putting together the different types of aero engines. And along with the knowledgeable and first class instructors, I soon found myself mastering the intricate workings of these engines. It was good training, giving me a deep satisfaction. I got on well with the instructors who noticed I had a certain amount of knowledge and practice to begin with.

There were the usual earwig attacks in the dormitories. Each one of us must have annihilated hundreds of these pests. Rabbits were plentiful, running around the station and aerodrome. We got rabbit for meals so frequently that there were many puns, jokes, poetry, and cartoons circulating around the station mainly concerning rabbits, pies and sausages.

Cranwell had plenty of sport arranged on the station, some of the performers being professionals. For many of the boys it was a pleasant relaxation to watch the various games played. HRH Prince Albert was a good tennis player. The station cricket team was good. Our Officer commanding the Boys Wing, Lt-Col Barnby, was a good batsman and scored some fine innings against teams from other stations, military teams from other units and Lincolnshire teams. I am certain we were an encouraging party to some of his big hits. Boxing and hockey were in plenty. We could also see some good fencing in the gymnasium by the Naval instructors.

Under station welfare the social side of activities were encouraged. Indoor recreation included billiards, rifle club, whist drives, concerts, dances, wrestling and swimming, etc. These were all arranged and controlled by a Central Sports Committee which was formed, the secretary being 2nd Lieut W. R. Castings (ex-RNAS) with a large committee of male and female service staff.

Football was getting started for the season. The Boys Wing was divided into two top teams known as Boys Wing "A" team and "B" team. These two teams were entered into the station competition of seven station sections in a league.

A group league was formed in which the boys "A" and "B" teams linked up to form the Boys Wing team. And a good team they became, playing against other RAF Stations Scopwick, Spittlegate, Hucknall, Waddington and other teams, performing so well as to be feared by teams containing professionals who were serving in the forces.

The "A" and "B" boys teams did well in competition against the men of the station. Some boys were selected for the Cranwell Station team. Some of the names to mention were Boy Lance-Corporals Myers and Shand, and Boys Allison, Francis, Giles, Owen and White.

One Boys Wing team, mainly RFC Boys, and some NCOs were as follows: Sgt Mills, Cpl Dunn, Sgt Murray, Boy Davies, Sgt Taylor, Boy Lance-Cpl Stewart, Boy Francis, Boy Giles, Boy Lance-Cpl Shand, Boys Bell and Owen.

I was keen on playing football, but never got above dormitory selection. The boys selected were very good. The Boys "A" team was at the top of the Station league many times.

It was comedy when the Boys teams played the Airships (Lighter-than-Air) team. The Airships team had its football pitch near the airships' hangars. As the Station did not permit personnel to stroll or wander across the long stretch of aerodrome, the boys had to parade.

We were "fell in" and marched with the Boys band leading us right across the aerodrome to the "away" pitch. We halted along the touchline, ordered "right turn" and "stand at ease" facing the pitch. Imagine it: we were expected to remain in this position "four deep" throughout the game. It does not stretch the imagination to say that orders were disobeyed. We broke ranks and created with the aid of the instrumentalists a huge din of encouragement in support of our team, who, on November 6, 1918, won by six goals to one. Caps of all type and issue flew into the air. We did not win all our matches with Airships, but they were well contested.

After these matches we were supposed to march back. It was impossible to get us "fell in". Boys were split up all over the pitch. We made our own way back to the dormitories in a long line of happy lads. This happened every time we played at Airships, the only thing for the team it assured plenty of supporters.

The other Station teams liked the boys to attend their matches against outside opponents because we created such a noise of encouragement and fun amongst ourselves it helped them on to a better performance and, along with some of the WRAF who joined in, spurred them on to greater effort, and a welcome win.

Three boys died while we were at Cranwell. One, Boy Lucas, died from a sickness whilst in Lincoln County Hospital on August 16, 1918.

One RNAS Boy, Boy A. H. Boucher, was the first and only boy in the Royal Air Force to die in uniform in face of the enemy. He had been on leave to his home in Ireland. Upon his return the ship, the Mail Boat *Leinster* was sunk in the Irish Sea by enemy action. On October 13, 1918, news was received at Cranwell that his body had been washed ashore.

In February 1919 one of my Halton hut pals, an RFC Boy Tom Dawkes, was taken to Lincoln Hospital where he died. I was detailed to join the bearer party.

With a Sergeant and five other boys, we carried his coffin on to a Crossley tender and proceeded from the hospital to the Railway Station. The Railway Authorities arranged for us to enter on to the side of the station. We carried him from the tender on to a reserved coach on the train to take him home to, I believe, Plymouth. We stood on the station platform and saluted as the train moved out on its journey, a sad farewell to a colleague who was in the same tent as myself Farnborough, my first hut at Halton, and the next bed to me at Cranwell. This sad duty took place on Monday February 24, 1919, having rehearsed the procedure with the Sergeant the day before.

One evening when all was quiet in the dormitory a boy came in with an old rugby ball he had "found". One or two boys demonstrated how it should be held, thrown and caught. This was champion. Most of us wanted to have a go and we did. When one tried to take it off another, keenness set in and without sides a real scrum developed. A dash for the loose ball came about so quickly that practically all the boys in the dormitory were in one mad scramble for the ball as it was thrown, dropped and carried from one end to the other of the dormitory. It became a bedlam.

I joined in the fun and with the ball with dozens of others we chased the thing, knocking beds, equipment and boys all over the place. Laugh, we all enjoyed it, but one boy named Harrison, during the whole of this mad sortie laid on what remained of his bed reading a booklet, oblivious to what was happening. When we had finished, hot, perspiring and bruised, Harrison laid on what was left of his bed on the floor apparently without concern to our riotous game, still engrossed in his reading.

It was a cheap magazine known in those days as a "Penny Dreadful". We sat around him laughing our heads off, but he never stirred one bit, just sadly looked up at us from amongst the debris of his bed and said, "You're bloody daft, the lot of yer." He was a good lad from Lancaster, a rugby player. He told us: "Next time you want to try rugby, try it on grass. It's like you lot, it's soft." A good pal, he looked older than his years, as he was going bald at the front, but a thin, wiry frame, supple and strong, proved his youth.

As we straightened up the dormitory we removed his pile of debris, lifting him bodily off the floor and on to his freshly made bed still reading his "Penny Dreadful" as though nothing had happened.

There was nothing so good as when the boys "got together". Spirit was good. We created a fine bond of comradeship amongst ourselves. On the whole a sense of companionship had developed, making a splendid foundation for what was soon to become the brand new peacetime Royal Air Force, well-trained ground staff, both at home and abroad. Many of us were posted abroad for the first build up of new Squadrons.

Leave came again. I was home on Friday October 25 until Wednesday October 30, 1918.

It was nice to be home again, but food was very short and makeshift meals were conjured up out of corned beef, potatoes, home grown vegetables and flour. Long queues formed at the shops often in hope that the shopkeeper had received some deliveries and a scamper away to another shop if he had not.

There was a good spirit amongst the people. The war had created a friendly atmosphere among the neighbours, who nearly all had a member of the family in the forces, many mourning the loss of a close relative killed in action, missing believed killed, or wounded – and the toll was mounting.

Rolls of honour were exhibited in halls, churches, schools, factories, shops and in our homes. With other relatives, our photographs were proudly exhibited over the mantlepiece in the sitting-room of our large house. Each day the list of the names of the casualties grew longer. The list of names and the photographs in the press were a constant reminder of the loss of someone you knew.

Newsboys running along the streets with special bulletins, newspapers being reduced to one or two printed sheets called out the headlines such as, "War special," "Zeppelin brought down," "Big liner sunk," "Belgian town captured," "Battleships in action," and so on. The price was one old penny ($\frac{1}{2}$p).

This was the only means of getting the news, there was always a rush to buy one. It was the only way of finding out the latest happening at home and abroad. The information was often very brief.

Dark nights brought the fear of the Zeppelins and raids. The Zeppelins had suffered badly at the hands of the RNAS. The selected night flying units of the RFC and gunnery from the ground forces severely mauled the Zeppelin raids on London and the east and north-east. Trying to get to the west coast they came over at such a great altitude they wandered all over the country, not knowing exactly where they were, they were not very successful.

The public were always kept aware of the possibility of a Zeppelin raid. My father told me he had heard the drone of Zeppelins passing over Sheffield after "alerts" more than once at what appeared a great height.

My brothers had both been in the fighting in France. Anthony was a Regimental Sgt-Major. After a long period in France with the "Old Contemptibles" he was now in this country training recruits. My other brother, Fred, was now a Sergeant in the KOYLIs and had been badly wounded in France and was in hospital in this country.

Both had been recommended for promotion to Commissioned rank. We three brothers never had a leave at the same time, but I met Fred on leave when he was a Lance-Corporal.

Leave over, it was back to Cranwell. The many duties meant mainly the handling of the huge British Zeppelin, the R25.

In the boxing tournaments we had some good boy boxers. Two were from our dormitory, Boy Lance-Corporal Mills and Boy Chappell. They did very well. Another good Squadron boxer was Boy Lance-Corporal Shand, a very good performer at all sports.

Other boys who won places of merit at sports are as follows: Boys Lees, Morley, Rigby, Snaith, Trapp and Yeomans and at rugby Carnill.

The station orchestra gave some first-rate concerts which I enjoyed. I had never previously heard an orchestra, only the piano, and the piano and violin in the local Picture Palace with the silent films, or the old gramophone. The splendid array of talented musicians and their music gave me great pleasure listening to good classical music. The conductor was PO J. Hales, RNAS.

The Cranwell Station magazine, *The Piloteer*, was well produced and popular. It had to be ordered from the Editor's "office", the Editor being journalist 2nd Clerk W. K. Seymour, RNAS. It was censored yet nevertheless gave interesting station news in plenty. I bought my first copy dated June 1918. The magazines I still have, although well used, contain valuable historical material and made good reading.

CHAPTER SEVEN

THE ARMISTICE. IN TO MAN SERVICE AGED 18. CHRISTMAS LEAVE. THE
END OF THE "DW" (DURATION OF WAR) MEN. TECHNICAL COURSE
COMPLETED. THE "LULL". POSTED TO LEUCHARS. BACK TO HALTON WITH
EX-BOYS ON OVERSEAS DRAFT. TO INDIA. BUILDING NEW SQUADRONS BY
EX-BOYS. FRONTIER SERVICE. HOME SERVICE AND ON TO RESERVE. EX-
BOYS OUT AND ON TO THE "DOLE" QUEUE.

On Monday November 11, 1918, came the great day of the signing, of
the Armistice. Hostilities ceased. There was great joy at Cranwell and
the whole attitude of many men changed. Those (practically all) on
"DW", Duration of War, engagement immediately started thinking and
preparing for discharge, but the station carried on with its training.
Flying training did not cease. The boys' training carried on as usual.
Our class commenced on a course of extended engine theory on
Monday November 18, 1918.

I got busy with more drawings in my book. The illustrations and
additional notes on the theory came in very useful during my service in
later years. A lot of valuable knowledge was gained about cooling
systems, lubrication, engine faults, mis-firing, overheating and other
forms of engine troubles that could arise and how to locate and rectify
them. In addition, our instructions on electric currents, accumulator
and the magnetic ignition were excellent. When stationed at Ambala,
India, I bought the book *Magneto and Electric Ignition* by W. Hibbert,
AMIEE, by post from Calcutta. This improved my study and
knowledge of the subject. Nevertheless, the RNAS at Cranwell, in its
method of instruction, proved first class. I learned more about the
internal combustion engine than I would have done as an apprentice in
a garage. The course on aero engines was second to none in those days.
I carry that knowledge to this day in grateful thanks. My book of notes
and drawings is one of my proudest possessions, and useful.

Friday November 22, 1918, came my birthday. I was now 18 years of age. I was remustered into man service as a 3rd AM. My pay was increased to two shillings per day, (10p,) with rank of Air Mechanic 3rd Class.

As the fighting in the war had ceased I think the authorities were temporarily put off their stride concerning what to do with us at Cranwell. Still under the same instructions, we had a slight "flap" on when on December 5, 1918, a party of Japanese Officers visited the station and inspected us on parade.

We were feeling that there would be some big movement of boys from the station. Many of the older boys had been posted. We few left of the original RFC Boys were 18 years of age or approaching it. Our classes of technical training were about completed and new RAF Boys arrived.

The instructors, and practically all of the Cranwell ex-RNAS personnel, were serving for "Duration of War" only. Some had already been demobilised. Training was getting cut to a minimum. The main topic amongst the men was getting back to civilian life. Hardly any spoke about the possibility of re-enlistment for a period engagement and it did not seem a great deal of preparation had been made for this future purpose. The winning of the war had been the priority, with all efforts rightly put to this purpose.

There had been a countrywide epidemic of acute influenza, with a huge loss of life. We were all inoculated against it on Friday December 6, 1918.

On Thursday December 18, 1918, we had the whole of "A" Squadron Boys Wing who were mostly RFC Boys gathered at the side of one of the large sheds. On raised platforms specially erected by the men we were photographed in one huge, long group, eight and nine deep. Sixty or more boys were in a row. The photograph was 14 inches in length and five inches wide. It contains 400 faces. They are recognisable, each one the size of a pinhead.

Though each face is recognisable, to be reduced in size for publication would hardly show the detail. One interesting point is the varying uniform, everything except for the new RAF blue. This was the only photograph that was taken of this Boys Wing or any other group of boys whilst at Cranwell RNAS Station.

We all had leave again. This time it was our Christmas leave, with New Year's leave for the Scottish boys.

It was a good leave, being the first Christmas leave I had at homewhilst in the forces. It was special, everybody was cheery and profoundly thankful hostilities had ceased. There was a general relaxation along with the hope that no further fighting would take place. This was in the hearts and minds of everybody. Our elders had had enough of it, both at home and abroad, with tragic reminders of so many who were lost never to be seen again.

The festive season was celebrated at home in quite a fashion. My sisters, Elizabeth and Nellie, took turns on the piano, playing the wartime songs and singing Christmas carols.

Family relations called in. My mother, who had brought up a large family, gave Christmas dinner with a rare treat of fowl my father collected on his bicycle from a relation who had a small farm and pork shop in Bawtry.

Food was still rationed and difficult to obtain so a lot of people started allotments on any available land, a Government suggestion was to "dig for victory". On my father's allotment at Meadow Head near fields and trees, he grew good vegetables. Sometimes a rabbit came for a feed off his stock. Being brought up as a boy amongst farmers, he caught them , but this "Catch" only happened on the odd occasion.

I took my ration book home with me which was welcomed. Issued at Cranwell, it was known as a leave or duty ration book and printed specially for when on leave. The rubber stamp of Royal Air Force, Cranwell, Sleaford, was impressed on it with my name, number, rank of 3rd AM, stating from reveille December 20, 1918, to 10 pm December 31, 1918. It had all the necessary coupons, which my parents used. On the book was the signature and rank of the issuing Officer, a name that became well known in later RAF years, Lieut N. J. Mitchell Innes.

I still have this ration book in my possession. Some of the coupons were taken out by the shopkeeper. It is a reminder that twice in our lifetime food has been in short supply and needed to be rationed. The cupboards had many bare shelves, causing problems of catering to my parents, a matter that had to be carefully and shrewdly organised. Hours were spent in the weariness and exasperating queueing up at any food shop that had any goods to open for.

I always felt that the forces stationed in this country got a good chance of better food than did the folk at home. When on leave one could see the amount of difficulty, care and study that had to be taken to put a meal on the table day after day.

There was only the slight chance of a little extra. Luxuries were impossible, unless something popped up on the "Black market". If lucky enough to get it, one had to pay extortionate prices.

So the joy of the Armistice was a tremendous event for celebration; home for the "DW" men and women who survived the war. The possibility of good meals in plenty for all, hoping for the end of the rationing, new clothes, family life, a new outlook with peace for all time as was generally quoted. "The lights went up again."

Rumour at Cranwell was that much of the flying and other training would be curtailed. This sounded reasonable. On some days there would be only one or two machines in the air.

The main topic of the men was: "It's all over now. Let's get out of it." We boys knew that we had to approach the situation in a different way.

We were in the Regular Service for a period engagement and knew we should be expected to carry on where the "Duration of War" men left off. As Senior Officers put it to us, "It is up to you boys, now. The opportunity to take over and work on the many jobs in the RAF will be a very important duty."

We knew it. Our talk was of the possibility of going out to France or even to Germany. Our training continued and, with others, our complete course finished on January 28, 1919.

There was no passing out parade, no presentation of prizes, no Reviewing Officers, no awards, or speeches. We had finished the course of instruction – and that was that. It was when I received my discharge papers on Form 280 that I saw I had a degree of proficiency as a boy under instruction of 80 per cent and obtained the Certificate of 2nd Class Education.

During our man service we ex-boys of the Royal Flying Corps never knew whether the "Fitters Aero" and the "Riggers" had passed with good marks or just about scraped through.

The sudden need for a completely new structure and creation of the Royal Air Force was a totally different proposition at home and abroad. The change from the pursuit of war to the Army of Occupation and the ultimate peacetime RAF, plus the process of demobilisation and the attendant thinning down of the service, gave us no surprise that we remained at Cranwell.

What was more we could be used on the many and varied

requirements on the station. As men were being posted for demobilisation and the huts became empty, we were given the fatigue duties of emptying the huts, moving bed boards, lockers and generally cleaning up.

Very few of the men were signing on for re-engagement in the RAF As some boys who enlisted after us at Farnborough were signed on for eight years and four Reserve. The nucleus of enlisted Regular personnel was assured to a certain extent to cover the coming years with a fair number of trained technical men to replace those leaving the service. The stalemate before peace was signed on Saturday June 28, 1919, gave the authorities time to reflect upon the formation of a peacetime Royal Air Force.

On Thursday March 6, 1919, I said good-bye to Cranwell. With a draft party we were posted and left Cranwell at 3 pm. Travelling by train up north, we reached Edinburgh and on to Turnhouse by train and arrived at Leuchars, RAF.

We were split up. I was put in the workshops on Aero Engine repair and assembly and so started my man service proper as a 3rd AM Fitter Aero.

This station was another ex-Naval (RNAS) station. At that time it had a long title and was known as "The North Sea Grand Fleet School of Aerial Gunnery and Fighting".

It was a nice station. The food was good, a feature that always made a good or bad impression. I settled in and enjoyed Leuchars and the parts of Scotland I visited when out on a pass with other RFC boys.

There was plenty of work and experience for us on the various aero engines, but with other RFC boys we were soon posted. This posting took us to Blandford for overseas duties. Some of us were put on a Russian draft for Archangel and drew the full kit of furs, etc.

I cannot say that any of us liked Blandford. The food was terrible, and conditions poor. After our arrival on April 2, we were inoculated and (kit left behind) went home on a six day draft leave on Saturday April 5, 1919. Back again at Blandford came another inoculation. On the same day, Wednesday, April 16, we went home this time on a 14-day leave, but were called back by telegram on the Monday May 28, 1919. The leave was spent in the usual manner of visits, but somehow different to the wartime spirit. At home it was over. For us, it was a beginning of uncertainty. Back at camp I admit I did not behave myself. I got punished more than once for insolence and other bad behaviour.

With a few others I was washed off the Russian draft on Tuesday May 13, 1919. To get rid of us we were sent home on a 28-day leave on Thursday May 15 to Wednesday June 11, 1919.

The leave was a good, long round of visits, walks with the dog and members of the family, but I was rather unsettled, mainly anxious to get working on aircraft, but not knowing the future plan. On Saturday June 28, 1919, peace was signed. I was confined to camp on CB when my pals went celebrating.

The Annual Sports were held at Blandford on Wednesday July 2, 1919, by kind permission of Brigadier-General F. G. Willock, DSO, GOC Halton and Blandford. This provided a relief from the moans and groans for many of us. None of our party was successful in any event, except in the canteen when we indulged in my newly-acquired taste for extra beer I had always enjoyed the odd glass.

On Monday July 7, 1919, our small party left Blandford, being posted back again to Halton North Camp in the overseas section.

I was placed on the Russian draft once more, again drawing the fur kit and inoculated so often it seemed they wanted to get rid of the stuff.

I am bound to say that our party did not behave very well, finding much to irritate us. After completing our technical training and ready for work we were not prepared to go back to the old "bull". I admit I was not putting up a good show and was a regular top candidate for defaulters' parade, getting six extra drill with full pack on August 18, 1919, for insolence to a sergeant whose name I will not mention, but an ignorant bully not popular with any of us.

On August 22, 1919, our Russian draft was paraded for departure. As each name was called, he picked up his kit and proceeded to a Leyland lorry and climbed in. When the roll was completed there was I standing all by myself on the parade ground.

I was "rollocked" for not answering my name. I said my name had not been called. Checking by the Officer in charge and by the RSM they agreed my name was not on the list. A reserve had taken my place.

I was instructed to hand all the fur kit and revolver in to the stores. This I did.

For a couple of weeks I was loose in Halton. There were postings galore, but I was never on any list and could not understand it as drafts came in and out. I did nothing at all. Finally I reported to the Orderly

Room that I was getting nowhere whilst parties were on the move. I was astounded, and the staff in the Orderly Room amazed, because as far as they knew I was on my way to Archangel.

Something had gone wrong. They had no record of me on the camp, except that I was on the pay roll and drawing my weekly pay. The Officer who told me saw the funny side of it. One NCO said I was a missing man with no records in this country. I could have gone home and come back every Friday for my pay. There was a lot of fussing about, the Serjeant-Major, S-M Cook recalled the facts and remembered that my name was *not* on the parade final roll call. A Reserve took my place.

We had some laughs about it, but I never knew of the reason how it came about. It was quickly rectified. I was placed on 99 draft for India. This time, instead of extreme cold, it was to be extreme heat so I drew out the tropical kit.

On the next day, after inspection, and having only just enough time to write home of the change in my posting, a party of us left the overseas camp at Halton North on the Saturday morning of September 6, 1919, for Liverpool.

We were on the dockside and should have embarked on the troopship *City of Marseilles* but something went wrong. Loaded on to a lorry our RAF party were transported to Knotty Ash camp, where we stayed the night. Next day we were transported to the dockside again. We boarded the transport, the SS *Derbyshire*, a "Bibby" line troopship, and sailed from Liverpool for the East on Sunday September 7, 1919.

My sister, Margaret, and husband, Tom, were in residence at Wallasey and were on the pier head on the New Brighton Pier waving to the troops as the ship passed down the river, little knowing I was on the ship. I did not know they were there.

Our small party of RAF was under the command of the Officers of a large body of a Northumberland Regiment who practically filled the ship.

After a very interesting sea voyage we arrived at Bombay, the RAF marching through the streets of Bombay to Colobar rest camp on October 1, 1919.

Posted from here, some of us proceeded by train to Ambala in the Punjab where we entered the number 114 Squadron Royal Flying Corps. Mainly all were ex-Boys coming in. As parties came in so did the men proceed to Home posting. They were mighty pleased because

they were DW enlisted men and well overdue for demobilisation. All
of us were the first regulars. We took over with 114 Squadron RFC,
being transferred to the RAF and becoming the new 28 Squadron
Royal Air Force.

We erected the new aircraft from crates by sea from England, 28
Squadron being newly equipped with Bristol Fighters. We later took
over at Kohat on the North West Frontier, exchanging places with 20
Squadron, when after this tour of service we were posted back home.

After the India service I had 43 days' overseas leave. At first it was
very strange, changing Rupees and Annas to Pounds, Shillings and
Pence. The life seemed to be different. The general public and
atmosphere in the country had changed. Conversation was no longer
about the pursuit of war, but the consequences of it with queues of men
seeking work at the Labour Exchanges. Women who had not been
engaged on war work or services of some sort were back in the home,
but you could sense unsettled relief, with not much spending money
and the political scene changing.

With the Government reduction of national expenditure upon the
advice of a committee under Sir Eric Geddes, the three forces were
drastically cut, with no further entries except special requirements.
This was called the "Geddes axe".

The required Royal Air Force Squadrons were up to strength and as
all the other necessary establishments were staffed and complete, it
could now embark upon its future to create achievements in the air,
supreme in the defence of our country.

Halton was gradually built up to a substantial School of Technical
Training, with boys being recruited in numbered entries, each with a
graduation parade held when the course completed. Some reached very
high rank.

On my 43 days' leave, my visits to Darnall became frequent. I had
spotted Lucy, now grown into a lovely young lady. We talked, had
strolls and got well acquainted. I took her to my parents. Back to a
posting to RAF Henlow, IAAD. Letters from Lucy were a great
pleasure. I liked the station with plenty of interesting work on the
Rolls-Royce aero engines, lecturing students, being in a select party
assisting the AID (Air Inspection Dept) of the Air Ministry.

Aero engines were brought in from crashes and accidents which we
stripped and minutely examined. I was playing in the station football
team in the Bedfordshire League. My service was completed and I was

placed on reserve, went home and was unemployed. I later started
work in Local Government. and married Lucy – we still enjoy extreme
happiness together. Lucy joined in all my activities, being awarded a
special ladies' commendation and brooch from the Air Ministry in the
Second World War.

A Royal Flying Corps Boys Association was formed with annual
dinners and reunions in London when my pocket diary was in great
demand. Members suggested that I become the Boys' historian. Not
keen to do it, I seemed to drift into it, scribbling bits down, colleagues
reminding me and pushing me on as it developed to written foolscap
sheets and finally the manuscript.

The reason this book has taken so long to produce is that I had to do
it all myself along with so many other duties, intermingled with
sickness. I had to make sure I had prepared it in a readable form to
make sure it was correct and had no fictitious journalistic sensational
exaggerations included in it. But it is worth the effort because I cannot
recall any other book of the Royal Flying Corps or the Royal Air Force
that even mentions the RFC BOY service. This only had the life of
about one year, but is of tremendous importance to the new Royal Air
Force foundation, a phase of history that must be recorded and never
forgotten.

The magnitude of its importance is referred to by my posting with
many others to India, because our man service began when we were
desperately needed to replace men still awaiting to go back home and
out of the service a year before. This applied to many other overseas
places. In addition, in the foundation of the Royal Air Force, the
pattern was built from the Trenchards "Brats". The later Royal Flying
Corps enlisted around 155,000 boys , who were becoming aged 18 and
men. They, too, swelled the ranks of the new RAF. The RAF on duty
with the Army of Occupation needed hundreds of men to work with
the remnants still held back for duty on the evacuated enemy
aerodromes. The priority of 1917, 1918 and 1919 was the liberation of
Europe, the need to make sure by presenting a strong, capable military
force backed by a new formidable Royal Air Force. The Royal Flying
Corps is fading into history, but the Service and the "Home Front" is
far better equipped, the whole second to none. The true value of the
introduction of the Air Training Corps, the Boy Service and the
Apprenticeship scheme absolutely proved itself as we know by the
graduation by colleges to the promotion of so many to high ranks

Marshal of the Royal Air Force and many others to Air Marshals.

The Women's Royal Air Force must also be mentioned along with the Royal Air Force Regiment, both playing an exacting role along with the Auxiliaries, a formidable force.

To have been one of the original 400 Boys in the Royal Flying Corps of 1917 and a Founder Member of the Royal Air Force gives me a sense of humble pride.

*A minimum roll of Ex-Boys of the Royal Flying Corps 1917-April 1918.
Note: Some with extended service were commissioned.*

Acres, J. B., Flt/Lt.
Adams, H. F.
Adamson, T.
Allen, B. D.
Allison
Amos, F. W.
Anderson, W.
Angless, J. H.
Antil, W.
Armitage, J.
Avern, H. L., 155258.

Baker, E. G., 90347.
Baker, G., 83187
Baker, J.
Baker, R. L.
Bangay, W. J.
Banney, C. E., Sqdn/Ldr.
Barber, T. W.
Barnard, W. J. S.
Barrell, T. F., 156552
Bartlett, V., 89804
Belcher, L., 157423
Bell, G.
Beverley
Biggs, A.
Bishop, F. T.
Bloomfield, R., 157240
Blunn, F.
Boddington
Bolt, Ben
Bosier, A. E.
Boucher, A. H.
Bowden, W.

Brandon, W.
Brereton, W., W/Co.
Brook-Lander, C., 149721
Brooks, W. L., 157151
Brown, R. G.
Browning, J. E., 157069
Bryant, F. R.
Bullimore, E.
Burdett, S.
Burdon, F., 157213
Burgess, H.

Carnill, G. A., 82494
Carter, A. R.
Carter, T. G., 156215
Cartwright, C. R.
Chandler, A. E., 87067
Chappell
Chatfield, Joe
Clark, A. E. R.
Cockcroft, Joe
Coleby, F.
Cox, F. L., 86650
Crossley
Crouch, C., 156770 W/Co.
Cunningham, J.
Cunningham, R., 183613
Curry 84767

Davies, T.
Davy, L. C.
Dawkes, Tom
Dennett, S. (Split)
Downes, L.
Duckworth, S.

Edwards, A., 84945
Edwards, T.
Ellis
Ennion, W.
Ewine, E. A.

Fidler, W. A.
Fisher, A.
Fleming, G., 83444
Forryman, T., 98752
Foster, J. W.
Foulds, W.
Francis
Freas, W.
Freeman, C. D.

Gunn, J. E., 149948
Gardiner, A.
Garnett, T. W.
Gayton, F. C.
Gibson, A.
Gilder, D. A., 87068
Giles
Gore, F. C.
Gough, R. D. W/Co.
Gower
Grant, H. W. D., 155549
Green, T. L. R.
Greenfield, R. G. 157164
Griffiths, H.
Grisbrook, T., 155866, Sqdn/Ldr.
Guyler, J. F.
Gwelman, P.

Habone, B. C.
Hadfields, H., 157533
Hancock
Handley, W., 81646 W/Off.
Hale, R., 157782
Harlow, F. C.
Harvey, W. G.
Hasted, R.
Harriott, J. P., 156386
Harrison
Hawkins
Head, A. E.
Heys, G.

Hodges, C.
Hodson, W.
Holt, N.
Horton, J. E., 157401
Hughes, H. V., W/Co
Hull, W. R., 155176
Humphrey, J. 88951
Hunt, C. F., W/Co
Hunt, G.
Hunter, J. W., 155805, Sqn/Ldr.

Imrie, J.
Ingram, J.

James, W.
Jenkins
Jenner, S. L.
Jush, A. B. E.

Keen, W. A.
Kenningham, A.
King, F.
Kirby, W. J.C., 157040, W/Co.
Kirkham, F., 90126
Knott, W.

Lambert
Lees
Leys, A., 155115
Littlejohn, J. W. L., 157572
Lloyd, J. N., 157472
Lord, W.
Lowdell, G. E.
Lucas

Machin, G. E.
Malone, H. 82430
Mann, G.
Mann, J. 157544
Manning, A. H.
Manning, J. W.
Marlow, H. G. V., 159666
Masters, J. W., 155736
Maybour, A. C.
Mayne, A. C., 89306
Mayo, F. 155653
McCardle, H. M.

McKeone, J., 155628
McLeod, W.
Mellish, H. R.
Middleton, U. A. R., 157541
Mildenhall, R.
Miles, E.
Mills
Mills, H. J., 159013
Morley
Moscrop, A.
Moulton, E. C. F., 157307
Murphy, A. E. F.
Murray, J.
Murray, W. T.
Murphy, J. D., 157174
Myers, J.
Myles, H.

Newport, D. J.
Nichols, E. C., 157993
Norris, E.
North, E. T.

Olfridi, W., 157310
Owen, G.
Opie, W., Air/V/M. CB. CBE
Oxley

Page, B. C.
Parker, F. W.
Peacock, A.
Peat, C., 197837
Penree, J. W. W.
Pegg, S. R.
Perkins, C. R.
Phythian, J.
Pickard, 86442
Plank, F.
Pobgee, R. D., 157267
Pointer, A. F.
Pope, G.
Potter
Price, H. S., 81361

Quilley, R.

Raby, Ben

Rawson
Record, S. E.
Rennie, W. L., 149765
Richards, A. W., 86642
Reid, G.
Roberts, C. L.
Robinson, J. F., 144708
Robinson, W. 125799
Rigby
Rogers, C. L.
Rollins, F.
Ross, J., 83445

Sankey, G., 91019
Saville, J.
Scammel, K. W., OBE
Scott-King
Scullard, L.
Shand
Shipley, F.
Simms, W. M., 155698., OBE
Simmons, H. G., 149452
Simpson, L.
Sinclair
Sladdon, J. R.
Slade, F. W., 155948
Smith, A. B.
Smith, F. S., 87867
Smith, S. E.
Snaith
Snellgrove, L.
Sparks, W. J.
Sparrow, E.
Spree, E. F.
Stark, W. G., 155581
Starkey, W.
Stevenson
Steers
Stewart
Strange, H.
Sudenham, N. W.
Sutcliffe, W. H.
Swannie, A. E.

Taylor, G.
Terry, V.
Thomas, G. W/Co., OBE

Thorne, F. W.
Townson, S. E. 83041., W/Co.
Trapp
Trim, F., 157036
Tucker, C. E., BEM
Turner, R. H.
Tye, T. F.

Vaudrey, W.
Vaughan, G.
Verity, B.
Vernon, F. 89977

Wagstaff
Walford, C. E. R.
Walker R., W/Co. OBE
Walker, R. H.
Wallsgrove, W.
Walster, W. W/Co.
Walters, H. W/Co.
Walton
Ward, F. H.

Ward, G.
Warrington, A. 83191
Watson, G.
Watson, A. H., 159510
Watts, C.
Weaver, A.
Webstead, R. G.
Weller, H. F. 156259
White, A. E.
Whitting, Joe., 155457
Wilkinson
Williams, T.
Wood, F. E. D., 156257
Wooley
Wright
Wragg
Wren, G.
Wrigley, E.
Wroe, J. H.

Yeardley, H.
Yeomans, T.

Some of these names are from a roll given to me by Joe Whiting., 155457.
   *Many names are from ex-boys. Lists of names attending Annual dinners
and re-unions held in London of ex-RFC Boys.*

Index

Four RFC Boys in uniform. Wearing "Cadet" (officers) white band. On leave.

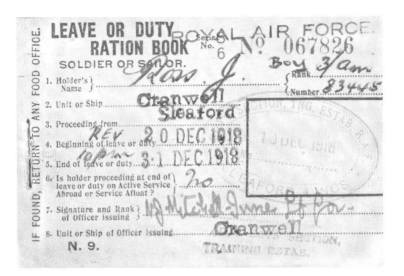

Leave or Duty Ration book, 1918

A. V. Roe, standing beside the wreck of one of his early machines.

Kapitan Leutnant Martin Dietrich.
Commander of Zeppelin L22 which raided Sheffield.

B. C. Hucks. Pioneer Aviator, pre 1914.

Boy George Watson and another at Cranwell RAF

Ten ex. RFC boys in main service aged over 18 years

Handley-Page O/400 Bomber A/C

George Fleming,
the boy from Sheffield, we enlisted together.

MILES MARTLET
AEROBATIC SINGLE SEATER
AEROPLANE

Complete   with
C. of A. £185

Miles Martlet aeroplane.

Herbert Latham, Brooklands 1911.

Roland Garros,french aviator, Hendon 1913.

Graham White ten seater aircraft, one engine 100 hp "green".